BLACK DOLLS

BOOK II

AN IDENTIFICATION AND VALUE GUIDE

BY MYLA PERKINS

COLLECTOR BOOKS

A Division of Schroeder Publishing Co., Inc.

On the cover:

Top — 14", vinyl head and jointed body, ©1963, courtesy of Lillian J. Ransom, $55.00.
Left Above — Georgene Novelties, "Beloved Belindy," 13½", all cloth, collection of Michele Bady. $1,200.00+.
Left Below — Davis Milling Co., "Diana," ©1905, uncut cloth doll from the set of Aunt Jemima rag dolls. $300.00.
Right — Original artist doll by Mary Van Osdell, "Elmo," 23½", porcelain and cloth, courtesy of Mary Van Osdell.

Searching For A Publisher?

We are always looking for knowledgeable people considered to be experts within their fields. If you feel that there is a real need for a book on your collectible subject and have a large comprehensive collection, contact us.

COLLECTOR BOOKS
P.O. Box 3009
Paducah, Kentucky 42002-3009

Cover design by Karen Geary.
Book design by Gina Lage.

Additional copies of this book may be ordered from:

COLLECTOR BOOKS
P.O. Box 3009
Paducah, Kentucky 42002-3009

or

Sugar 'n Spice
16555 Wyoming
Detroit, Michigan 48221

@$17.95. Add $2.00 for postage and handling.

CONTENTS

DEDICATION 4

INTRODUCTION 5

SHOWCASE OF DOLLS...7

CHAPTER 1
Creche, Papier-Maché, China, and Wax Dolls.....................24

CHAPTER 2
Bisque Dolls, Late 1800's to 1925+ 34

CHAPTER 3
Cloth Dolls, Late 1800's to present 44

CHAPTER 4
Composition, Rubber, Wood, and Celluloid Dolls, 1900–1950+...........107

CHAPTER 5
Vinyl and Plastic Dolls, Mid 1900's to Present....................140

CHAPTER 6
Artist and Reproduction Dolls...352

INDEX 438

DEDICATION

This book is lovingly dedicated to my two beautiful granddaughters, Haille Nichole Perkins and Mackenzie Gayle Scott.

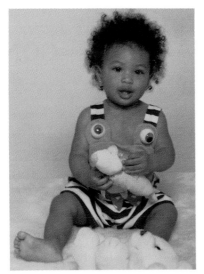

Haille

Mackenzie

PHOTOGRAPHIC RECOGNITION

Vickie Anguish of Vickie Anguish Originals; Barray; Floyd Bell; Pat & Bill Biskie; Maureen Braeden; Lois Bro; Frasher's Auctions; Jerel Black; Dorothy E. Bordeaux; Bradley Dolls; Jane Cameron; The Collectibles by Phyllis Parkins; Marge Crunkleton; Cynethea Cunningham; Frasher's Doll Auctions, Inc.; Susan Girardot; Mary June Hill; Etta Houston; Kor January; Jack L. Johnston; Virginia Kiley; Patricia Kolesar of Kolesar Kreations; Kathe Kruse (Puppen GmbH); Lu Lane; Lawton Doll Co.; Stephanie Lisoski; Marlene Sagar Long of Violet Vision; Darlene Luther; Jackie Maphis; Cheryl Pabst May; McMasters Doll Auctions; Lee Middleton; Kay Morton; Lin Murphy; Olmec Toys; Mary Van Osdell; Heidi Ott; Jim and Sue Parker of Parker People Dolls; Connie Parsons; Annis Rogers; Patricia Rose of Patricia Rose Studios; Sarah's Attic; Phyllis Schlatter; Rotraut Schrott; Lynn Shay; Shindana Toys; Gail J. Shumaker Originals; Sharon Smelser; Frances L. Smith; W. Donald Smith; Frank Sposato; Linda Lee Sutton; Carla Thompson; Pat Thompson of Vlasta Dolls; Jean Turner; Virginia Ehrlich Turner; Victoria Ashlea Originals, Goebel United States; Rosalie Whyel Museum of Doll Art; Joyce A. Wilkinson; Faith Wyse; Robert Zacher; Zambardon Corp.; Richard Hines Photography for Johannes Zook Originals.

SPECIAL THANKS
For Lending Dolls to be Photographed

Artchees; Michele Bady; Joan Banks; Mary A. Beard of The Corner Shop; Linda Boulware, Dolls of Color, Inc.; Tina Burbank; Valerie Burbank-Pugh; J.C. Carmichael; Tanya Mitchell Charles; Clara Levy Clark; Kitty Dade; Valda Dillon; Betty Formaz; Tony Formaz; Michele Hill Grier; Patricia Hall; Emma Hayward of Aunt Em's Workshop; Beverly Alison Hill; Clara Phillips Hill; Verna Hill; Zenobia Holiday; Dianna Jackson; Shirley Jackson; Melven Baines Jolley; Patricia Whittler-Martin; Xzena Moore of the Cubbyhole; Hannah and Harry Mumin; Museum of African American History (Detroit); Lillian J. Ransom; Robert G. Ransom; Jeff Sakarins; Donald N. Thurber; Reevah Turner; Patricia Tyson of Cultural Accents; Michael Wolk-Laniewski; Beverly Dooms; Dr. Ingrid Dooms-Cook.

Doll Collecting! What is doll collecting? What is a "doll collector?" Are there doll collectors in other countries? How many do you have to have to be considered a doll collector? What kinds of dolls do doll collectors have? Where do doll collectors keep their dolls? Do they have them on display or store them in closets? Why do collectors feel a need to own dolls made as playthings for children? Where do most collectors find dolls? What kinds of dolls are collectible? Where do dolls get their names? The answers to all of these questions are as broad and varied as the dolls you will see photographed on the following 437 pages.

According to *World Book Encyclopedia,* "Whether it be books, beer mugs, or antiques, people have the instinct to collect." People who follow, refine, and cultivate this natural instinct become what are called "collectors." They not only try to amass a collection of the items they are interested in but also search diligently for written information on the history of the object and consequently become very knowledgeable about the subject. Simply put, a doll collector is therefore defined as someone who collects dolls and tries to learn as much as possible about the subject.

Many of these collectors do not limit their collecting to one subject. Very often a collector of dolls will also have a collection of thimbles, quilts, matches, perfume atomizers, etc. The collector is putting inhibitions aside and following the "natural" instinct to collect. Many times an entire family will become collectors, each specializing in a different item. This can result in positive family unity as many hours (or even miles) can be spent together in the great "search" for another specimen for one's collection.

Collecting dolls is said to be one of the three most popular hobbies in the world. The other two hobbies are collecting stamps and coins. There is some dispute as to the order the three hobbies are ranked. (Of course a doll collector believes that doll collecting is and should be number one.)

Once one admits to being a doll collector, another big decision is sometimes required. One can choose to have a general collection of dolls, anything that appeals at the moment of purchase, or one can limit the collection to a specific type of doll. The latter can be much more challenging as it is usually harder to find the specific doll that will fit into your category. Some of the categories that collectors often specialize in are the following: ethnic dolls, antique dolls, artist dolls, reproduction dolls, china head dolls, paperdolls, composition dolls, Barbie dolls, cloth dolls, personality dolls, dolls by a certain manufacturer, boudoir dolls, historical dolls, German dolls, mechanical dolls, Kewpie dolls, advertising dolls, and hard plastic dolls. Many times a collector will begin with a general collection and later become fascinated with a particular type of doll and then begin to concentrate on that type only. There are many, many options and no set rules to follow in the "doll collecting" game.

How many dolls does a person need to have before being called a "doll collector?" There is no magical number. Many doll clubs only require that a collector have as few as ten dolls in order to apply for membership. As we all know, once a person has ten dolls, he or she is "hooked," usually for life. It is not unusual for a collector to have hundreds or even thousands of dolls in their collection. However, once this accumulation is amassed, another problem surfaces. Where does one keep all of the dolls? Many collectors set aside one room in their house and call it "the doll room." Others display a few dolls at a time while keeping the majority in boxes stored in closets. Some collectors have turned their entire home over to the dolls and created their own magical dream world! All choices are appropriate and acceptable.

Usually when a beginning collector sees the collection of an advanced collector, the first question asked is, "Where did you find all of these good dolls?" Dolls can be found in a wide variety of places such as antique shows, antique shops, flea markets, garage sales, doll shows, and doll conventions. Dolls vary in cost from less than a dollar to thousands of dollars. Any doll is collectible. My favorite dolls are not necessarily my most expensive. For the collector of black dolls, black doll shows are becoming popular and are held frequently in many cities around the country.

In looking through this book, you will see that many of the dolls have names. Where do these names come from and why don't all of the dolls have names? The dolls that have names were verified by an accompanying original box or hang tag. In cases where neither was available, the original owners supplied names as they remembered when dolls were purchased. Occasionally, manufacturer catalogs were used to identify dolls. A great majority of the earlier dolls and antique dolls are not named in this book. If a name did not accompany a doll, I did not feel I had the liberty to name the doll. My duty at this point was to simply describe the doll as accurately as possible.

Although I do have an extensive collection of black dolls, my goal is not limited to identifying dolls that I own or would love to own, but to identify with a description and photograph, *every* black doll ever created. In short, even if I personally don't like the doll, I feel it should be documented. With the help of collectors, doll dealers, and museums all over the country, I feel it is an obtainable goal. If you have a doll that can be documented and is not included, please contact me at 16555 Wyoming, Detroit, Michigan 48221.

Plate 1: Jumeau. "Creole Lady." 23" tall. Porcelain head portrait doll made by Emile Jumeau of France for the Jumeau display at the 1884 New Orleans Exhibition. Doll was sold at auction by Frasher's Doll Auctions on August 8, 1993, for $231,000, setting a world record for a doll sold at auction. The doll was from the collection of the late Ann Rost of St. Louis, Missouri. She had entered the doll in competition at the United Federation of Doll Clubs exhibits during the 1950's and always came away with the blue ribbon. Photograph courtesy of Barbara Frasher of Frasher's Doll Auctions, Inc. $231,000.00.

Left — Plate 2: Male china doll with molded turban. 11" tall. Circa 1870. China shoulder head, painted eyes and mouth, china arms and legs, black cloth body. All original. $2,800.00.

Right — Plate 3: China doll with molded headband. 8½" tall. Shoulder-plate china head, painted eyes, china arms and legs, black cloth body stuffed with sawdust, painted on red earrings. Clothing looks very old, could be original. Circa 1870. $1,200.00.

Plate 4: Saalfield #2160. "Patches and Petunia." 1937. Paper dolls. 17" tall. Includes 10 outfits and 16 accessories. Dolls are unmarked. $85.00.

Plate 5: Topsy-turvy with black china shoulder head on one end, bisque white shoulder head on the other end. 10" tall. Black doll has molded kinky hair, painted eyes and mouth, china arms, and shares a joint cloth body with the white head. White head has molded blond hair in curls, painted eyes and mouth, bisque arms. All original. Unmarked. Circa 1870. $2,000.00.

Plate 6: Saalfield Publishing Co. "Topsy." 1911. See plate 138 for a complete description.

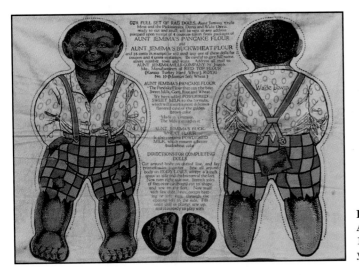

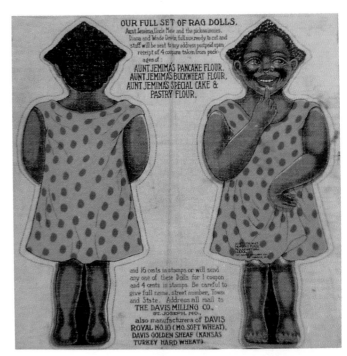

Plate 7: Davis Milling Co. "Diana," ©1905. Uncut cloth doll from the set of Aunt Jemima rag dolls. Cloth is approximately 12" x 12". Completed doll would be approximately 11" tall. Notice the almost triangular shaped head. This was changed on later Diana dolls. Dress is yellow with orange dots. Marks: AUNT JEMIMA'S/PANCAKE FLOUR DOLL,/DIANA,/THE DAVIS MILLING CO.,/ST. JOSEPH, MO., on the front of the dress near the hemline. $300.00.

Plate 8: Davis Milling Co. (Now Quaker Oats Co.). "Wade," 1910, son of Aunt Jemima. Printed on cloth uncut doll. Cloth is approximately 12" x 18". Wade is wearing a white shirt with orange print and orange and yellow checkered pants. Marks: WADE DAVIS, on back. $250.00.

Plate 9: R.T. Davis Mill Co. Original paperdoll set of "Aunt Jemima and her Children," 1895 premium. Printed on the paperdolls are the doll's names and "Before the Receipt was sold." Each doll came with one set of clothes. Printed on the clothing are the doll's names and "After Receipt was sold." Dolls vary in size from 3¼" to 5" tall. Children's names are, from smallest to the largest: Dinah, Zeb, Dilsie, Abraham Lincoln, and Rastus. Directions for cutting out and assembling the dolls so that they will stand alone are printed on back of the dolls, as well as descriptions of new outfits. Also included is promotional material from R.T. Davis Mill Co. on the "Three Staffs of Life" — wheat, corn and rice. Price for original set $125.00.

Reprints of this set of paperdolls were made in the 1970's. The backs of the reprints are missing the directions and all promotional information from R.T. Davis Mill Co. The reprints are stamped on the back as follows: COMPLIMENTS OF RALPH'S ANTIQUE DOLLS AND DOLL MUSEUM/RALPH GRIFFITH ELMER BELL/OWNERS. 1970's reprint set $25.00.

Plate 11: Babyland topsy-turvy doll made by Horsman, circa 1910. 12" tall. All cloth with lifelike lithographed faces. Black doll wears a deep red blouse and turban, red checkered skirt, white scarf around neck. White doll wears the same red checkered dress. Cap is missing from the white face. Gimbel Brothers, department stores in New York and Philadelphia, pictured a similar "Babyland" topsy-turvy rag doll in their 1912 catalog. The price was listed at $1.00. $1,000.00.

Plate 10: Topsy-turvy doll with embossed pressed paper faces, very unusual. 1890's. Straw-filled body. Both dolls have red print bodices, plaid bonnets, red striped skirts. Neither of the dolls have arms. All original. 11" tall. Unmarked. $400.00.

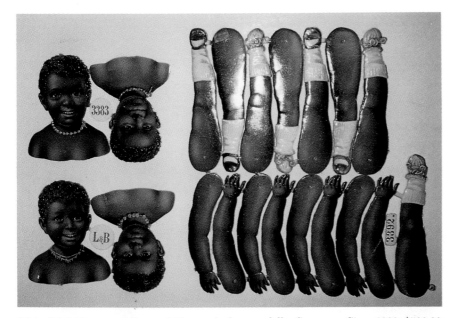

Plate 12: Littauer and Bauer. Lithographed paper dolls. Germany. Circa 1880. $500.00 for complete set.

Plate 13: Roberta Doll Co. 17½" tall. Hard plastic walker doll, black wig in original set, amber sleep eyes, open mouth with four upper teeth, red felt tongue. All original in red plaid dress, red socks, white shoes, natural straw hat. Unmarked. 1950's. $300.00.

Left — Plate 14: Creche figure. 10½". Molded hair, glass eyes, molded on boots. All original. $1,200.00.

Right — Plate 15: Creche figure. 12½" tall. Terre cotta head and limbs, inset glass eyes, molded hair, cloth body. All original. Paint is flaking badly off the face and hair. $900.00.

Left — Plate 16: Early terre cotta creche figure. 12½" tall. Molded curly hair, painted eyes. All original. $1,000.00.

Right — Plate 17: All original creche figure with painted eyes, molded curly hair. Scabbard over shoulder with removable sword. Pearls are handsewn on headpiece. $1,500.00.

Plate 18: Collection of Norah Wellings dolls. Sizes range from 7" to 19" tall. Dolls were made in England from 1926–1960. $75.00–325.00.

Plate 19: Chad Valley. "Bermuda Sailor." 10½" tall. Painted eyes, black lamb's wool hair, painted closed mouth, applied ears, velvet head, hands, and feet. Blue velvet sailor's outfit forms the body. Bermuda is printed on the cap. Doll looks very much like the Norah Wellings dolls. Tag sewn to left foot: HYGIENIC TOYS/MADE IN ENGLAND BY CHAD VALLEY CO. LTD. $250.00.

Plate 21: Character face doll. 14" tall. Bisque head, glass eyes, black wig, open mouth, jointed composition body. Marks: MADE IN GERMANY. Photograph courtesy of Frasher's Doll Auctions. $3,000.00.

Plate 20: Alexander. "Rumbero and Rumbera" of Cuba. 9" tall. 1942–1943. Composition heads, painted eyes, black mohair wigs, jointed composition straight leg bodies. All original. Marked on back. $300.00 each.

Plate 22: Top: Martha Chase. 27" tall. Circa 1900. Stockinette head, painted features. The Chase dolls were made with heads of stockinette stretched over a mask. The molds for the masks were reproduced from dolls with bisque heads. Courtesy of Frasher's Auctions. Sold at auction in 1992 for $7,875.00.
Bottom left: Heubach Koppelsdorf. 14" tall. Bisque head, glass eyes, molded painted hair, open smiling mouth, composition body. Marked mold number 418. Photograph courtesy of Frasher's Auctions. $2,000.00+.
Bottom right: "Alabama Baby." 13½" tall. Cloth doll made by Ella Smith in Roanoke, Alabama. She made dolls from 1904–1924. She called her dolls "Alabama Indestructible Dolls" and made them in both black or white versions. Photograph courtesy of Frasher's Auctions. Doll was sold at auction in 1992 for $6,090.00.

Below left — Plate 23: Babyland Rags with hand painted features. Early 1900's. Photograph courtesy of McMasters Doll Auctions. $1,000.00+.

Below center — Plate 24: Carved hair wooden Schoenhut boy. Painted features, paint is flaking off face. Doll was offered at auction by McMasters, June, 1993, Gaithersburg, Maryland. Photograph courtesy of McMasters Doll Auctions. 14" tall. $1,500.00.

Below right — Plate 25: Volland. "Beloved Belindy." 18". Early Beloved Belindy. Missing scarf and apron, original dress. Photograph courtesy of Susan Girardot. $1,000.00+.

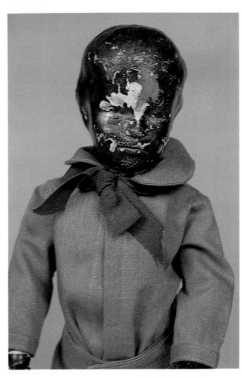

Plate 26: 17" Simon & Halbig 1009. Photograph courtesy of Maureen Braeden. $2,000.00+.

Plate 27: Simon & Halbig, mold #739 with original clothing. 22" tall. Photograph courtesy of McMasters Doll Auctions. $2,500.00.

Plate 28: Georgene Novelties. "Beloved Belindy." 13½" tall. All cloth, white button eyes, painted nose and mouth. Replaced apron, skirt, and bandanna. Collection of Michele Bady. $1,200.00+.

Left — Plate 29: Georgene Novelties. "Beloved Belindy" with dotted feet and blouse. 19" tall. Collection of Michele Bady. All original. $1,200.00+.

Right — Plate 30: Georgene Novelties. "Beloved Belindy" with red feet and blouse. 20". All original cloth character doll from the Raggedy Ann and Andy stories. Photograph courtesy of Susan Girardot. $1,200.00+.

Plate 31: 13½" tall. Circa 1900. Lithographed facial features, hair, and clothing. Features have faded a great deal. Dress is blue with white stars on the front and red and white striped on the back. Stuffed with horsehair. Unmarked. $600.00.

Plate 32: Heubach Koppelsdorf. "Abyssinian Baby." 9" tall. Bisque head, stationary brown eyes, open mouth with two upper teeth, jointed five piece composition body, black mohair wig. All original in white cotton and felt outfit with red sash at waist, silvertone sword tucked into sash. Marks: HEUBACH KOPPELSDORF/ 458 . 16 (slash) 0/GERMANY, on head. Original tag attached to clothing: ABYSSINIAN BABY/MADE IN GERMANY. $650.00.

Plate 33: Armand Marsielle. Mold 1894. 14" tall. Fired bisque socket head, stationary brown glass eyes, open mouth with four upper teeth, brown mohair wig, composition and wooden body. Clothing is said to be all original. Marks: 1894/AM 1 DEP, on head. $1,000.00.

Plate 34: Sea Island Sugar. "Gobo, South African Boy." ©1935. Cloth doll is printed on the back of a ten pound bag of Sea Island Sugar, manufactured by the Western Sugar Refinery, San Francisco, California. Bag is 15" x 9¾". Directions were printed on the bag for making the doll. $150.00.

Plate 35: 7½" tall. Hard plastic, movable arms and head, molded hair with loop for ribbon, painted eyes, closed mouth, molded on shorts with unpainted suspenders and socks, painted black shoes. Marks: CIPSA (or GIPSA), on back. $65.00.

Plate 36: Nancy Ann Story Book. "Nigeria." 5½" tall. Jointed hard plastic, brown sleep eyes, black mohair wig, painted mouth, painted on black slipper shoes. All original in long white dress trimmed with gold rickrack, matching long headpiece. Marks: STORY BOOK/DOLLS/U.S.A./TRADE MARK/REG., on back. $100.00.

Plate 37: Averill Manufacturing Co. "U-Shab-Ti," (Tutanahamen.) 1923. See plate 405 for a complete description.

Plate 38: Effanbee. "Suzette." Composition head, painted brown eyes, closed mouth, jointed composition body. 11" tall. All original in long grass skirt, orange bra top, orange and yellow lei. Marks: SUZETTE/EFFANBEE, on head; SUZETTE/EFFANBEE/MADE IN/USA, on back. $350.00.

Plate 40: Ideal. "Shirley Temple" doll as "Marama" from the movie *Hurricane.* 18" tall. Composition head, painted side-glancing eyes, open-closed mouth with four painted upper teeth, black yarn hair, jointed composition body. All original in ecru hula skirt made of string with gold felt waistband, two paper leis around the neck, orange flower in hair. Marks: SHIRLEY TEMPLE/18, on head; 18, on back. Doll was also available in 8", 13", and 15" sizes. $1,300.00.

Plate 39: Effanbee. "Patsyette," left; and "Patsy, Jr." right. See plates 428 and 429 for complete descriptions.

Plate 41: Ideal. "Snow White." 16½". 1938. Jointed composition. Swivel head, molded hair with center part with molded red bow, painted eyes. Jointed straight leg body. Doll is wearing a red and white dress that is appropriate with the period and could be original. Unmarked. $600.00.

Plate 42: Effanbee. "Bubbles." 20" tall. Composition and cloth baby, open mouth, two upper teeth, tin sleep eyes, painted hair. Original tagged clothes. Photograph courtesy of Phyllis Schlatter. $550.00.

Plate 43: Effanbee. "Candy Kid." 13" tall. Circa 1924. All composition, fully jointed, brown sleep eyes, closed mouth, molded-painted hair. Original clothes, boxing gloves are missing. Head has been repainted. Photograph courtesy of Phyllis Schlatter. $600.00.

Plate 44: Hard plastic jointed dolls from the 1940's. 27" tall. $350.00 each.

Plate 45: "Mammy Castoria." 11" tall. Lithographed cut out and sew doll offered by Fletcher's Castoria in the 1930's. $200.00.

Plate 46: Terri Lee. "Bonnie Lou and Benjie." 16" tall. Painted hard plastic. All original in matching outfits of pink print with bunnies and carrots. Photograph courtesy of Susan Girardot. $1,500.00 pair.

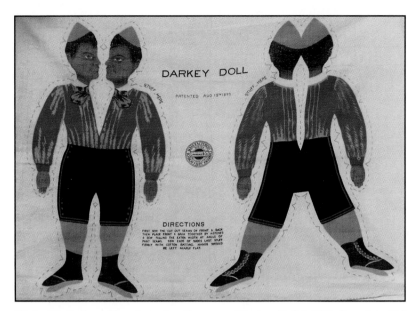

Plate 47: Cocheco Manufacturing Company. "Darkey Doll." 1893. See plate 139 for a complete description. $650.00.

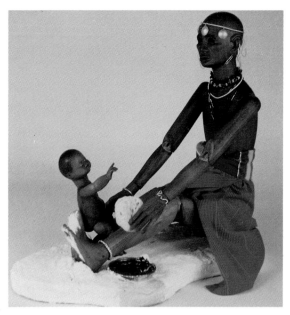

Plate 48: Bell, F. "Grandmother and Child." 27" and 6". Both dolls are handcarved from walnut and represent the Woodobee Tribe. Grandmother has inset glass eyes and fifteen piece jointed body. The child has a five piece jointed body. Both dolls are one-of-a-kind by doll artist Floyd Bell. Photograph courtesy of Floyd Bell. $11,000.00.

Plate 49: Souvenir doll from the Virgin Islands. 9". $100.00.

Plate 50: Ideal. "Diana Ross." See plate 791 for description.

Plate 51: Mattel. "Parsley Bunch." 20" tall. 1983. All cloth doll, painted eyes, black yarn wig. All original in red dress with white dots, red and yellow lace-up shoes, yellow bloomers. Cloth tag on body: EMOTIONS, A DIVISION OF MATTEL TOYS, MADE IN TAIWAN. Photograph courtesy of Stephanie Lisoski. $75.00.

Plate 52: "Generations." Vignette by doll artist Mary Alice Byerly. Porcelain head, hands, and legs, wired cloth body. Father is "Renny," mother is "Rita," son is "Sweet William," and daughter is "Wileen." Photograph courtesy of Mary Alice Byerly. $3,000.00.

Plate 53: "Dr. George Washington Carver" by artist I. Roberta Bell. Photograph courtesy of Frances L. Smith. $425.00.

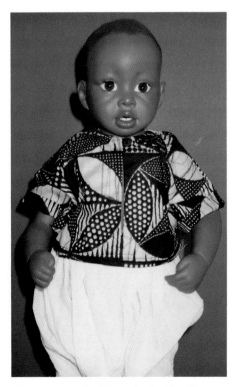

Plate 54: Thompson, Carla. "Cyrus." 24" tall. Soft sculpture by artist Carla Thompson. Limited edition of five. Photograph courtesy of Carla Thompson. No price available.

Plate 55: Heath. "Kumbah" from "Children From Gambia" series by English doll artist Philip Heath. 24" tall. Porcelain and cloth. Limited edition of 30 dolls. Circa 1989. Collection of and photograph courtesy of Phyllis Schlatter. $1,500.00.

Plate 56: Heath. "Yankuba." 18" tall. From "Children From Gambia" by Philip Heath. Porcelain and cloth. Limited edition of 30 dolls, 1989. Photograph courtesy of Phyllis Schlatter. Also in the series was another doll "Lamin," 20" tall. $1,250.00.

Left — Plate 57: January. 16".
1993. Hand carved by artist Kor
January. Molded painted hair,
glass eyes. Photograph courtesy
of Kor January. $600.00.

Right — Plate 58: Frances L.
Smith. "Miss Veatrice." See plate
1684 for complete description.
$2,000.00.

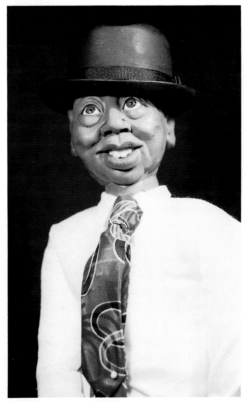

Plate 59: Maphis. "Alona." 26" tall.
One-of-a-kind by Jackie Maphis. Porcelain head, shoulder-plate, arms, and
legs. Photograph courtesy of Jackie
Maphis. $1,600.00.

Plate 60: Johnston. "Bo Jangles." 21" tall. Original doll by artist Jack L. Johnston. One-of-a-
kind. Sculpted of cernit with a wire armature
cloth body. Photograph courtesy of Jack L. Johnston. $900.00.

Plate 61: Lawton. "Ndeko/Zaire." ©1991.
14" and 8". Porcelain dolls from the "Cherished Customs" collection. Ndeko is the Lin-
gala word for sister. In Zaire, the children
often carry their siblings on their back
because it is the mother's responsibility to
carry loads of water, wood, and food. Edition
of 500 dolls. Photograph courtesy of The
Lawton Doll Company. $600.00.

Plate 62: Middleton, Pauline. "Joseph." 24" tall. Original doll by Australian artist Pauline Middleton. Limited edition of ten. Porcelain and cloth, glass eyes, weighted body, mohair wig. Photograph courtesy of Phyllis Schlatter. Available on the market in 1992. $3,500.00.

Plate 63: Schrott. "Bilan of Burkina Faso." 27½". Original doll sculpted in cernit by German doll artist Rotraut Schrott, 1991. Photography courtesy of Rotraut Schrott. No price available.

Plate 64: Schrott. "Little Chief of Kango." 31" tall. Sculpted of cernit in 1984 by artist Rotraut Schrott. Photograph courtesy of Rotraut Schrott. No price available.

Plate 65: Schrott. "Black baby." 25". Sculpted in cernit by artist Rotraut Schrott in 1984. Photograph courtesy of Rotraut Schrott. No price available.

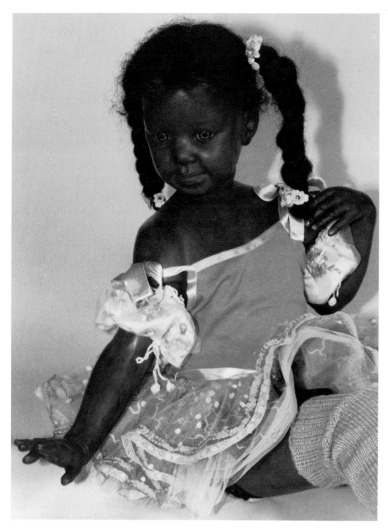

Plate 67: Parkins. "Chelsea" by artist Phyllis Parkins. Vinyl doll. 21" tall. Photograph courtesy of The Collectibles by Phyllis Parkins. Edition of 2500. $200.00.

Plate 66: Schrott. "Jasmine." Original sculpture by artist Rotraut Schrott. Doll was sculpted in 1989, of cernit. 40" tall. Photograph courtesy of Rotraut Schrott. Doll is also available in vinyl and is shown on page 422, plate 1673. No price available.

Left — Plate 68: Smelser. "Dusty." 28" tall. A Sharon Smelser original, limited edition of 50. Porcelain head on a jointed hard body. Dusty comes in assorted outfits. ©1992. Photograph courtesy of Sharon Smelser. $1,200.00.

Right — Plate 69: Patricia Rose. "Pam." 14" tall. All porcelain, acrylic wig, and eyes. Limited edition of 50 dolls. All original dressed as a flower girl in long white gown trimmed with pink ribbon with pink floral headpiece of dried roses. Made in 1991. Photograph courtesy of Patricia Rose Studios. $500.00.

Plate 70: Osdell. "Lucinda." 29" tall. Limited edition of 15 by Mary Van Osdell of Van Osdell Originals. Each doll is dressed in a one-of-a-kind outfit made entirely of antique fabrics. Porcelain head, arms, and legs, cloth body, goat hair wig. Osdell marketed Lucinda mold to doll-makers. Photograph courtesy of Mary Van Osdell. $1,700.00.

Plate 71: Shumaker. "Tanteen." 28" tall. 1993. Vinyl limited edition of 250. Courtesy of Gail J. Shumaker Originals. $400.00.

Plate 72: Ott. "African Girl and Baby" by doll artist Heidi Ott. 1988. 18" and 12" tall. Girl is all vinyl with rooted hair, set-in glass eyes. Boy is vinyl and cloth with painted and molded hair, weighted cloth body. Photograph courtesy of Phyllis Schlatter. Girl, $600.00. Baby, $450.00.

Left — Plate 73: Johannes Zook Originals. "Kanika." 22" tall. Kanika was issued in 1993 and is limited to 1,000. The head was also used on Claire and Cody in the 1993 Zook doll line. Issue price was $220.00. Photography by Rich Hines Photography.

Right — Plate 74: Osdell. "Elmo." 1993. 23½". Original artist doll by Mary Van Osdell. Porcelain head, arms, and legs, cloth body. Molds were sold to make reproductions. Photograph courtesy of Mary Van Osdell. No price available.

Plate 75: Grace Drayton type composition dolls. 6¾". One piece composition head, body, and legs, with movable arms. Molded hair in a "bob" style popular in the 1920's, painted side-glancing eyes, painted closed mouth. All original in brown print cotton dresses. Unmarked. $75.00 each.

Plate 76: "Golliwogg." 20". Probably made from this English pattern. Photograph courtesy of Lu Lane. $300.00.

Plate 78: Alexander. "Leslie." See plate 513 for description.

Plate 77: Terri Lee. "Patty Jo and Benji." Photograph courtesy of McMasters Doll Auctions. $1,500.00 pair.

CHAPTER 1
CRECHE, PAPIER-MACHÉ, CHINA, AND WAX DOLLS

Upon looking at a display of antique black dolls, one of the most frequently asked questions is "where were these made?" The response that they were made in Europe raises many eyebrows and comes as a surprise to the viewer. However, it is an accurate statement, the great majority of the dolls commercially made in the 1800's and early 1900's were made in Germany, including the black ones. An article entitled "Where Santa Claus Buys His Dolls" from *Leslie's Illustrated Weekly Newspaper*, December 5, 1912, page 580, describes the doll manufacturing industry as follows:

> Away up in the forests of Thuringia and Bavaria, men, women, and children are working day after day fashioning dolls — dolls of every description, which will be shipped to this country to delight our little American girls on Christmas morning. Santa Claus sends in his orders early, for he will brook no disappointment for his little friends on this side of the Atlantic. Many of these dolls are the products of the cottage industry, for hundreds of them are made in the homes of the peasants. They are not as fine and beautiful, perhaps, as those which are turned out in the large factories; but they are nevertheless unique in many ways, and their very quaintness is attractive to the restless little American who, like the grownups of the present day, is ever longing for something new — something different.
>
> The United States is Germany's best customer for toys of every description, especially dolls, and each year new types are put on the market. In Sonneberg the greater part of the population is engaged in this industry, and it is the chief source of revenue for the town and gives employment to whole families during the entire year.
>
> The making of the composition dolls as seen in the German factories is an interesting process, even though some of the rooms are hot, steamy places where one does not care to stay long at a time. First, there is the kneading-room, where a big mixing trough is set up, and in this all sorts of rag-bag material are to be found — old gloves, rags, bits of cardboard, etc., and gum tragacanth. This mixture is kneaded by hand to the consistency of a paste, heated and carried into the mod-room. There it is dipped up by women and poured into the patterns, which are set up in rows.
>
> The molds are put away until they are cold enough to handle when a workman, by a dexterous movement of his hands, separates the leaded sides, and the doll's head is revealed.
>
> The polisher then trims off the ragged seams and sends the heads to another room, where the holes for the eyes are cut out. This is an extremely delicate task, as all the sockets must be of uniform size. The work is done by hand, a long, sharp knife being used.
>
> The heads are next painted, waxed, or glazed, depending upon the character of the material from which they are made. The arms, legs, and hands are molded in the same manner as the heads — a special machine being used for stamping out the hands. These parts are painted in flesh color, while the heads must have rosy cheeks, red lips, and dark or light eyebrows, as the color of the eyes used may require. Putting in the eyes is a simple operation, unless the eyes are to open and shut, in which case the balancing of the lead becomes a matter of some skill. Germany possesses a secret formula for the enamel used on the faces...
>
> ...The assembling of the parts is often very complicated, as the best jointed dolls have a stout elastic cord on the inside, to which the movable parts are attached. The bodies are stuffed with shavings of cork, sawdust, excelsior, or cotton, and the arms and legs must be sewed in place with precision, or a crippled doll would be the result. The entire work demands practice and skill, both of which are acquired early in life by the workers.
>
> At Vincennes, France, there is a large factory where the very best type of French doll is made. Parts of all dolls are imported from Germany, for that country has a monopoly on the heads, and the factories all over the world depend on the German factories for their supply of this part of the dolls.

A special branch of the industry is devoted to making dresses and hats. The latest styles are copied. The woman in charge is ever on the alert for novelties, and this year the "character doll" has given her no little study. These dolls are made to represent different nations. They are clothed in the picturesque costumes worn in Germany and other European countries before the French fashions spread over the works, and the doll dressmakers have been compelled to study various museums of costumes in order to fashion the proper dresses. Dolls of this type have an educational value and will likely prove popular.

In Paris there is a large doll dressmaking establishment where hundreds of girls (many of them fashion experts) are employed. Prizes are offered each year for the most artistic creations in doll dressing and manufacture. This accounts for the fine finish of the French doll, which is a genuine counterpart of the stylish French woman of the period.

Germany, too, has made rapid strides in the perfection of the doll, and as far back as 1851 there was a school for the purpose of teaching the art of coloring the faces, and the beautiful, lifelike baby dolls, with faces painted from living models, are the work of some of its pupils.

Each Christmas season brings its crop of freak dolls, and this year one made of what is commonly known as the "dishrag plant" has made its appearance. I saw a number of these in the toy stores in Nuremburg, and their oddity seemed to appeal to the German child. The queer toy is light in weight, will stand hard wear, and has rather an attractive face made of celluloid. Dolls made of very durable porcelain have been the "best sellers" in Europe this season and a few of them have reached the United States. Their durability, however, is their highest merit, as they are by no means beautiful.

Few people realize how much it costs to amuse the American child. Not a small part of this expense arises from the purchase of imported dolls. It is known that the wholesale dealers have bought more extensively this year than heretofore, and some ideal of the extent of the trade in this article may be formed from the reports of our consuls in Germany.

George N. Ifft, the United States consul at Nuremburg, in a recent report to the Bureau of Manufactures at Washington, states that in one year six million dollars worth of toys were exported from Nuremburg alone to the United States. This represents the cost to the consumer, as to the original price of the manufacturer must be added an import duty of thirty-five percent, and an additional one hundred percent for freight charges and profits of the wholesalers and retailers. The Christmas shipments usually begin in the early autumn and continue until the middle of December.

Photographs of dolls were included with the article. One of the dolls was a black doll and is shown on page 108, plate 375. No mention was given as to what material was used to make the doll.

During most of the 1900's, doll manufacturers and designers targeted two distinct markets when producing and promoting black dolls. The two can be defined as follows:

1. Dolls made for and marketed to black children. These were generally the dolls made from the same molds as those used for the white dolls. They also were sold wearing the same clothing as the white dolls. White parents many times bought these black dolls for their children also. In the late 1900's, some manufacturers marketed black dolls for black children with ethnically correct features.

2. Dolls representing blacks to white children and parents. These were usually the stereotypical rag doll "Mammy." Dolls falling in this category are "Aunt Jemima," "Pickaninny," "Topsy," "Golliwog," etc. Black parents did not buy these dolls for their children generally. They, the dolls, did not represent an image blacks wanted for their children.

Both types of these dolls are highly collectible today. Dolls made between 1920 and 1960 are more readily available in the second type of doll. Dolls made after 1960 are usually from the first category of dolls above.

In the early 1920's, W.E.B. Du Bois along with A.G. Dill, published a monthly magazine for black children. The magazine was called *The Brownies' Book*. The goal of the magazine was to help foster a proper racial self-respect. As reported in *The Crisis*, June, 1921, page 75, the magazine did a New York survey which revealed the following:

"With every doll a specimen of the Nordic type, every picture book and magazine illustration of child life representative of the white race, it is difficult for colored children to grow up by way of that imaginative world when Anderson and Stevenson and Maeterlinck and all the story-tellers and artists since the days of Gutenberg have made the common country of childhood.

"Not only this, but with a literature to which Negroes at best are amusing pickaninnies or faithful servitors, it is difficult for the colored child to gain the sense of human dignity without which the efforts made in recent years to increase and improve his educational opportunities must be largely wasted."

Although noteworthy, Du Bois' efforts were in vain as abundance and variety of black dolls as proper playthings for black children diminished greatly by the 1930's. Following are photographs of dolls made in the 1800's and early 1900's of various materials.

Plate 79: All original creche figure with painted eyes, molded curly hair. Scabbard over shoulder with removable sword. Pearls are handsewn on headpiece. 12" tall. $1,500.00.

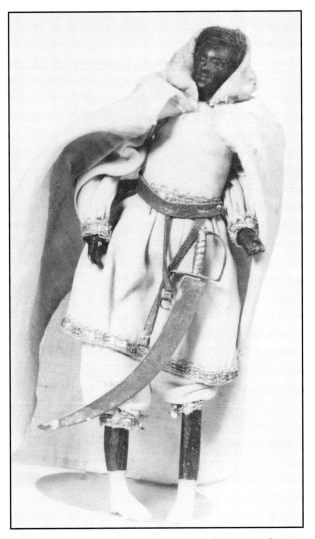

Plate 80: Early wax creche figure; bead eyes; wooly wig; dressed in a Moorish costume, probably original. Wood body, lower arms and legs; painted boots. 8" tall. Courtesy of Evelyn Ackerman. $1,000.00.

Left — Plate 81: Creche figure. 12½" tall. Terre cotta head and limbs, inset glass eyes, molded hair, cloth body. All original. Paint is flaking badly off the face and hair. $900.00.

Right — Plate 82: Early terre cotta creche figure. 12½" tall. Molded curly hair, painted eyes. All original. $1,000.00.

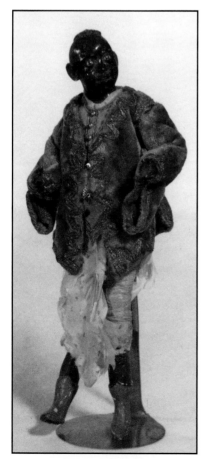

Left — Plate 83: Creche figure. 10½". Molded hair, glass eyes, molded on boots. All original. $1,200.00.

Right — Plate 84: 12" tall. Papier-maché head, arms, and lower legs, and painted blue boots. Molded painted eyes, molded turban (yellow with blue dots), molded hair sticks out around turban. Cloth body with wooden middle. When you press her stomach, her mouth opens. Redressed. Unmarked. Photograph courtesy of Connie Parsons. $650.00.

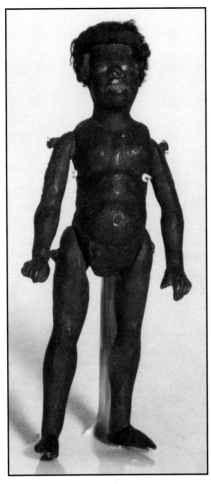

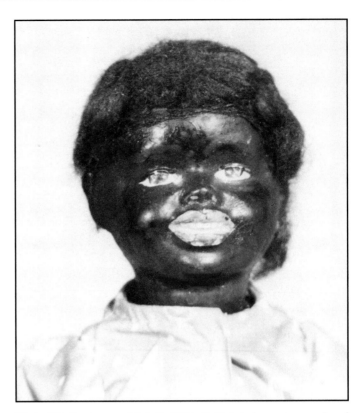

Plate 86: Papier-maché doll. 12" tall. Painted eyes, open-closed mouth with molded upper teeth, bent-leg body, mohair wig. Doll has negroid features. Clothing is handmade and is old but probably not as old as the doll. Unmarked. Doll was said to have been made in Germany. $400.00.

Plate 85: Papier-maché. 6" tall. Negroid features, part of old mohair wig remains on head, painted eyes. Body looks like loin cloth had been attached at one time. Unmarked. Collection of Michael Wolk-Laniewski. $250.00.

Plate 87: 18" tall. Papier-maché head, black glass eyes without pupils, closed mouth, pierced ears, original wig (feels like wool but probably mohair). Wig is in tight rolls all over her head. Silky looking lady body with painted bisque arms and lower legs. Replaced dress and shoes but doll has on original underwear. Unmarked. Collection of and photograph courtesy of Connie Parsons. $600.00.

Plate 88: Molded hair papier-maché, circa 1830. 6" tall. Painted eyes, molded hair, cloth body, turned wood arms and legs. Unmarked. Clothing is very old, it is not known whether it is original or not. One unusual feature on this doll is that she has two right hands. Collection of Michael Wolk-Laniewski. $350.00.

Plate 89: Papier-maché. 7" tall. Papier-maché head and body in one piece, jointed arms and legs, painted eyes, closed mouth. Hair is black wig made of material that is hard to identify, it appears not to be lamb's wool or mohair. Although the features are definitely negroid, doll is originally dressed in native outfit that would be more fitting on a Native American. Glued-on outfit is made of felt. Unmarked. $250.00.

Plate 90: 7" tall. Head is of unidentifiable material, could be some sort of composition of papier-maché. Swivel head, exaggerated negroid features, glass eyes, molded hair, wooded jointed stick body. Old clothing could be original. Early 1900's. Collection of Michael Wolk-Laniewski. $250.00.

Plate 91: Topsy-turvy with black china head on one end, bisque white head on the other end. 10" tall. Black doll has china shoulder head, molded kinky hair, painted eyes and mouth, china arms, and shares a joint cloth body with the white head. White head has bisque shoulder head, molded blond hair in curls, painted eyes and mouth, bisque arms. All original. White doll is dressed in a beige dress trimmed with matching ribbon. The black doll is dressed in a beige print dress with matching headscarf. Unmarked. Circa 1870. $2,000.00.

Plate 92: China shoulder head. ©1870. 1½" tall. Faintly molded hair, painted eyes rolled to the top of the head, mouth could have been painted at one time, if so, paint is now worn off. Shoulder head does not have sew holes. It was at one time glued onto a body as traces of glue remain. Marks: 9, incised on back. $125.00.

Plate 93: China doll with molded headband. 8½" tall. Shoulder-plate china head, painted eyes, china arms and legs, black cloth body stuffed with sawdust, painted on red earrings. Clothing looks very old, could be original. Circa 1870. $1,200.00.

Plate 94: "Filipino." Circa 1899. 13". China shoulder head and limbs on a cloth body, painted eyes, ethnic features of the Philippino aborigines. According to Coleman's *Collectors Encyclopedia of Dolls*, Butler Bros., the exclusive distributor, included these dolls in their WAR doll lines after the Spanish American War. Marks: 1, on back of head. Collection of Michael Wolk-Laniewski. $200.00.

Plate 95: Male china doll with molded turban. 11" tall. Circa 1870. China shoulder head, painted eyes and mouth, china arms and legs, black cloth body. All original. $2,800.00.

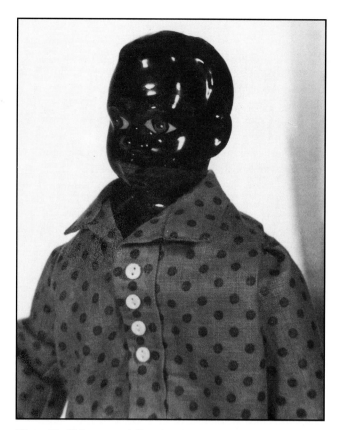

Plate 97: China frozen Charlottes. 4" tall. Molded hair, painted eyes and lips. All original in crudely made clothing. Unmarked. Collection of Michael Wolk-Laniewski. $250.00 pair.

Plate 96: China man doll. 11" tall. China shoulder head, cloth body, celluloid hands marked Germany with the turtle mark, painted features. Clothing is probably not original to the doll. Collection of Michael Wolk-Laniewski. $350.00.

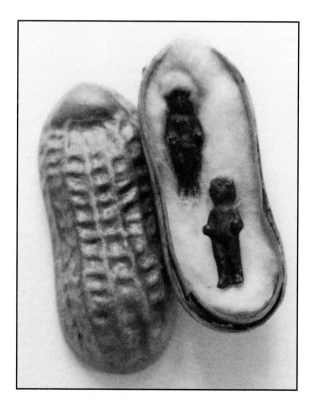

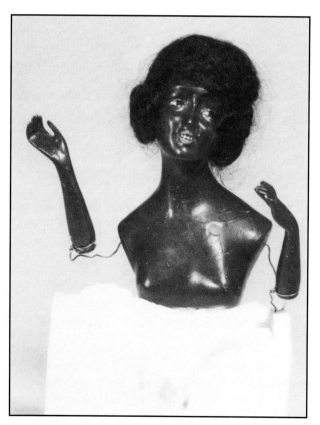

Plate 98: Two china frozen Charlottes in a papier-maché peanut filled with cotton. Dolls are 1" tall. Cotton has been glued to the heads for hair, painted features. Peanut is 3" long. $100.00.

Plate 99: Wax shoulder head to make a fashion doll. Circa 1912. Head and shoulders are 5" tall. Head is solid wax, painted features, original black mohair wig, black bisque arms extending out from the body connected by wires to torso. Wax fashion dolls are extremely rare. Unmarked. $500.00.

Two Leo Moss dolls were presented for auction October 22, 1983, by The Country Bumpkin Doll Shop & Auctions of Rochester, Michigan. The auction was called "Autumn in Arizona" and was held in Scottsdale, Arizona. No further information of the dolls is available (size, etc.). Photograph of the dolls is in *Doll Reader,* October, 1983, page 19. Although the photograph is small and not very clear, the dolls appear to have closed mouths and molded hair.

"Leo Moss," is a self portrait doll by Leo Moss. Papier-maché balding head with full beard, closed mouth, stationary eyes. All original in "formal" outfit, tuxedo, white shirt, and bow tie. Doll is approximately 16" tall and was offered at auction March 30, 1985, at Boca Raton, Florida. It is not known whether or not the doll was sold. Doll is pictured in *Doll Reader,* Feb./March, 1985, page 29.

Another Leo Moss doll is "Vesa." She has a solid dome papier-maché head, composition arms and legs, cloth body, glass eyes, molded hair, tears on face. Marks: L.M., incised on head. Body has a cloth label on stomach marked "VESA 1930." Doll was sold at auction in May, 1987, for $6,750.00. Doll was on the market again in 1989. It is not known if doll was sold and if so, what the selling price was. Vesa was a ribbon winner at U.F.D.C. See *Doll Reader,* August/September, 1987, page 302 for photograph.

"Peggy," 22", is a baby doll by Moss with papier-maché shoulder head, molded hair, stationary brown glass eyes, closed mouth, three molded tears on cheeks, composition lower arms and legs, and brown cloth body. Marks: L.M., incised on shoulder-plate. Peggy was sold at auction for $5,500.00 by Marvin Cohen Auctions, January 11, 1987, Mesa, Arizona. For photograph, see *Doll Reader,* October 1985, page 101 and *Doll Reader,* April, 1987, page 66.

A Leo Moss child doll, 27" tall, papier-maché head, molded hair composition arms and legs, bulging glass eyes, closed mouth, no tears was offered for sale by the Country Bumpkin Doll Shop, Metamora, Michigan, February, 1987. The asking price of the doll was not indicated. Photograph of the doll is shown in *Doll Reader,* February/March, 1987, page 54.

Two Leo Moss dolls were brought to the Franklin Park Mall in Toledo, Ohio, September 27–30, 1984, for appraisals. The dolls were signed by Leo Moss and dated 1912 and 1932. Both had molded hair, papier-maché socket heads, glass eyes, closed mouths, molded tears, cloth bodies signed in ink by Leo Moss, composition arms and legs. Dolls are pictured in *Doll Reader,* December, 1984/January, 1985, page 96. Dolls were appraised for $5,000.00 each in 1984.

"Leo" and "Lillian," circa 1900. Approximately 13". Papier-maché heads with molded hair. Lillian has molded tears and molded loops in hair to hold hairbows. Dolls are in the collection of Lenon Hoyte of Aunt Len's Doll and Toy Museum.

A 19" Moss doll with papier-maché head, brown glass eyes, smiling mouth with painted teeth, and molded hair was offered on the market in the fall of 1989, by Melton's Antiques for $6,850.00. The doll was said to date circa 1910. Photograph from the ad is in *Doll Reader,* October, 1989, page 71.

Two Moss dolls are featured in the same edition of *Doll Reader,* October, 1989, page 108. One of them looks very much like the doll available from Melton's Antiques, smiling mouth with painted teeth and is unmarked. The other is described as a crying Leo Moss child, 16" with glass eyes, two molded tears on her cheeks, closed mouth, composition lower arms and legs, cloth body. Marks were "1901, L.M." The dolls were reported as being from the June 25, Cohen auction of Pat Stall's collection in New Lebanon, New York. It is assumed the auction was June 25, 1989. Prices the dolls brought at auction were $6,100.00 for the marked doll, $3,000.00 for the unmarked one.

A Leo Moss baby with three molded tears was sold at auction for $4,000.00 against a $5,000.00–$7,000.00 estimate at Theriault's, Newport Beach, California, January 3, 1987, "Departures" sale. The doll was 20" tall and is pictured in *Dolls, The Collector's Magazine,* July–August, 1987, page 19.

A Moss child doll was sold at auction by Theriault's, October 7, 1990, in San Francisco, California for $13,000.00. The doll was said to be the "star of the show." The doll had three molded tears on her cheeks, molded hair, glass eyes.

Seven additional Leo Moss dolls are described and shown photographed for an article by Steva Roark Allgood in UFDC's *Doll News,* Fall, 1987, pages 26–30. Allgood is an owner of Moss dolls. The first doll is "Pearl," 21", thought to be one of the last dolls made by Leo Moss. The doll is incised "LM." A chest patch sewn onto the cloth body reads "Pearl/Christmas 1932." (Some believe that patches sewn to some of the cloth bodies indicate the year the child was born, not the year the doll was made.) Pearl has molded hair, glass eyes, three molded tears, closed mouth, composition arms and legs, and a cry box inside the body that usually works. The next doll is "Zoletta," 17" pouty girl three to four years of age. Her molded hair has a loop for inserting a ribbon. She has composition arms and legs, cloth body, a molded tear on each cheek, pierced nostrils, and glass eyes. It is said that the real "Zoletta" in the Moss family married at the age of sixteen and had four or five children. The doll is incised "LM." The third doll in the article is "Prissy," a pouty girl of about six to eight years of age. She is marked "11821," incised on the back of her neck. She has molded hair parted in the middle, stationary brown glass eyes, pierced nostrils, composition arms and legs, and brown cloth body. The fourth doll is an adult named "Callie," thought to be the mother of Leo Moss. She is 19" tall, stationary brown glass eyes, pierced nostrils, closed mouth, molded gray hair pulled into a bun, composition arms and legs, cloth body. The fifth doll is "Buzzy," a very unhappy little boy, 21" tall. He has brown glass eyes, pierced nostrils, a turned down closed mouth, composition arms, cloth body and legs. A cloth patch sewn to his chest reads "To Buzzy Jackson, May, 1914." The sixth doll in the article "Rose," is shown in the author's earlier book, *Black Dolls, 1820–1991,* page 18. The last doll in the *Doll News* article is "Flora," 19" tall and a lady doll. Her molded hair comes down over one side of her forehead. She has stationary brown glass eyes, pierced nostrils, a slight smile, and is incised "LM." Quoting from the article by Allgood: "Flora is thought to be a sister of Ruby Moss and was last seen 1936–1937 working in a cannery in Macon, GA. Flora left Macon after one of her two children drowned in a mill pond. The drowned child was named Floyd and his doll belongs to another Moss enthusiast." All of the Moss dolls have the customary papier-maché heads.

A collector has to be very careful before purchasing a Leo Moss doll. In today's market, many look-alike and reproduction Moss dolls are offered for sale, as some unknowing individuals try to sell them as original Moss dolls. See page 417, plate 1655 for an excellent example of a new Moss look-alike. They should not be confused with the authentic Moss dolls pictured below.

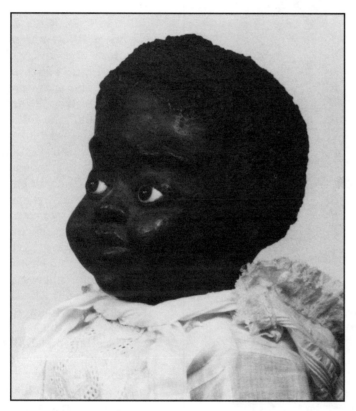

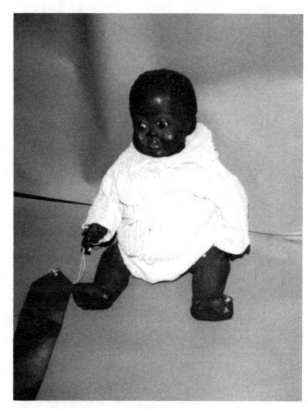

Plate 100: Leo Moss character face doll. 21" tall. Circa 1900. Papier-maché swivel head, stationary glass eyes, molded hair, cloth body, papier-maché lower limbs. One-of-a-kind doll, hand sculptured by Leo Moss. Photograph courtesy of Frasher's Auctions. $14,000.00.

Plate 101: Leo Moss. "Baby Floyd." 13". Doll won six blue ribbons for its owner, Annis Rogers. Photograph courtesy of Annis Rogers. $9,000.00.

CHAPTER 2
BISQUE DOLLS,
LATE 1800'S TO 1925+

Plate 102: Advertisement showing a black child with a black doll. Ad appeared in *The Illustrated London News,* February 8, 1902, page 217. $75.00.

In 1892, Marshall Field & Co. advertised "Negro Jointed Dolls — Fancy Shirts" #542, length was 6". Dolls came one dozen in box, $4.75 per dozen.

In 1895, Butler Brothers, a wholesale distributor, advertised under the listing "Penny" Solid China Goods, No. 551, "Glazed Nigger Baby." The dolls had open arms and legs, were 1¼", came one gross to a box, and were seventy-eight cents per gross. On the same page under the listing "Glazed Nigger Dolls," the following two dolls were advertised: No. 560, Glazed Nigger Doll, free arms and legs, size 3¼", one dozen in box, six dozen or more were twenty-two cents. The other doll No. 561, also called Glazed Nigger Doll, was the same as previous doll only taller, 4½".

Also in 1895, Butler Brothers advertised double dolls under the category "Miscellaneous Dolls" as follows: "No. 718, Double Head Dolls — Natural glass eyes, two styles of dress, one darkey head and the other a bisque head with pretty baby face and lace cap. Appropriate dresses. Full length, including dress, 14", one dozen in box." Cost was $2.05 per dozen.

Heubach Koppelsdorf made a baby doll called "Baby Coon." ca. 1920. 7½". Bisque head, painted hair, closed mouth, glass brown sleep eyes, five piece bent-leg jointed composition body. Original tag attached to doll is labeled: BABY COON. The doll is marked: HEUBACH KOPPELSDORF DRGM. Original clothes were a checked shirt and diapers.

A brown Emile Jumeau doll, circa 1880, marked: JUMEAU MEDIALLE D'OR PARIS and DEPOSE E 7 J was sold at auction for $9,570.00 by Richard Withington's, Nashua, New Hampshire, May, 1993. The doll was 16" tall, and had brown glass eyes and wore a white dress with a straw bonnet.

Simon Halbig of Germany made a black doll with mold #729. The doll was 23" tall, stationary brown eyes, open mouth, black wig, and composition body. Simon Halbig also made a character face doll, mold #969. The doll had stationary brown eyes with painted upper and lower lashes and red dots in corners, open mouth with teeth, slightly dimpled chin, black wig, composition body. The doll was 22" tall.

Simon Halbig mold #739 sold at McMaster's Gaithersburg, Maryland auction, September, 1991, for $3,300.00. She had a bisque socket head, glass eyes, black wig, composition body, and was 20" tall. Doll was marked: S 12H 739 DEP. The doll new, in the early 1900's, cost around $5.00.

Gebruder Heubach made a bisque shoulder head character doll, circa 1910. The doll was 17" tall, molded hair, open-closed mouth. Sold at auction by Theriault's Auctions, Long Beach, California, November, 1988, for $2,600.00.

Kammer & Reinhardt (K*R), mold #101, 15" tall, was auctioned for $5,975.00 in 1990. Novelty black doll "Snowflake," a painted bisque doll, 3¾" tall, was made by Oscar Hitt. Doll has exaggerated Negroid features, including eyes that are glass bubbles with bits of black metal for pupils which "float" in the glass domes. Doll is marked: SNOWFLAKE/©BY/OSCAR HITT/GERMANY.

Many of the rarer, finer examples of the bisque dolls are no longer in the hands of individual collectors, but are in the hands of museums. The Strong Museum in Rochester, New York, is fortunate enough to have many of these dolls. Some examples from their collection are described as follows with information supplied by the Strong Museum.

Bru, Casimir. Paris, France. Bisque head, chocolate color, brown blown glass eyes, closed mouth with parted lips, pierced ears, gold and coral earrings, black mohair wig, bisque shoulder, swivel neck, white kid body, chocolate color lower bisque arms, white underclothing, maroon silk dress, maroon net socks, maroon velvet hat with ribbon trim, leather shoes.

Bru, Casimir. Paris, France. 1879–1885. Bisque head, chocolate color brown blown glass eyes, closed mouth with parted lips, pierced ears, black mohair wig, bisque shoulder swivel neck, kid body lightly stained brown, chocolate color lower bisque arms, white underclothes, rust colored silk dress with inserts of rust colored velvet, velvet jacket and hat to match, black wool socks, leather shoes.

Bru, Casimir. Paris, France. 1879–1885. Black bisque head and shoulder, swivel neck, brown blown glass eyes, closed mouth, pierced ears, black wig, black kid body, upper arms kid, lower arms unglazed porcelain, gold bead bracelets on each arms, cream colored silk and lace dress, purse sewn on side, natural straw hat with black ribbon, white socks, brown leather shoes.

Bergner, Carl. Sonneberg, Germany. 1904–1905. Two faced bisque head, one white, one black, brown glass eyes, closed mouth, compo head and shoulders, lower arms and legs, cloth body over cardboard wood knobs in torso for squeak box, head turned by metal ring on top of hood. (Note: this is not the more popular topsy-turvy of flip doll.)

Germany. 1830–1880. Lady doll. Brown glazed porcelain shoulder head with short black hair, brown eyes, red lips, low sloping shoulders with three sewholes on each side, brown leather body stuffed with sawdust, one brown wood arm and one brown wood leg with red flat boots trimmed with green paper strip. Body dates from 1850, head from 1880. Pantaloons with top, petticoat, yellow plaid cotton skirt,

Give the Child a Doll

The Most Beautiful of All the Toys on the Market Are the

NEGRO DOLLS

¶ YOUR child would be happy if it had a Negro doll such as are sent out by the National Negro Doll Company, Nashville, Tennessee. Every race is trying to teach their children an object lesson by giving them toys that will lead to higher intellectual heights. The Negro doll is calculated to help in the Christian development of our race. All dolls are sent by express, charges paid.

DOLLS FOR THE SEASON 1911-1912 NOW READY

Prices from **50c.** up to **$8.50**

For Illustrated Booklets, Prices and Other Information, Send Five Cents to the

National Negro Doll Company

519 Second Avenue N., Nashville, Tenn.

R. H. BOYD, President | H. A. BOYD, Manager

Plate 103: Advertisement for Negro dolls by the National Negro Doll Company, Nashville, Tennessee. Advertisement was placed in *The Crisis,* July, 1911, page 131. The same ad also appeared in August and September of the same year. Dolls sold by the National Negro Doll Company during this period were bisque dolls.

Plate 104: Advertisement for Negro dolls with a price list from the National Negro Doll Company. Ad was placed in *The Crisis,* November, 1911, page 50.

batiste apron with lace, top blouse with lace, red ribbon trim and red belt.

Lanternier, A & Cie. Limoges, France. 1915–1916. Black bisque swivel head, black curly skin wig, glass eyes, open mouth with upper teeth, composition body and hands, wooden arms and legs, printed purple dress.

Heubach, Ernst. Koppelsdorf, Thur, Germany. 1900–1910. Brown bisque swivel neck, glass eyes, black natural skin wig, open mouth with four upper teeth, completely jointed composition body. Print dress with matching bandanna, white apron, red shoes.

Heubach-Koppelsdorf. Koppelsdorf, Germany. 1900–1925. Black bisque swivel head, tiny eyes without pupils, open mouth, two painted upper teeth, lower lip extends about five cm out from face, painted brown molded black afro hair, open nostrils, two brass rings in pierced ears, composition body with bent arms and straight legs, both one piece.

This is a small portion of the black dolls in the Strong Museum collection. The dolls are always on exhibit and the museum is open to the public.

Plate 105: Advertisement for colored dolls from the E.M.S. Novelty Co. in Jamaica, New York. Dolls were probably bisque. Ad was placed in *The Crisis* magazine, September, 1913, page 255.

Plate 106: Advertisement from *The Crisis,* January, 1914, page 162 for "A Colored Dolly for the Child." Ad was placed by the E.M.S. Novelty Company, Jamaica, N.Y.

Plate 107: Advertisement for 18" undressed dolls with hair for $2.00 and 12" dressed dolls without hair for $1.00. Ad was in *The Crisis,* January, 1917, page 154, placed by Otis H. Gadsden, New York City.

Beautiful Colored Doll Free

This Negro doll has light brown color, long black hair, jointed limbs, sleeping eyes. For selling our artistic Negro post cards and other beautiful cards. Large assortment; very cheap. Agents and dealers are making big money handling them. Terms free. Sample of all post cards sent postpaid for 15 cents.

J. GRIFFITH ART COMPANY
36-38 Beekman St. New York

Plate 108: Advertisement for a free doll from the J. Griffith Art Company on Beekman St., New York. Doll was a premium for selling the company's cards. Ad appeared in *The Crisis*, February, 1914, page 205. The same ad also ran in March and April of the same year. At that time, 1914, *The Crisis* had a circulation of 50,000.

Plate 110: November, 1917, advertisement for dolls in *The Crisis*, page 50. Ad was placed by Gadsden Doll Co., a frequent advertiser of dolls in this magazine.

There can be no better gift than a colored doll to a colored child. Our dolls are beautiful. They are jointed and can be adjusted to any position. Nineteen inch doll with natural hair, undressed, $2.00 prepaid. Sixteen inch doll dressed in the latest style, $1.75. Fourteen inch boy doll dressed, $1.00. All of our goods are shipped prepaid. Send 10c. extra for postage. 50c. extra on Canadian orders. All orders given prompt attention. Terms strictly cash.

GADSDEN DOLL CO.
Room 439.
30 Church St.,
New York City.

19 Inch Hair Doll

Plate 109: Advertisement with a photo of a black doll from *The Crisis*, December 1917, page 102. A 19" doll undressed with hair was $2.00, a 16" dressed doll was $1.75, and a 14" dressed boy doll was $1.00. Ad was placed by the Gadsden Doll Co. on Church St. in New York City.

DOLLS   DOLLS   DOLLS

A complete line of colored dolls of every description ready for immediate delivery at popular prices. Catalog on request.

GADSDEN DOLL CO.
30 Church St., Room 439, New York City.

DOLLS—DOLLS

Beautiful Colored Dolls and Calendars With Negro Subjects for 1920

Sleeping eye, solid bisque, fully jointed, natural brown color, dark hair, eighteen inches high. Sent prepaid for $4.00. This is without a doubt one of the greatest doll bargains of the season. These dolls are popular priced and fully guaranteed to be just as represented. All bisque Kewpie doll, no hair, fifteen inches high, sent prepaid for $2.25.

A great line of Art and Commercial Calendars for the home and for the advertising trade; about thirty-five subjects from which to select, including rural and various scenes. Prices, $4.00, $5.00 and $9.00 per hundred, $30.00, $40.00 and $80.00 per thousand. Samples for agents sent for 50c. Our agents are doing well selling these goods. This is one of the best bargains of the season. Send for samples and make money. Address:

OTIS H. GADSDEN
63 Park Row, New York, N. Y.

Plate 111: Advertisement for 18" bisque dolls for $4.00 and 15" all bisque Kewpie dolls for $2.25 from Otis H. Gadsden, New York, N.Y. Ad appeared in *The Crisis*, November, 1919, page 334, and December, 1919, page 94.

DOLLS   DOLLS

Beautiful Colored Dolls at popular prices

Also beautiful Patriotic Pictures of Negro Officers and Soldiers.

SPECIAL PRICES TO AGENTS

Otis H. Gadsden Co.
30 Church Street
Room 339
New York City

Plate 112: Advertisement for dolls by the Otis H. Gadsden Co., October, 1918, from *The Crisis*.

DOLLS—DOLLS

Beautiful Colored Dolls of Distinction. Red Cross Nurse fully dressed, 18 inches high, black hair, natural color. Sent postpaid for $3.00.

Our Soldier Boy doll, full uniform, including hat and boots, 18 inches high. Sent prepaid for $2.50. We also have Sailor and Cupie dolls in beautiful brown colors. All these dolls are fully guaranteed to satisfy or money refunded.

Patriotic pictures of the great war showing Negro officers and soldiers, including *colored heroes*. Hand to hand battle. "The Love Letter" and post cards of colored soldiers. The pictures are in beautiful water colors, new, just off the press. They are without doubt the greatest agents' offer of the day as they are sold on a money making basis. Some are 16 x 18, some 18 x 20 inches. These are the only pictures on the market today, so far as we know, that show the great part the colored women are doing in this great war. They are 25c a copy. Special prices to agents and dealers. Send for a copy and be the first agent in your town.

OTIS H. GADSDEN
ROOM 339
30 CHURCH ST., NEW YORK CITY

Plate 113: Advertisement for "colored" dolls, a Red Cross Nurse and a soldier boy, both 18" tall. Also available from the same company were sailor and kewpie dolls. Ad was placed by Otis H. Gadsden in *The Crisis* magazine, November, 1918, page 46.

DOLLS   DOLLS

Colored Dolls of Distinction. Red Cross Nurse fully dressed, dark hair, natural brown color, 18 inches. Send postpaid for $3.00.

Soldier boy, full uniform, 18 inches. Sent postpaid for $2.50.

Large undressed dolls at special prices.

Beautiful pictures for the home at 25¢ each or 5 for $1.00. Special prices to agents.

OTIS H. GADSDEN
Room 416
5 Beekman St., New York City

Plate 114: Advertisement for dolls by Otis H. Gadsden, New York City, placed in *The Crisis* magazine, December, 1918, page 102. Shown in the ad is the "Red Cross Nurse" doll.

Dolls — Dolls —

High grade colored dolls that you can depend on in natural brown colors at reasonable prices—also beautiful Negro calendars with colored children for a subject. These calendars come in a great number of subjects. We are now making them up for the trade also for home use. Our agents are doing well selling these goods. Send for proof and get started to making good money. Reliable selling agents wanted.

All our goods are sold on their merits.

OTIS H. GADSDEN
63 Park Row   **New York City**

Plate 115: Advertisement for sale of dolls from Otis H. Gadsden, New York City, from *The Crisis* magazine, August, 1919, page 220. *The Crisis* is the official publication of the National Association for the Advancement of Colored People (NAACP). The same ad was placed in the September, 1919 issue of the same magazine.

COLORED GIRLS IN A DOLL WIG FACTORY, BOSTON

Plate 116: Photograph captioned "Colored Girls in a Doll Wig Factory, Boston." Photograph appeared in *The Crisis* magazine, June, 1921, page 83. No further information was given about the factory or the wigs.

Plate 117: Stereopticon photo titled "She had so Many Children" #88, from the "Group Series." Opticon shows the subservient roll black doll has in a tea party with a little white girl and her white dolls. Black doll is on the left and is holding a serving tray. A similar opticon photo is shown in my earlier book *Black Dolls 1820–1991*. The same doll and props are used but the scene is different. $25.00.

Plate 118: Francois Gaultier. Circa 1860. 14" tall. Fashion lady with bisque shoulder head, painted features, closed mouth, pierced ears, cork pate, black string wig, white cloth body, leather hands and feet. Ecru print long dress, said to be original, with white apron. A small white all bisque baby doll came with this doll. Baby is 2½" tall and is jointed. Baby is not shown as it is not known if she is original to the large Gaultier. Marks: F o G, on back of shoulder head. Francois Gaultier also made a fashion doll 12½" tall with glass eyes and black kid leather body. This doll is also marked: F.G. $3,000.00.

Plate 119: Gaultier. 15½" fashion dolls attributed to Francois Gaultier, France, circa 1880. Bisque swivel head on kid leather body. Clothing is not original. Dressed as "cake walkers" of the nineteenth century. Collection of and photograph courtesy of Rosalie Whyel Museum of Doll Art. $3,000.00 each.

Plate 120: Armand Marsielle. "1894," Germany. Fired brown bisque socket head, brown sleep eyes, open mouth with teeth, black mohair wig, composition body jointed at shoulders, elbows, wrists, hips, and knees. 9" tall. Dressed in a simple pink print cotton dress. Marks: 1894/AM . DEP/GERMANY/10 (slash) O, on head. $350.00.

Plate 121: 9" tall. Bisque head, five piece composition body, black stationary glass eyes, open-mouth with five upper teeth, red dots in corner of eyes. Hole on each side of head above the ears, probably used for stringing. Marks: 10/0 MADE IN/GERMANY. Dressed in original red and white striped cotton chemise. Collection of Valda Dillon. $350.00.

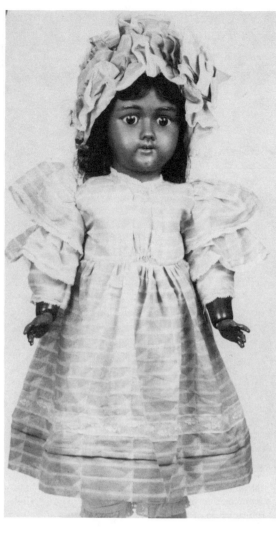

Left — Plate 122: Heinrich Handwerck. 24" tall. Bisque head, open mouth with teeth, glass eyes, wig, jointed composition body. Doll is marked: 69-127. Photograph courtesy of Frasher's Auctions. $2,000.00+.

Right — Plate 123: Bisque head doll. 13" tall. Glass eyes, composition jointed body. Doll is marked: E 4 D. The head was probably made by the French doll maker, E. Denamur. However, there were also several other French doll manufacturers who had the same initials. Late 1800's. Courtesy of Frasher's Auctions. $2,000.00+.

Left — Plate 124: SFBJ. "Unis France." 8½" tall. Painted bisque socket head, five piece jointed composition body, stationary black eyes, closed mouth, black mohair wig. All original in Caribbean Island outfit with hoop earrings attached to the mohair wig. Marks: UNIS/FRANCE (in oval)/60, on head. $300.00.

Right — Plate 125: SFBJ. "Unis France," 1920–1930. Fired brown bisque socket head, stationary black glass eyes, open mouth with four upper teeth, joined inexpensive five piece composition body. 10½" tall. Dolls were made in France but dressed in the Caribbean Islands for the tourist trade. All original in muslin dresses with print overskirts. Dresses have handmade lace sewn to the hemline. Marks: UNIS/FRANCE (in oval)/71 (to the left of the oval) 149 (to the right of the oval)/60. $375.00.

Plate 126: SFBJ. "Unis France." 8½" tall. Painted bisque head, stationary black glass eyes, open mouth with four glass teeth, original black mohair wig, five-piece jointed composition body with painted on black t-strap shoes and socks. Doll is all original in red print dress and matching headscarf. Marks: UNIS/FRANCE (very faint inside an oval)/60, on head. $375.00.

Plate 127: Schuetzmeister and Quendt, Germany. 14" baby doll, 1920's. Bisque socket head, composition bent-limb baby body. Mold #252. Collection of and photograph courtesy of the Rosalie Whyel Museum of Doll Art. $1,500.00.

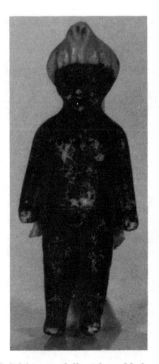

Plate 129: 2½" tall placecard holder doll. Bisque head and upper body, painted features, cardboard lower body which is her skirt. Bisque hands attached to her body by springs. She has a small hole in top of her head to hold stick with a placecard. Unmarked. Photograph courtesy of Connie Parsons. $125.00.

Plate 128: Solid bisque doll with molded on turban. 2¼" tall. Painted features. Much of the paint has been rubbed off the doll. Collection of Michael Wolk-Laniewski. $175.00.

Plate 130: Early 1900's. 15". Head is made of a pottery type porcelain, sleeping brown eyes, dark brown mohair wig, ball jointed body. Doll is said to have been made in Russia from K*R molds. All original in floral cotton print outfit with many layers of skirts. Miniature tambourine is tied to doll's wrist. Unmarked. $600.00.

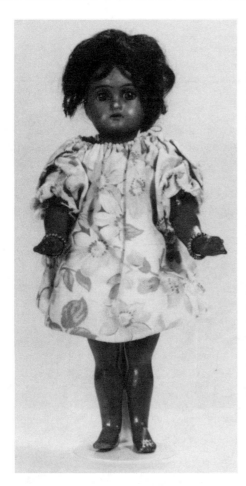

Left — Plate 131: German doll. 7" tall. Bisque head, sleeping brown eyes, black mohair wig, open-mouth, five-piece composition body. Original bracelets of gold-tone beads. Old floral print cotton dress could be original. Marked: 192, on head. This is said to be a K*R mark. $800.00.

Right — Plate 132: Simon & Halbig. Mold #1009. 17" tall. Character child 1900–1920. Bisque head, composition ball jointed body, stationary black eyes, black human hair wig in braids. White cotton dress with eyelet bodice. Clothing probably not original but old. Marks: S 7 2 H 1009/ DEP/GERMANY. Photograph courtesy of Maureen Braeden. $2,000.00.

Plate 133: Bisque twins. 3" tall. One piece bisque dolls with painted eyes, painted black hair with three tufts of hair attached (hair looks like human hair) molded on white dress with orange, green, and blue trim, molded on gold painted shoes. Dolls are in the original box. Dolls are unmarked. Dolls were made in Occupied Japan. $125.00 a set in original box.

Plate 134: Boy and girl all bisque doll similar to previous girl twins. These are a little smaller, 2½" tall. Painted bisque with molded on clothing. Marks: JAPAN, on back. $95.00 set.

CHAPTER 3
CLOTH DOLLS,
LATE 1800'S TO PRESENT

The Delineator, November, 1887, described with illustrations "how to make a black face" for a cloth doll that was called "Mammy Chole." In that same issue, there was a pattern for making clothing for a black nurse doll to be named either "Miss Dinah" or "Aunt Sally." Instructions were given for a dress, apron, handkerchief (to cover neck and bodice) and cap. It was suggested that the dress be made of gay colors.

In 1914, Butler Brothers (wholesale distributor) advertised a 23" "Mammy," cut out and sew doll, and a 17" "Topsy-turvy." The cost was $1.25 per dozen. The mammy doll is wearing a dotted bandanna on her head, a check-ered shawl around her shoulders, a print dress, and print apron. The topsy-turvy doll is not pictured in the ad.

"Gold Dust Twins," 4½" tall, were made in the 1920's by Nelke and used as premiums by the Fairbanks Soap Co., makers of Gold Dust Soap Powder. Dolls were made of cloth.

Merrythought Limited of Ironbridge in Shropshire, England, made black dolls in the late 1930's and 1940's. The dolls had pressed felt faces and velvet cloth bodies. Included in the lines were an 8" "Topsy"; 8" "Yah Sah," dressed as a chef; and 14" "Dixie." Golliwogs with black felt faces and usually wearing a tuxedo were produced beginning in 1932.

In 1991, a black Martha Chase doll was offered by Richard Withington Doll & Toy Auctions. The doll was of the same basic design as the more common white dolls by the maker but is extremely rare in a black version. The doll was sold at auction for $10,340.00 to a collector/dealer from Massachusetts. The doll is shown in a photograph in *The Inside Collector,* June, 1991, page 86.

Plate 135: 1917. Advertisement for pattern for "Dinah Doll" from *McCalls* magazine, December, 1917, page 47. Pattern No. 7550, Character Doll's Set; Dinah Doll and Peasant Doll, dress, apron, cap, and petticoat. It is not clear what the Peasant doll looked like. Only Dinah is shown in the ad. Pattern came in five sizes; to make dolls 14"–22". Pattern cost ten cents. This ad with Dinah and all the white dolls clearly shows how some black dolls were marketed in the early 1900's and what role they were meant to portray.

NO. 7500, DOLL'S SET; cape, jumper dress with guimpe, bathrobe, petticoat and drawers. Pattern in 5 sizes; 14 to 30 inches in height (10 cents).

No. 6860, DOLL'S EMPIRE SET; coat, hat and dress. Pattern in 5 sizes; 14 to 30 inches in height (10 cents).

No. 7480, DOLL'S SET; consisting of coat, hat, dress and romper. Pattern in 6 sizes; 16 to 30 inches in height (10 cents).

No. 8066, BABY DOLL'S SET OF LONG CLOTHES; coat, cap, dress, wrapper or sacque, Gertrude petticoat and stork pants. Pattern in 5 sizes; 14 to 30 inches (15 cents).

No. 6030, DOLL'S SET; coat, hat, dress, petticoat-chemise and drawers. In 5 sizes; 14 to 30 inches (10 cents).

No. 7550, CHARACTER DOLL'S SET; Dinah Doll and Peasant Doll; dress, apron, cap and petticoat. Pattern in 5 sizes; 14 to 22 inches (10 cents).

No. 5640, DOLLS' SET; one-piece dress, undergarment, kimono, night-gown and boudoir cap. Pattern in 5 sizes; 14 to 30 inches (10 cents).

*No. 8090, DOLL'S SET OF SHOE CLOTHES; coat, hat, dress with or without bolero, envelope chemise and petticoat. In 5 sizes; 14 to 30 inches (10 cents).

..870, Doll's Set; dress ..ticoat and envelope chemise. ..n 5 sizes; 14 to 30 inches in..

The quantity of material required for each size of any of these patterns will be found on the pattern envelope.

FOR YOUNG ANNIVERSARIES

No. 1931. Every youngster has at some time the ambition to own a "life sized" doll—and it's an easy ambition to gratify. Adorable rag dolls, as "Sue and Sandy", above, present a really life-like appearance with cunningly shaped and stuffed bodies, wool hair and real clothes made like a child's. Sizes 22 and 30 inches high. Pattern for two dolls, with blue face transfers and directions. Price, 35 cents.

No. 1937. They might have stepped out of a nursery picture book, these appealing little stuffed animals about 5 inches high. Clever mothers make these simple two-piece pets to illustrate, for the toddler, the nursery classics such as "gootic goosie gander," the gingham dog and the calico cat and other favorite story book characters. Pattern for four stuffed animals. Price, 25 cents. Blue.

No. 1939. Frisky lambs gamboling in a daisy field are an adorable decoration for baby's crib or carriage robe. White lambs, lightly padded, on pink or blue eiderdown covers are favorite color combinations, with the daisy fields embroidered in silk floss. One would make a marvelous gift for a favorite godchild. Transfer (blue) gives motif 16½ x 19¼ ins., small motif for kimona, etc., 40 cents.

No. 1938. These perky bunnies and mischievous pickaninny are just the kind of amusing stuffed toys you can't resist sewing together for the youngster. The long eared rabbit can be made of old fashioned calico print, the bunny with print rompers. The velvet Topsy wears calico in very bright colors. Grace Bibber, designer. Pattern for doll 12 ins., and 2 bunnies 8¼ and 10 ins. high. 25 cents.

No. 1935. He may be too small to go to the circus, but he isn't too small to enjoy the rowdy clowns and agile acrobats that disport themselves on his cunning appliqué quilt. These gay colored figures on white, with a color repeated in the wide border would make a gift to please the mother as well as the lucky child who receives one. Pattern for quilt about 41¾ x 64½ ins. Price, 45 cents.

No. 1936. Marionettes are the newest hobby of both grown-ups and youngsters—and it's easy to understand their fascination when you see this delightful new type of rag doll marionette that performs in such an amusing life-like manner. They are simple to make and string; pattern gives full directions. Pattern for 2 marionettes about 24 ins. high. 50 cents. Blue. Designed by Edith Asfry.

Plate 136: Advertisement for pattern for "Topsy," cloth doll, from *Women's World*, 1931. The completed doll would be 12", made of black velvet cloth with calico clothes in bright colors. Grace Bibber designed the doll.

A Josephine Baker doll as sold in Paris

Plate 137: "Josephine Baker" doll photographed in *The Crisis*, May, 1927, page 105. Photo was included in an unrelated column by W.E.B. Dubois. No further information about the doll was mentioned in the column. The doll was probably made by Lenci as Lenci was known to have made a Josephine Baker cloth doll in 1926–27. Josephine Baker was also reported to have been a close friend of dollmaker Madame Lenci. $10,000.00+.

Below — Plate 139: Cocheco Manufacturing Company. "Darkey Doll," 1893. Cut out and sew cloth doll. Uncut cloth is approximately 24" x 17". Finished doll would be about 15" tall. Cloth is marked: PATENTED AUGUST 15TH, 1893. Circle logo in the center of the cloth reads as follows: COCHECO MANUFACTURING COMPANY 1827/LAWRENCE & CO./BOSTON NEW YORK & PHILA. Doll was designed by Ida A. Gutsell, an 1892 graduate of Syracuse University. $725.00.

Plate 138: Saalfield Publishing Co. "Topsy" from "The Rag Family," c. 1911. A set of six dolls were sold together printed on one piece of cloth. They were French, Dutch, Scotch, Spanish, German, and this one, Topsy. They were to be cut, sewn, and stuffed at home. 8" tall. Topsy is wearing a red dotted dress, yellow shoes, and is holding a watermelon. $400.00.

Left — Plate 140: "Mammy Castoria." 11" tall. Lithographed cut out and sew doll offered by Fletcher's Castoria in the 1930's. Skirt has green, red, and blue stripes, yellow dotted apron, blue bodice on dress, yellow dotted shawl, and headwrap. Doll is holding a box of Fletcher's Castoria. Marks: MAMMY CASTORIA, at front hemline. $200.00.

Right — Plate 141: Georgene Novelties. "Beloved Belindy." 19" tall. Collection of Michele Bady. Doll is shown in color on page 13, plate 29. $1,200.00 and up.

Left — Plate 142: Georgene Novelties. "Beloved Belindy." 13½" tall. All cloth, white button eyes, painted nose and mouth. Replaced apron, skirt, and bandanna. Collection of Michele Bady. $1,200.00+.

Right — Plate 143: The Toy Works. "Beloved Belindy." 8" tall. Printed on red blouse, cap, shoes, and white undies. Removable yellow print skirt. Printed on lower back: ©1991 Mcmillan, Inc. Tag sewn to body: THE TOY WORKS. $15.00.

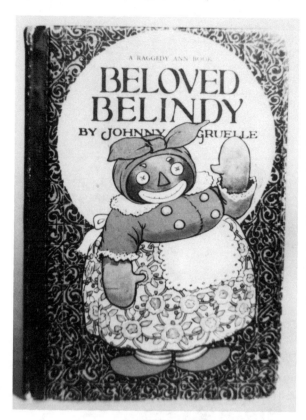

Plate 144: Children's book, *Beloved Belindy* by Johnny Gruelle, published by the Bobbs-Merrill Co., Inc., 1960. Popular Beloved Belindy dolls were based on character in this book. Book had first copyright in 1926 by the P.F. Volland Company; ©1941 by Myrtle Gruelle; renewed in 1953 by Myrtle Gruelle. Collection of Michele Bady. $60.00.

Plate 146: Another Beecher type cloth doll. 20½" tall. Original dress. This one has nose damage but dolls are very similar. Courtesy of Patricia Whittler Martin. $1,000.00.

Plate 145: Beecher type cloth doll. Circa 1910. 20" tall. All cloth, black dome shaped button eyes, embroidered mouth, black lamb skin wig. All original in turkey red print dress. Collection of Michael Wolk-Laniewski. $3,000.00.

Plate 147: Advertisement for "Aunt Jemima's Rag Doll Family." Ad was in color in the magazine, *Woman's World,* Volume 32, Number 12, December, 1916, page 17. *Woman's World* was published by Woman's World Magazine Company, Inc., 107, South Clinton Street, Chicago, Il. In 1916, there were two million subscribers to this publication. $30.00.

Plate 148: 1949 advertisement for vinyl "Aunt Jemima" family dolls. Aunt Jemima, Uncle Mose, Wade, and Diana. Dolls are shown in my book *Black Dolls, 1920–1991,* page 62.

Plate 149: Advertisement for Aunt Jemima rag dolls from *The Ladies Home Journal,* January, 1926. In the color ad, Aunt Jemima has her arms folded in front of her, is not holding pancakes, has a yellow dress with black dots, a red and white striped apron. Uncle Mose has on a red shirt with white dots, blue jeans with a patch on only his right knee. Diana has a white dress with red dots, has a ribbon in her hair, is holding a cat, has a yellow patch on her dress, and a yellow scarf around her neck. Wade is holding his hat straight in front of him, not sidewards as in some Wade dolls and has patches on both knees of his bluejeans. A similar ad appeared in the February, 1926 edition of *The Ladies Home Journal.* Both ads were full page ads for Aunt Jemima Pancake Flour. The rag dolls and the coupon for ordering were in the bottom right hand corner of the page. $15.00.

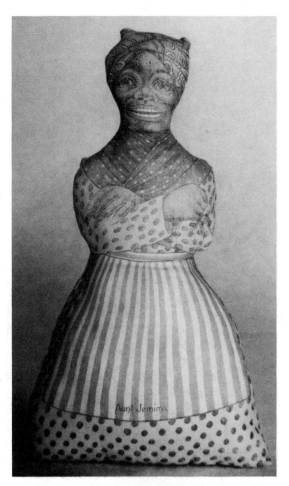

Plate 151: "Aunt Jemima," 15" tall. Circa 1916. Red bandanna with yellow print that has tied ends sticking up near the top. This way of tying the bandanna changed in later Aunt Jemima dolls. Smiling mouth, red dotted shawl around her neck, red and white striped apron, yellow dress with black dots. This doll is the one shown in the December, 1916 *Women's World* magazine. Marks: AUNT JEMIMA, on front of apron. $300.00.

Plate 150: Davis Milling Co. "Aunt Jemima." 15" tall. 1905. Doll has yellow dress with tiny black dots under a red and white striped apron. The dots and the stripes on this Jemima doll are smaller than any of the other Jemima dolls shown in this book or my earlier book. Doll was damaged and has been mended at the neck, distorting the original big wide grin with upper and lower teeth showing. The neckerchief is red with white dots and a striped border; the head bandanna is red with yellow circles. Marks: AUNT JEMIMA'S PANCAKE FLOUR PICKANINNY DOLL/THE DAVIS MILLING CO./ST. JOSEPH, MO., on lower corner of the apron. $325.00.

Plate 152: Aunt Jemima Mills Co. "Aunt Jemima." 15" tall. Two sets of Aunt Jemima dolls were issued in 1924. This doll is from the first edition. It is very similar to the first set except that she has more wrinkles on her face and her bandanna has more folds than in the later edition shown on page 61 in my earlier book, *Black Dolls, 1820–1991.* Marks: AUNT JEMIMA, on apron. $275.00.

Plate 153: "Uncle Mose," 16" tall. Circa 1916. This Uncle Mose has on a yellow hat, red shirt with a pipe in his pocket, yellow suspenders, black pants. His arms are crossed, he has a full white beard, and closed mouth. He is the only Uncle Mose that I have seen with soles sewn on the bottom of his feet. It is a separate piece of fabric and is yellow. This is the Uncle Mose shown in the 1916 ad for "Aunt Jemima's Rag Doll Family" in the magazine *Women's World,* Volume 32, Number 12, December, 1916, page 17. Marks: UNCLE MOSE, on back. $300.00.

Plate 155: Aunt Jemima Mills Co. "Uncle Mose." 16" tall. Printed on cloth doll is wearing a red print shirt with white circles, black pants, brown shoes, yellow suspenders. This one does not have a separate piece for the feet. Marks: UNCLE MOSE, printed on back. $275.00.

Plate 154: Davis Milling Co. "Uncle Mose," ©1905. Uncut cloth doll from the Aunt Jemima rag doll family. Cloth is approximately 31" x 8½". Completed doll would be about 14½" tall. This is the earliest of the Uncle Mose dolls that I have seen. He is wearing a white and red striped shirt with black pants, has a pipe in his pocket, and is holding what appears to be a spoon. The following information is printed on the cloth: Our Full Set of Rag Dolls, Aunt Jemima, Uncle Mose and the pickaninnies, Diana and Wade Davis, full size, ready to cut and stuff will be sent to any address postpaid upon receipt of four coupons taken from packages of Aunt Jemima's Pancake Flour, Aunt Jemima's Special Cake and Pastry flour, and 16 cents in stamps, or will send any one of these Dolls for one coupon and four cents in stamps. Be careful to give full name, street number, town, and state. Address all mail to The Davis Milling Company, St. Joseph, Mo., also manufacturers of Davis Royal No. 10, (Mo. Soft Wheat) Davis Golden Sheaf, (Kansas Turkey Hard Wheat.) Uncle Mose doll is marked: AUNT JEMIMA'S/PANCAKE FLOUR/DOLL, UNCLE MOSE./THE DAVIS,/MILLING CO.,/ST. JOSEPH, MO., on front of shirt. $300.00.

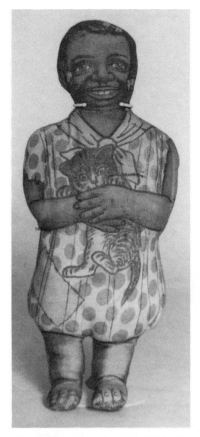

Plate 156: Aunt Jemima Mills Co. "Diana Jemima." 11" tall. From the first edition of 1924. Diana is holding a cat and is wearing a red and white dotted dress, unlike the Diana redesigned later in 1924, where she is wearing a blue print dress. Marks: DIANA JEMIMA, on back. $200.00.

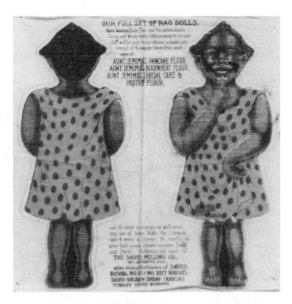

Plate 157: Davis Milling Co. "Diana," ©1905. Uncut cloth doll from the set of Aunt Jemima rag dolls. Cloth is approximately 12" x 12". Completed doll would be approximately 11" tall. Notice the almost triangular shaped head. This was changed on later Diana dolls. Dress is yellow with orange dots. Marks: AUNT JEMIMA'S/PANCAKE FLOUR DOLL,/DIANA,/THE DAVIS MILLING CO.,/ST. JOSEPH, MO., on the front of the dress near the hemline. $300.00.

Plate 158: Arnold Print Works. "Topsy." 8" tall. All cloth doll from printed cloth made to be cut out and sewn at home. Doll has on a red dress and is holding her hat. Larger, more common, 14" version of the same doll is in author's book *Black Dolls, 1820–1991* on page 59. The larger doll is named Pickaninny. $350.00.

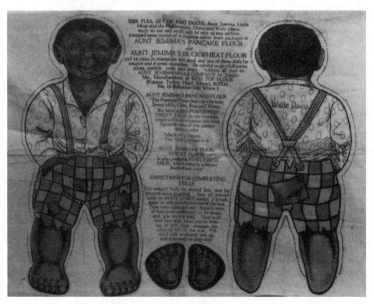

Plate 159: Aunt Jemima Mills Co. "Wade," son of Aunt Jemima. Printed on cloth uncut doll. Cloth is approximately 12" x 18". Wade is wearing a white shirt with orange print and orange and yellow checkered pants. Marks: WADE DAVIS, on back. $250.00.

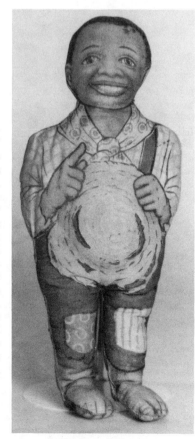

Plate 160: Aunt Jemima Mills. "Wade." 11" tall. Original Wade from the first set designed in 1924. Redesigned 1924 Wade doll is shown in my earlier book on black dolls on page 61. Doll is almost identical except one hand has a finger pointing, he is holding his hat for a full view of the brim, and is marked. Doll is wearing a white and yellow window pane print shirt. Marks: WADE DAVIS, on back. $150.00.

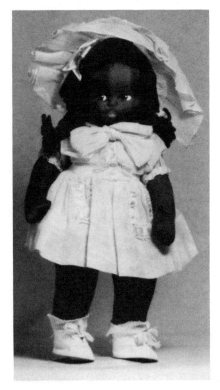

Plate 161: Cloth mask face doll. 14" tall. 1940's. Black satin-like face and limbs, pink body, black yarn hair, painted features. All original in Alexander quality beige organdy dress and bonnet. Unmarked. $250.00.

Plate 164: Berea College Student Industries. 23" tall. All cloth doll, felt eyes and mouth, embroidered nose, sewn on kerchief with attached hoop earring. All original with white cotton blouse, green cotton skirt, and red print jacket. Marks: BEREA COLLEGE/STUDENT INDUSTRIES/BEREA, KENTUCKY, on tag sewn to right leg. Courtesy of Michael Wolk-Laniewski. $100.00.

Plate 162: November, 1944 advertisement for McCall's pattern 1167 for a bean bag black boy doll. $5.00.

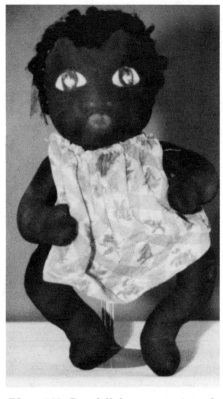

Plate 163: Rag doll from approximately 1914. Black shiny material, printed features, nubby black hair. 12" tall. Frog legs. Collection of and photo courtesy of Etta Houston. $575.00.

Plate 165: 6½" felt native-type doll. Fully jointed at neck, shoulders, and hips, glass eyes, applied ears, excelsior stuffed, detailed stitching on fingers and toes, center seam down the middle of the face. Collection of and photograph courtesy of Lynn Shay. $125.00.

Plate 166: Stuart Co. "Honey Suckle," cloth Mammy sachet. 8". Lithographed face, printed cloth forms body and sachet bag. Tag attached to hang string: NO. 38/MAMMY SACHET/MFG. BY/STUART CO. ST. PAUL MINN./HONEY SUCKLE; reverse side: HANG ME UP OR LAY ME DOWN/HONEY SUCKLE. $65.00.

Plate 167: American cloth folk doll. 25" tall. Painted features. Photograph courtesy of Frasher's Auction. (Price not available.)

Plate 168: Biarritz. 10½". Made in France. 1920–1940. Cloth mask face, lamb's wool hair, painted features, cloth felt covered body and limbs over wire armature. All original, including guitar. Tag sewn to jacket: CREATIONS/LARREA/BIARRITZ/MADE IN FRANCE. $95.00.

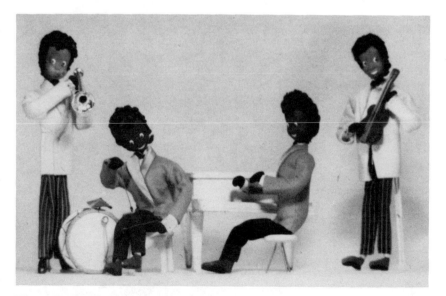

Plate 169: Biarritz. All approximately 10½". Left — Group of four musicians. 1920–1940. Cloth mask face, lamb's wool hair, cloth bodies over wire armature. Two of the dolls are a light shade of brown, the other two are darker. All original. Unmarked. $500.00 set. Right — Close-up of one of the musicians.

Plate 170: "Golliwog." 11". All cloth. Clothing forms body, red and white striped pants, blue, red, and yellow top. Unmarked. $125.00.

Plate 171: Collection of cloth "Golliwogs." 9", 11½", and 13½". The two taller ones are cotton stuffed. The smaller one is straw stuffed (most unusual) with glass eyes and mink hair. Photograph courtesy of Lu Lane. $175.00 each.

Left — Plate 172: Dean's Childsplay Toys Ltd. "Golliwogg." 12½". All cloth, black button eyes, painted face, clothing forms the body (red and yellow). Tag sewn to body: DEAN'S CHILDSPLAY TOYS LTD./RYE, SUSSEX/...Collection of Michael Wolk-Laniewski. $175.00.

Right — Plate 173: Another Dean's Golliwogg similar to the previous doll. This one is 16" tall. Tagged body. Photograph courtesy of Susan Girardot. $200.00.

Left — Plate 174: Pedigree. "Golliwog." Red jacket, yellow shirt, black and white striped pants. Clothing forms the body. Tag has been cut off at the back neckline, but enough remains to tell it is from the Pedigree Company. Photograph courtesy of Pat & Bill Biskie. $200.00.

Right — Plate 175: Dean's Childsplay Toys Ltd. "Golliwog" #800. 1978. 13" tall. Cloth with removable blue felt jacket. Red pants, yellow vest, black shoes with white spats form the body of the doll. Sewn on black synthetic hair. Original hangtag is attached to the doll. Collection of the Museum of African American History (Detroit). The same doll was also made in 16" size by Dean's. $75.00.

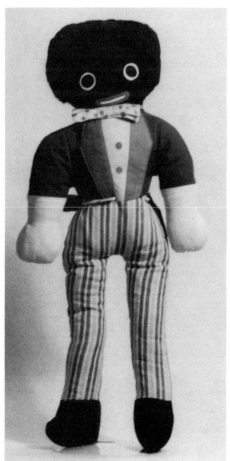

Left — Plate 176: 18". "Golliwog" from England. 1977. All cloth with sewn on clothing that forms the body, black acrylic wig. Unmarked. Collection of the Museum of African American History (Detroit). $75.00.

Right — Plate 177: "Golliwog." 15½" tall. Felt head, felt sewn on mouth, glued on eyes and nose, black yarn hair. Felt clothing forms the body, yellow shirt, blue jacket, red pants, white spats, black shoes. Unmarked. Collection of Michelle Bady. $175.00.

Plate 179: 24" "Golliwog." Removable clothing. Photograph courtesy of Lu Lane. $200.00.

Plate 178: Chad Valley Chiltern. 24" tall. All cloth, felt eyes and nose, applied cloth mouth. Sewn on clothing forms the body, navy blue jacket, yellow shirt, red striped pants. Hang tag: ANOTHER/SOFTTOY/BY/CHAD VALLEY CHILTERN/MADE IN ENGLAND; reverse side: CHAD VALLEY BY APPOINTMENT/TO H M QUEEN ELIZABETH/THE QUEEN MOTHER/TOYMAKERS. $125.00.

Left — Plate 180: Chad Valley Co. "Golliwog." 17" tall. Clothing forms the body, blue jacket, yellow shirt, red and white striped pants. Tagged: CHAD VALLEY CO. LTD. Photograph courtesy of Pat and Bill Biskie. $200.00.

Right — Plate 181: Merry Thought Ltd. "1930–1990 Merry Thought Diamond Jubilee." 20" tall. Fake fur wig, velvet face, hands and arms, plastic eyes. Velveteen tuxedo in red and blue forms the body. Tagged. Courtesy of Robert G. Ransom. $75.00.

STORY LORE Dolls

For "you know who"—provided of course, that she's good

*Listen, my children, and you shall hear
The story leaves rustle, and drawing near
The voices of friends like Gay Gingerbread Man
Who says "Run, run, run and catch me if you can"!*

A Gay Gingham Dog

Here's proof that the Gingham Dog of poetic Field fame was Scotch; just look at this plaid descendant of his. And there will be hundreds like him this Christmas all standing firmly around, each with a hi'land bonnet cocked over his weather eye! He's 12 inches long, 9 inches tall with button eyes and everything, except the stuffing, ready-cut in packet No. 128.

Gingham Dog No. 128

Black Sambo No. 184

Golliwog No. 185

*Look here, my children, and you shall see
Hansel & Gretel as Dutch as can be;
Little Black Sambo in red coat so bold
Pants, shoes, umbrella in colors as told*

We've seen miniature Golliwogs atop perfume bottles and real live Golliwogs dancing in a smart review, and someway their startling inquisitive pertness is always irresistible! Our clever edition will be jolly amidst the pillows on a bed or sofa. He's 20 inches tall with bright blue, red, black and white, in proper solids, stripes and polka dots and his hair raising wig—ah, that's a secret, but it is all in the packet No. 185, all materials except stuffing.

Never was there a Story Lore girl with more imagination than Alice, and so the lucky child who owns this Alice doll may step right into a wonderland of fun! She stands 16 inches high with glossy brown hair pompadoured back, authentically cut apron and black felt slippers. Packet No. 922X contains the stamped cloth dolly, 3 colors of embroidery thread, hair ribbon and yarn for her hair, felt shoes, organdie sleeves, collar and apron and dainty print dress. Lace and braid may be added if you choose, but they are not in the assortment.

They come cut and stamped, with all materials, ready to stuff and sew together

Gretel No. 478G

Hansel No. 478H

Rooster No. 133

Gingerbread Boy No. 183

*Order, my children, and sew as directed
And there will evolve just as you have expected—*

*A Golliwog, say—with such talent for knowledge
Big sister will carry him right back to college!*

Alice in Wonderland No. 922X

The Black Sambo packet contains ever so many bits of material, enough for a brown boy with a black wool pigtail wig, red coat, blue trousers, purple shoes with crimson soles and the green umbrella of felt. He finishes 11 inches tall. All material except stuffing included in packet No. 184.

This chesty, cock-sure little rooster is either the crooner who joined the Bremen-town Musicians or the crower who refused to work for little Red Hen! Anyway he's just the thing for dad's sock on Christmas morning. His tail is three brilliant layers of felt feathers with spots and top knot to match. He wears a w'scoat instead of wings, stands firmly 11 inches tall; all materials except kapok stuffing in packet No. 133.

Hansel and Gretel have the funniest round faces with sewed on ears and noses. Their wooden shoes are felt, but the rest of their clothes may be made of any bright materials from your scrap bag. Stamped muslin dolls, wig yarn, and embroidery threads are in the packets with cutting patterns and directions for their garments. They finish 12 inches tall. Hansel is No. 478H and Gretel No. 478G.

How a sleepy tot will adore this cuddly, chubby gingerbread boy all made of lustrous ginger tan broadcloth. His raisin eyes and currant buttons are blue and purple, his mouth is orange peel color while the nose which was a blob of dough is a stuffed applique. Sugar white ricrac looks like it might have been squeezed from a pastry tube for his cap and jacket trim. He's 10 inches tall with stamped broadcloth, ricrac and four colors of embroidery thread included in packet No. 183.

Plate 182: Advertisement for "Golliwog" No. 185 and "Black Sambo" No. 184 from *Women's World,* December, 1936, inside front cover. The completed Golliwog would be 20" tall and the completed Black Sambo would be 11" tall. All materials except stuffing are included in the packets. More information on Golliwogs can be found in author's previous book, *Black Dolls, 1820–1991,* on page 66.

Plate 183: 16½" cloth doll with very skillfully done embroidery features, knotted black wool embroidery floss hair. All original. Doll appears to have been made from a commercial pattern as face is three pieces and back of head has a dart to give form to head. Collection of Emma Ransom Hayward. $85.00.

Plate 184: Handmade cloth doll made from a commercially sold pattern. 15" tall. Black cloth head and body, felt eyes and mouth, painted nose, attached gray beard and hair around the back of head. Top of head is bald. Dressed in blue and white striped shirt, black pants with a patch. Black plastic hat looks like a recent replacement. 1940–50. Collection of the Museum of African American History (Detroit). $65.00.

Plate 185: Left — Sea Island Sugar. "Gobo, South African Boy." ©1935. Cloth doll is printed on the back of a ten pound bag of Sea Island Sugar, manufactured by the Western Sugar Refinery, San Francisco, California. Bag is 15" x 9¾". Directions were printed on the bag for making the doll. $150.00. Right — Reverse side of Sea Island Sugar bag.

Plate 186: Above — Victor Flour. ©1939. Cloth puppets, one black the other white, printed on the back of a 48 pound bag of Victor flour milled by The Crete Mills in Crete, Nebraska. Black boy is wearing a yellow shirt and red checked pants. White boy has a red shirt with blue and white striped pants. Finished puppets would be approximately 12" tall. Flour sack measures 15½" x 28". $150.00. Right — Reverse side of Victor Flour bag.

Plate 187: 16½" handmade cloth doll. Muslin head, embroidered features, needle sculptured nose, bristle-like hair, stumps for legs. All original in natural linen type sleeveless blouse, two-toned brown and white plaid skirt. Doll was found in a house on top of Civil War letters. Private collection. $700.00.

Plate 188: 17" all cloth souvenir doll from the Caribbean Islands. Circa 1950. Shell necklace and bracelet, straw bag and hat, embroidered features, black braided fabric hair. All original. Collection of Michael Wolk-Laniewski. $65.00.

Plate 189: 13" mask face cloth doll. Black striped cloth body, faded white apron and matching headwrap, gold earrings, painted facial features, red and white gingham skirt. Circa 1940. Collection of the Museum of African American History (Detroit). $65.00.

Plate 190: Sock doll. Doll is made out of a gray sock, attached plastic eyes, embroidered nose and mouth, black and white yarn pigtails all over the head. Dressed in blue print dress. Collection of the Museum of African American History (Detroit). $20.00.

Plate 191: Souvenir dolls from the Virgin Islands. 10" tall. All cloth with embroidered features, attached black yarn hair with attached goldtone earrings. All original. $40.00 each.

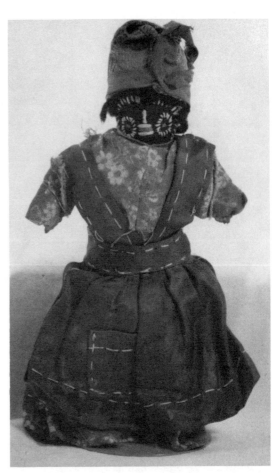

Plate 192: Mammy type cloth doll. 8½" tall. Commercially made doll, painted facial features. All original in red print dress, red headwrap with goldtone hoop earring attached. 1940–50. Unmarked. $55.00.

Plate 193: Handmade cloth doll with embroidered facial features. Said to have been made during the Civil War. Doll has no arms, body and legs are made out of blue floral print cloth. Private collection. $200.00.

Plate 194: 36" cloth doll. Circa 1970–80. Handmade of black cloth, painted hair with yarn pigtails, painted features. Blouse and pantaloons are made of feed sack type cloth; skirt is granny-patch quilt, apron fabric is in Dutch tulip design. Private collection. $85.00.

Plate 195: Cloth half doll. Embroidered features, black yarn hair, attached plastic hoop earrings, embroidered fingernails. 10" tall. Mid 1900's. Collection of Michele Bady. $125.00.

Plate 196: 7". Early stockinette face, wooden legs and shoes, print two piece outfit. Collection of Reevah Turner. $35.00.

Plate 197: 9½". Brazilian souvenir doll. Brown felt body and glued on facial features. Marked: BONECAS TIPICAS, on base. Collection of Reevah Turner. $35.00.

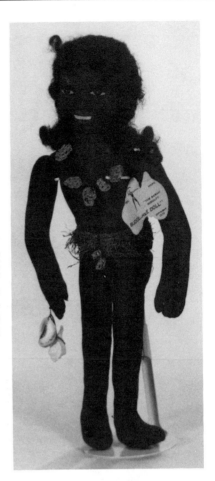

Left — Plate 198: 10" cloth doll with baby on her back. Dressed in authentic African cloth. Stitch features. Still available in 1993. Collection of Reevah Turner. $20.00.

Right — Plate 199: "The Sarah Midgley Budgerree Doll." 12" tall. ©#15775. Cloth mask face, painted features, black mohair wig, coral beads around neck. Portion of original grass skirt remains around waist. Hang tag: THE SARAH MIDGLEY BUDGERREE DOLL/ ©#15775. Reverse side of tag: AUSTRALIA, stamped on; KUMMERA OF AUSTRALIA, hand written. Collection of Michael Wolk-Laniewski. $125.00.

Left — Plate 200: 10" toaster cover doll. 1940's. Button eyes, embroidered mouth. Cloth head is made of faille. Collection of Michael Wolk-Laniewski. $80.00.

Right — Plate 201: Cloth toaster cover. 8½" head to waist. Early 1930's. Blue cotton print dress. Collection of Michael Wolk-Laniewski. $80.00.

as Seen in
GOOD HOUSEKEEPING

SINGING SAM AND MANDY
BW-94

General Materials One pair woman's lisle hose, beige or brown. Cotton wadding for stuffing. Four black buttons for eyes. White felt for whites of eyes. Brown felt for hands. J. & P. Coats or Clark's O.N.T. Six Strand Embroidery Floss in red and brown. Chadwick's Red Heart Knitting Worsted in black for hair. J. & P. Coats or Clark's O.N.T. Mercerized Sewing Threads to match.

Materials for Sam Red and white striped cotton (shirt); blue denim (overalls); yellow felt (hat); black felt (shoes and hat band); Printed cotton (patches on overalls); narrow black velvet ribbon (bow tie); five small pearl buttons; short pair of doll's socks in a bright color.

Plate 202: Directions for making cloth dolls "Singing Sam" and "Mandy" #BW-94. Directions are in three page booklet #G46 by the Spool Cotton Co. The dolls were made from women's hose. Finished height was not given but head circumference was 10½". No information was available on date of publication. $5.00.

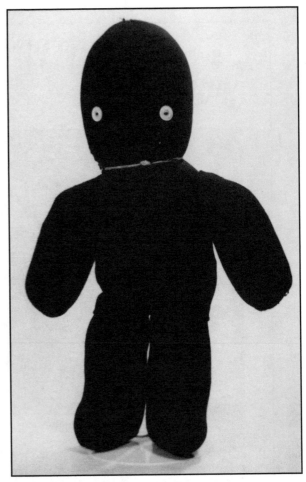

Plate 203: Homemade 16" cloth doll. Embroidered eyes and mouth, applied nose and ears, black yarn hair, crystal beads for teeth. 1930's. Collection of Michael Wolk-Laniewski. $125.00.

Plate 204: 15". Stuffed black sock doll with white button eyes. Doll is extremely heavy. It is not known what it is stuffed with. Collection of Michael Wolk-Laniewski. $60.00.

Plate 205: Sock doll, 11½" tall. Doll was made for Connie Parsons in the early 1950's by her aunt. Doll has button eyes, embroidered mouth and nose, plastic rings for earrings. Plastic rings make her hands and feet. Original clothes. Photograph courtesy of Connie Parsons. $75.00.

Plate 206: Artist doll. "The Sawdust Doll." 18". Handpainted cloth face. All original recreation of an antique doll. 1980's. Collection of Michael Wolk-Laniewski. $150.00.

Left — Plate 207: Peck. 9½" souvenir type doll. Embroidered features, attached earrings. All original with fruit basket on head. Sticker attached to front of skirt: HAND MADE IN THE/VIRGIN ISLANDS/BY/MYRA LINN PECK. 1970's. Collection of Michael Wolk-Laniewski. $75.00.

Right — Plate 208: 17" knitted boy doll. Probably homemade in the 1890's. Head, hands, and legs are knitted in brown yarn, clothing is knitted in red and white with blue accents. Collection of Michael Wolk-Laniewski. $225.00.

Left — Plate 209: Sock doll. 15". Button eyes, embroidered nose, applied fabric mouth (partially missing,) attached hoop earrings. All original in green print dress with red scarf and headpiece. Collection of Michael Wolk-Laniewski. $125.00.

Right — Plate 210: 11" tall. Cloth mask face. Circa 1940–50. All original in red dotted dress and headpiece, white apron. Collection of Michael Wolk-Laniewski. $125.00.

Plate 211: Souvenir type cloth doll. 13" tall. Embroidered features, wooden bead earrings. All original. Circa 1950. The shape of the legs is an interesting feature. Collection of Michael Wolk-Laniewski. $65.00.

Plate 212: Sock doll. 13" tall. Button eyes, stitch-tacked nose, embroidered nostrils and mouth. All original in plaid dress with red print bandanna scarf and kerchief. Collection of Michele Bady. $85.00.

Plate 213: 11" tall. Cloth doll handmade from a commercial pattern. Two seams down front of face, felt eyes and mouth, painted nostrils, black yarn hair, jointed arms and legs. All original in red print shirt, light blue pants. Collection of Michele Bady. $75.00.

Plate 215: "Yo' Aunt Cloe." 15" tall. All original sock doll, mid 1900's. Button eyes, embroidered nose, applied cloth mouth is damaged, attached hoop earrings. Hang tag:

Plate 214: Cloth toaster cover. 1960–70. Button eyes, embroidered nose and mouth, attached goldtone hoop earrings. Collection of Michele Bady. $85.00.

RIGHT FROM DIXIE/YO' AUNT CLOE/SOLD BY/LAFAYETTE GRILL/WALTERBORO, S.C. BRUNSWICK, GA. Collection of Michele Bady. $175.00.

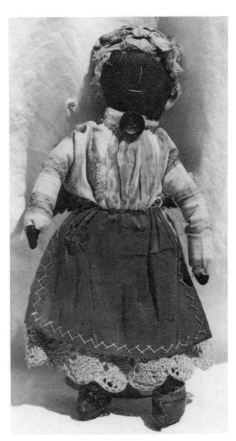

Left — Plate 216: "Aunt Peachy." 17" tall. All cloth, embroidered mouth and nostrils, painted eyes with embroidered outline, gray yarn hair, attached hoop earrings. All original in red print dress, red bandanna, white bibbed apron. Tag sewn to dress: AUNT PEACHY/SOUTHERN DARKY DOLLS/"JUST FOLKS" REG. U.S. PAT. OFF./HELEN WALKER, STAUNTON, VA. Collection of Michele Bady. $225.00.

Right — Plate 217: 9½" cloth doll from late 1800's or early 1900's. Doll has no hair, head is covered with cap, embroidered French knots for eyes, stitched mouth and nose. Clothing is extremely well made but doll's arms are different lengths. Private collection. $250.00.

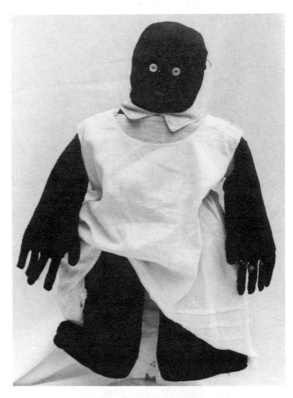

Plate 218: 20" handmade cloth doll. Early 1900's. Outstanding feature of this old doll is the beautifully made two-piece green dress with yellow needlework. Facial features that remain are very crude. Private collection. $350.00.

Plate 219: 21" handmade cloth doll made in 1916 or before. Doll has no hair, button eyes, two red stitches for nose, embroidered mouth and teeth (does not show up in photo). Doll is dressed in blue wool dress with some moth holes, wearing two slips and a separate collar. Under the black cloth on the body, you can see a blue and white striped material. Private collection. $125.00.

Plate 220: 9½" handmade cloth doll. Black muslin head and body, rolled muslin arms and one seam legs, braided wool hair. Reverse appliqué technique was used to make facial features with red fabric underneath the black used in the face. Private collection. $250.00.

Plate 221: 15" male cloth doll. Late 1800's. Black bead eyes with white stitching behind, nose and mouth are badly worn off. Original old clothing. Private collection. $400.00.

Plate 222: Smaller version of plate 223. 10" tall. Pressed face, painted black eyes with green accents, tuft of black yarn hair under sewn on cap. All original in red dotted dress with white apron. Unmarked. $35.00.

Left — Plate 223: Commercially made cloth doll with pressed mask face, looped black yarn sewn under bonnet for bangs, two sewn on black yarn braids, painted features including green eyes, brown cloth arms and legs, red cloth body, feet and dress and matching bonnet with removable white apron. This type of doll was very inexpensive during the 1930's and 1940's and was usually given as a prize at a carnival. Similar dolls were available in varying sizes. 16" tall. Unmarked. $100.00.

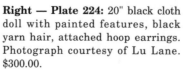

Right — Plate 224: 20" black cloth doll with painted features, black yarn hair, attached hoop earrings. Photograph courtesy of Lu Lane. $300.00.

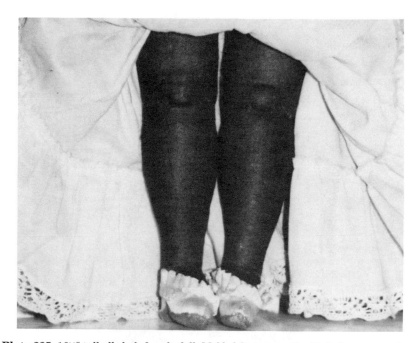

Plate 225: 16½" tall all cloth female doll. Molded features with stitched eyes, mouth and teeth. Cloth on entire doll is stuffed very tightly. Fingers are individually stitched and have real fingernails. Modeling on this doll is outstanding. Her hands, feet and knees are realistic. Original elaborate dress and shoes and wearing rings, bracelets, necklaces, and earrings. Unmarked. $300.00.
Above — Close up of knees. Photograph courtesy of Connie Parsons.

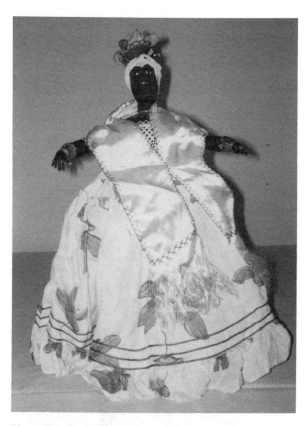

Plate 226: Brazilian "Bahai" doll. 15" tall. All cloth with needle sculpted features, stitched fingers and feet. All original. Collection of Emma Ransom Hayward. $300.00.

Plate 227: 12" cloth doll with embroidered features, molded nose, separate fingers with fingernails, anatomically correct, has elbows and knees. Original clothing. Private collection. $250.00.

Left — Plate 228:
16½". Anatomically correct cloth doll. Circa 1910. Glass eyes, quill finger-nails, embroidered features. All original. Collection of Michael Wolk-Laniewski. $300.00.

Right — Plate 229:
11" souvenir doll from New Orleans. Cotton stuffed, painted features, cotton added for bustline. Photograph courtesy of Lu Lane. $125.00.

Left — Plate 230:
17" sateen type cloth doll with needle sculpted features. Photograph courtesy of Lu Lane. $125.00.

Right — Plate 231:
12" cloth doll with button eyes. All original. Photograph courtesy of Lu Lane. $125.00.

Left — Plate 232: 13" cotton stuffed doll, cotton hair, embroidered features, stitched flat fingers. Photograph courtesy of Lu Lane. $225.00.

Right — Plate 233: 20" cotton stuffed cloth doll with button eyes and nose, 11" topsy-turvy with button eyes, embroidered nose and mouth. Photograph courtesy of Lu Lane. $175.00 each.

Left — Plate 234: 18" cotton stuffed child doll with embroidered features. Photograph courtesy of Lu Lane. $250.00.

Right — Plate 235: 14" cloth doll with painted features. All original in skirt made of feathers. Photograph courtesy of Lu Lane. $225.00.

Plate 236: 15" cotton stuffed cloth doll, oil painted features. Photograph courtesy of Lu Lane. $250.00.

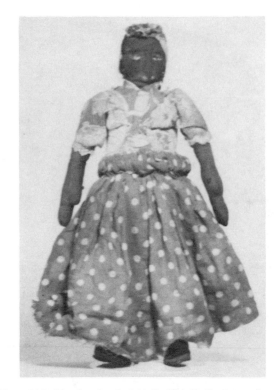

Plate 237: Handmade cloth doll. 8" tall. Sculptured nose, painted eyes and mouth, black human hair or mohair, tiny beads sewn on for earrings, cloth wire armature body. All original in green dotted skirt, print blouse, shawl, and kerchief. 1940's. Unmarked. $75.00.

Plate 238: Souvenir type cloth dolls. Left — 9½", without hat, probably from one of the Carribean islands, circa 1960; right — 15", sawdust stuffed, probably from a Pacific island, embroidered features, black yarn hair. Photograph courtesy of Lu Lane. $65.00 each.

Plate 239: Cloth doll with commercially painted on facial features, sewn in black yarn braids, red dotted cloth body for clothing, removable white apron and neckscarf. 14" tall. Unmarked. 1930–1940. $85.00.

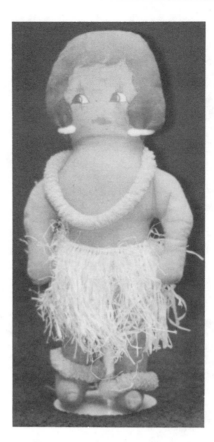

Plate 241: 10½" brown cloth doll, painted features, grass skirt, orange lei and anklets. Germany is stamped on foot. Photograph courtesy of Faith Wyse. $125.00.

Plate 240: 24" handmade one-of-a-kind cloth doll. Cotton stuffed, shoe button eyes, individual fingers. Photograph courtesy of Lu Lane. $375.00.

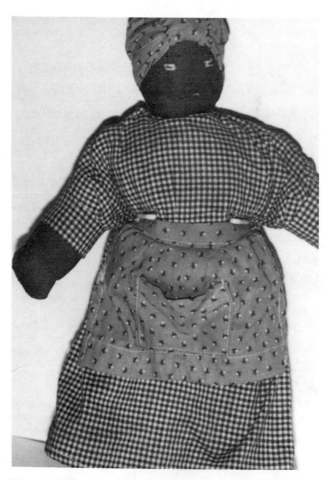

Plate 242: 7" cloth toaster cover with embroidered features. Photograph courtesy of Lu Lane. $85.00.

Plate 243: Approximately 9" cloth mammy-type doll, embroidered features. Photograph courtesy of Lu Lane. $125.00.

Left — Plate 244: 11" cloth girl. Painted features, white button earrings, black yarn hair. Photograph courtesy of Lu Lane. $95.00.

Right — Plate 245: 20" handmade cloth doll made of black wool fabric. Applied red wool lips, ecru cotton for teeth and applied eyes, black wool pupils. Doll was made by a black woman named "Elizabeth." Her last name has been lost. Collection of Mary A. Beard. All original. Missing one white shoe. $125.00.

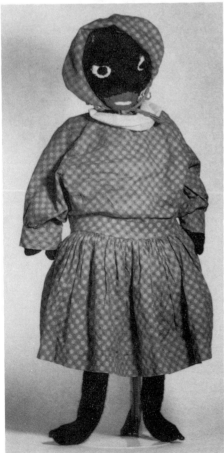

Left — Plate 246: 30" handmade cloth doll made by "Elizabeth" along with previous doll. Head and body made of black stockings with wig made of human hair, features applied out of fabric. It is stuffed with cotton as it would have come from the fields. Collection of Mary A. Beard. $125.00.

Right — Plate 247: 19" handmade cloth doll, early 1900's. Body is made of black stockings and black fabric, stuffed hard with fabric or cotton. Eyes, mouth, teeth, and eyebrows are embroidered. Nose and dimpled mouth are needle sculpted. Nubby-textured fabric forms hair under bandanna. Wire armature in body. Hand sewn clothing. Collection of Pat & Bill Biskie. No price available.

Left — Plate 248: 13" handmade cloth doll. Face appears to be crepe, arms and legs appear to be some type of polished cotton, torso is blue and white cotton check, back of head is velvet. Hair is of cording material. Removable clothing, embroidered mouth and nose, fabric covered button eyes with black ink painted on. Doll appears to have been made from a "scrap" bag. Photograph courtesy of Pat and Bill Biskie. $200.00.

Right — Plate 249: Cloth mask face musical doll. 11½" tall. Black yarn hair, painted side glancing eyes, painted mouth, black velvet body and limbs. Key wound musical doll plays "My Old Kentucky Home." All original in red and white striped dress with matching panties, red hair bows and red ribbons around the ankles. 1930's. Unmarked. $200.00.

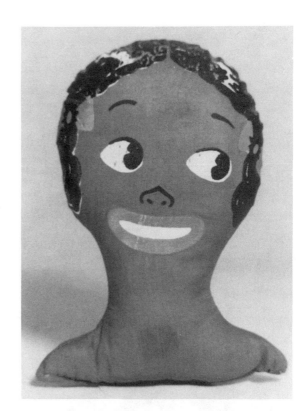

Plate 250: Approximately 7" cloth doll in dress made of a red bandanna, red felt shoes and purse, embroidered features. Photograph courtesy of Lu Lane. $65.00.

Plate 251: Commercially made cloth doll head. 6¼" tall. Painted black hair with red painted bows, painted side glancing eyes, watermelon mouth. Unmarked. 1940's. $45.00.

Plate 252: Lenci-type cloth doll. 9½" tall. All felt, movable arms and legs, black mohair wig, painted eyes. All original in dress made of felt with organdy trim at hem. $125.00.

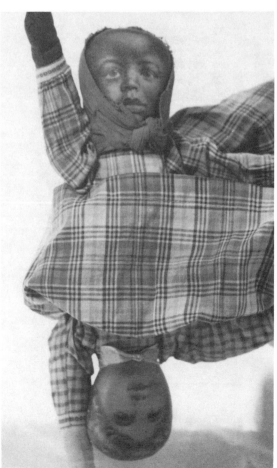

Plate 253: Babyland topsy-turvy doll made by Horsman, circa 1910. 12" tall. All cloth with lifelike lithographed faces. Black doll wears a deep red blouse and turban, red checkered skirt, white scarf around neck. White doll wears the same red checkered dress. Cap is missing from the white face.

Gimbel Brothers, department stores in New York and Philadelphia, pictured a similar "Babyland" topsy-turvy rag doll in their 1912 catalog. The price was listed at $1.00. $1,000.00.

Plate 254: "Babyland Topsy-turvy" in another all original outfit. Private collection. $1,000.00.

Plate 255: 14" cloth topsy-turvy from the late 1800's. Photograph courtesy of Susan Girardot. $350.00.

Plate 256: Handmade topsy-turvy. 14" tall. One end is happy, the other end sad with eyes closed and embroidered "tears" on her cheeks. All cloth with black yarn hair, embroidered features. $35.00.

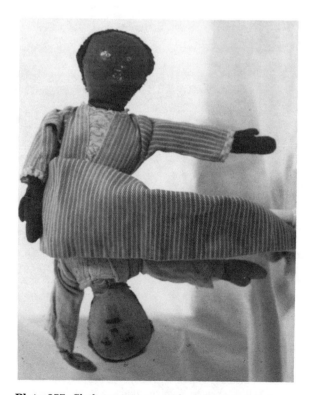

Plate 257: Cloth topsy-turvy with embroidered features. Circa 1900. 12" tall. Primitive painted faces, hair is made of textured material. Private collection. $175.00.

Plate 258: Cloth topsy-turvy. 9" tall. Both heads have hand painted features. Black head has black yarn hair and is dressed in red print dress with matching bandanna. White head has yellow yarn hair and is dressed in print dress with a blue bonnet. Clothing has been cut out with pinking shears. 1950's. Unmarked. $50.00.

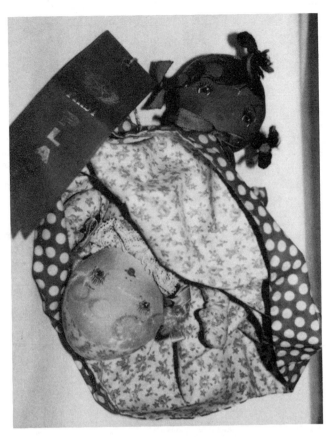

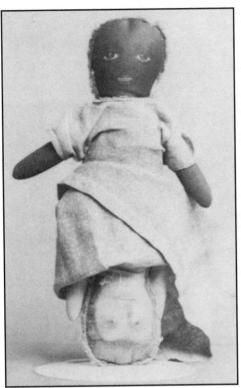

Plate 260: Printed cloth topsy-turvy, unsigned. Black face on one end, white face on the other. Black face has painted smiling mouth with both upper and lower teeth showing, hat and hair are missing, if there was hair originally. Usually in this type of doll, tufts of mohair is sewn under cap at the forehead. White doll has painted blue eyes, blond hair and is missing her cap and dress. The only clothes on the doll are the lavender print blouse and skirt on the black doll. 10" tall. This is not the more common Bruckner topsy-turvy but is very similar. Early 1900's. $275.00.

Plate 259: "Topsy and Eva." 9½" tall. Blue ribbon winner in antique rag dolls category. All original. 1930's. Collection of and photo courtesy of Etta Houston. $450.00.

Plate 261: Topsy-turvy doll with embossed pressed paper faces, very unusual. 1890's. Straw-filled body. Both dolls have red print bodices, plaid bonnets, red striped skirts. Neither of the dolls have arms. All original. 11" tall. Unmarked. $475.00.

Plate 262: Cloth topsy-turvy. 14" tall. Embroidered features, black yarn hair on the black doll, yellow yarn hair on the white doll. Black doll has a blue dress with white dots, white doll has a pink print dress with children and geese. Handmade and unmarked. Circa 1950. Courtesy of Patricia Whittler Martin. $85.00.

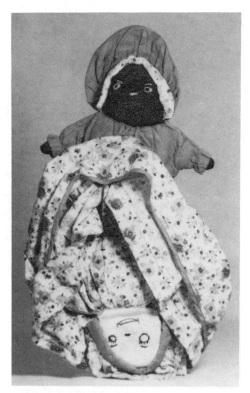

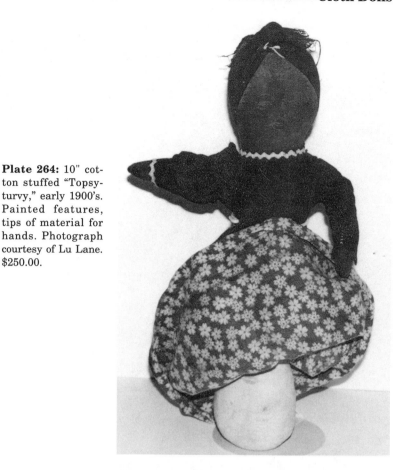

Plate 264: 10" cotton stuffed "Topsy-turvy," early 1900's. Painted features, tips of material for hands. Photograph courtesy of Lu Lane. $250.00.

Plate 263: Cloth topsy-turvy from 1930–40. 14" tall. Embroidered features. All original in green dress and matching cap on the black doll, lavender print dress with matching cap on the white doll. Unmarked. $75.00.

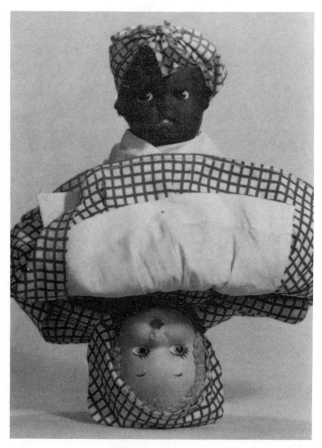

Plate 266: Mask face topsy-turvy. 9" tall. Painted features, stuffed with sawdust. All original in green and white striped dress with white bodice on black side, red dress with white dots on the white side. Unmarked. 1940's. Collection of Emma Ranson Hayward. $200.00.

Plate 265: Junel Novelty Company, N.Y. "Topsy and Eva." Cloth double doll with pressed cloth faces, painted features. The black doll, Topsy, has an open mouth, three tufts of black yarn for hair and is dressed in red and white checked dress and headscarf. Eva has yellow yarn hair, closed mouth, and is dressed in blue and white checked dress matching the bonnet. Doll was probably made in the 40's and cost $2.00 when it was new. Original hang tag is still attached to doll and reads: JUNEL/A QUALITY PRODUCT/MFR./JUNEL NOVELTY COMPANY/NEW YORK; reverse side: "TOPSY & EVA"/™/FIBRE CONTENT OF/THIS DOLLS HAIR/NEW WOOL — 50%/RAYON — 50%. $250.00.

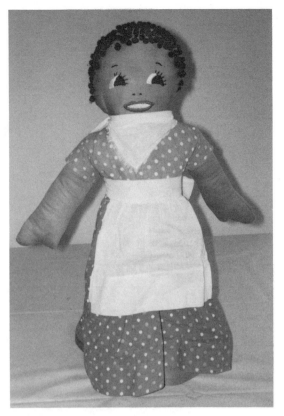

Plate 267: 19½" Mammy-type rag doll. Extremely well done, embroidered features, hand knotted individual wool knots for hair, polished cotton body stuffed with cotton. All original. Collection of Emma Ransom Hayward. $150.00.

Plate 268: 11½" sock doll. Button eyes, large red felt lips, yarn braids with oil cloth ribbons, cotton red and white checked dress with cotton stuffed bosom, organdy apron. Collection of Emma Ransom Hayward. $60.00.

Plate 269: 7" sock doll. Button eyes, felt lips, pelt of animal type black hair attached to scalp, sting attached to back of scalp in order to hang or suspend doll. All original in cotton outfit with medical staff drawn on shirt. Collection of Emma Ransom Hayward. $75.00.

Plate 270: Cloth topsy-turvy doll. 12" tall. Embroidered features, sewn on orange headscarf with one attached earring. All original in "shared" dotted blue cotton dress. White doll at the opposite end is shown in following plate. 1940's. $150.00.

Plate 271: White side of previous topsy-turvy doll. Doll is wearing a floral print dress.

Plate 272: "Topsy-turvy." 13" tall. All cloth, painted features, red print dress with white apron and bandanna, earrings. 1940–50. White half is shown in the following photo. Dolls were sometimes called "flip" dolls. Photograph courtesy of Faith Wyse. $95.00.

Plate 273: Reverse end of previous topsy-turvy doll. This end is white with blond yarn hair, painted features and green print dress. Photograph courtesy of Faith Wyse.

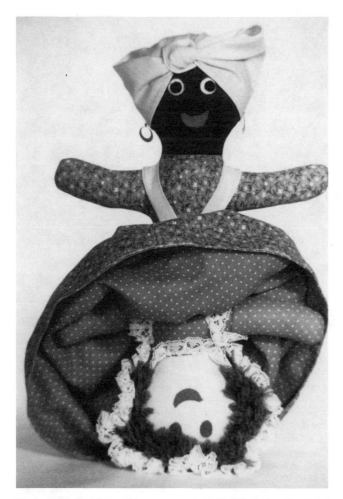

Plate 274: Gambina. "Topsy-turvy." 13½". All cloth, felt facial features, brown yarn hair on the white end. Available in the 1990's. Collection of Valerie Burbank-Pugh. $20.00.

Plate 275: Cloth topsy-turvy doll. Both heads are black, one is awake and the other sleeping, black yarn hair, painted features. 13" tall. Dressed in red print dress with white lining for sleeping side, sleeping doll has white bodice on dress, awake side has print bodice on dress. Unmarked. 1980's. $25.00.

Norah Wellings made dolls in England from 1926 to 1960 under the company name, Victorian Toy Works. She produced the dolls and her brother, Leonard Wellings, managed the company. The dolls were made for children to play with and were often sold as souvenir dolls. The South Sea Island dolls in the grass skirts were marketed and sold in the British Colonies. All of the Wellings' dolls were extremely well made and today most examples are still in excellent condition. She made dolls representing many nationalities. She is known to have made black dolls in the following sizes: 42", 36", 18", 17", 14½", 14", 12", 11½", 11", 9½", 9", 8½", 8", 7". There are undoubtedly more sizes available, but these are ones that the author has seen. Some of the dolls have glass or glassine eyes, others have painted eyes. Most of the dolls are made entirely of velvet, however, an example of one with a composition head is included in the chapter on composition dolls. Names used by Wellings for some of the black dolls are: Dudu, Zulu, Zuzu, Tak-Uki, Desiree, Bermuda, South Sea Islander, Islander, Maori Boy, West Indies Girl, and Nassau Policeman.

Plate 276: Norah Wellings. 8" tall. All original velvet cloth doll. Sewn on turban hat with decorated with flowers, painted features, sewn on brass hoop earrings, bead and wire necklace, grass skirt. Marks: MADE IN ENGLAND/BY/NORAH WELLINGS, tag sewn on bottom of left foot. $85.00.

Plate 277: Norah Wellings. "West Indies Girl." 8". Velvet movable head, black mohair wig, painted features, velvet body. All original in long red print dress, white organdy shawl and apron, carrying a burlap sack filled with cotton. Original tag attached to doll: NORAH WELLINGS/PRODUCTIONS (drawing of a doll is in the center of the tag.) On an identical doll, "West Indies Girl" is stamped on the reverse side of the tag. $150.00.

Plate 278: Norah Wellings. 29" tall. Tan velvet head, limbs and body, brown glassine eyes with painted, painted hair and eye lashes, painted open mouth with teeth, applied ears. All original in burnt orange velvet pants, removable velvet jacket, brown satin waist sash. $500.00.

Plate 279: Norah Wellings. "Turkish Boy." 8". Light brown velvet doll, painted eyes, painted smiling mouth with teeth, attached velvet fez in the same color as the doll, printed sash around the hips. Tag sewn to right foot: MADE IN ENGLAND/BY. Remaining line was cut off tag before it was sewn to the foot. $90.00.

Plate 280: Wellings. "Tak-Uki." 18" tall. All velvet, glass eyes, reddish brown mohair wig styled in upsweep hairdo, painted mouth with teeth, applied ears. Orange velvet dress with sewn-on yellow felt circles forms the body. Necklace and arm and leg bracelets made of plastic sewn on to the doll. Early 1930's. $325.00.

Left — Plate 281: Wellings. Girl, 14" tall. Velvet movable head, black curly mohair wig, glass eyes, smiling mouth with painted teeth, attached ears with wooden beads for earrings, matching necklace made of wooden beads. Red velvet blouse forms the body and arms, attached brown print skirt. Skirt and blouse are trimmed with pale green and gold felt. Sewn on shoes are black velvet. Skirt is tagged: MADE IN ENGLAND/BY/NORAH WELLINGS. $260.00.

Right — Plate 282: Wellings. Boy, 15" tall. Brown velvet movable head, applied ears, glass eyes, reddish brown mohair wig, smiling mouth with painted teeth. Orange velvet trousers form the lower body. Tag on right foot: MADE IN ENGLAND/BY/NORAH WELLINGS. $265.00.

Left — Plate 283: Wellings. "Nassau Policeman." 8½" tall. Velvet face and body, painted eyes, closed mouth. White policeman's jacket forms the upper body, navy blue velvet pants with red felt side stripes, removable white hat with green felt under the brim. Hang tag: NORAH WELLINGS/ PRODUCTIONS; stamped on reverse side: Nassau Policeman. $150.00.

Right — Plate 284: Wellings. 11". Painted eyes and mouth, yellow velvet sewn on pants with black stripes, black velvet shirt with four buttons, yellow felt hat, printed cloth bowtie. Tagged on bottom of right foot. $200.00.

Plate 285: Wellings. 8". Brown velvet with movable head, painted eyes, bald, painted closed mouth. Gold velvet pants form the body. Tagged on left foot. $95.00.

Plate 286: Attributed to Norah Wellings. 19" tall. Velvet head and arms, brown cotton cloth body and legs, glass eyes, mohair wig. All original in orange, yellow, brown, and white plaid dress and headwrap with white apron and shawl. Unmarked. $275.00.

Plate 287: Wellings. 7". Painted eyes, painted closed mouth, sewn on orange pants. Head is bald and looks like a hat was originally on doll's head. Tagged on foot. $85.00.

Plate 288: Wellings. 18". Velvet head, reddish brown mohair wig, glass eyes, gold velvet sewn on bibbed pants, applied ears. $325.00.

Plate 289: Wellings. "Islander Girl." 13½" tall. Glass eyes, swivel head, black wig, original grass skirt made of red and gold plastic raffia-like material. This same material is wrapped around the bodice. Doll has bracelets on wrists, ankles, and matching earrings attached to applied ears. Unmarked. $225.00.

Left — Plate 290: 15" tall. Attributed to Norah Wellings. Brown felt face, applied ears and soles of feet, brown velvet body and limbs, stitched fingers and toes, painted features, brown "fuzzy" wig of unknown material. All original in natural colored grass skirt, rust colored lei around neck, bangles on ankles and wrists, hoop earring. Unmarked. $200.00.

Right — Plate 291: Wellings. 8½" tall. Brown velvet head and body, black wig, painted features, closed mouth. Removable clothes, blue cotton shirt, orange felt pants, natural straw hat. Marks: MADE IN ENGLAND/BY/ NORAH WELLINGS, on bottom of left foot. $100.00.

Plate 292: Wellings. 8" tall. Velvet swivel head and body, painted side-glancing eyes, painted smiling mouth with teeth, brown mohair wig styled in an upsweep. Aqua checked dress forms the body. Marks: MADE IN ENGLAND/BY/NORAH WELLINGS, on left foot. Black label with "Nassau" handwritten is sewn to front of dress. $100.00.

Plate 293: Wellings. "Nassau" boy. 8" tall. Velvet head, arms, and feet, painted eyes and mouth. Clothing forms the body, velvet shirt with two buttons, blue striped cotton pants, gold felt hat. Shirt is tagged "Nassau." Marks: MADE IN ENGLAND/BY/NORAH WELLINGS, on left foot. $100.00.

Plate 294: Wellings. 16" tall. Velvet swivel head, glass eyes, painted mouth, movable velvet arms bent at the elbow, velvet body and legs, black mohair wig. All original in grass skirt, orange lei, orange ribbons at wrists, ankles and in hair, bangles at shoulders and ankles. Unmarked. $300.00.

Plate 295: Wellings. 8". All velvet with movable head, black synthetic wig, painted eyes and teeth. Natural colored raffia wrapped around body for skirt. Tagged on left foot. $85.00.

Plate 297: Postcard printed by "The London Toy & Model Museum," London, England, of Wellings velvet cloth dolls. Dolls are described on back of card as: TRIO OF NORAH WELLINGS DOLLS/©1935 — BRITISH. The museum is said to have closed several years ago. Postcard courtesy of David Salmanowitz. $25.00.

Plate 296: Wellings. 8". Velvet doll with movable head, black wig, painted eyes, and closed mouth. All original in sewn grass skirt in natural color and green. Tagged on left foot. $85.00.

Plate 299: Chad Valley. "Bermuda Sailor." 10½" tall. Painted eyes, black lamb's wool hair, painted closed mouth, applied ears, velvet head, hands and feet. Blue velvet sailor's outfit forms the body. Bermuda is printed on the cap. Doll looks very much like the Norah Wellings dolls. Tag sewn to left foot: HYGIENIC TOYS/MADE IN ENGLAND BY/CHAD VALLEY CO. LTD. $250.00.

Plate 298: Lenci-type felt doll. 7½" tall. Painted googley eyes, closed mouth, jointed felt body. All original in muslin safari outfit. Marks: MADE/IN/ITALY, sticker on bottom of right foot. $95.00.

How Our English Cousins
Trim Their Doll Windows
Dolls, Dolls, Nothing But Dolls Displayed by this London Store

Plate 300: 1930. *Playthings,* January, 1930, page 229. Window display of dolls in England. Black doll in the center is the Norah Wellings "Tak-Uki." The black doll on the far left is hard to attempt to identify as it is in the shadows.

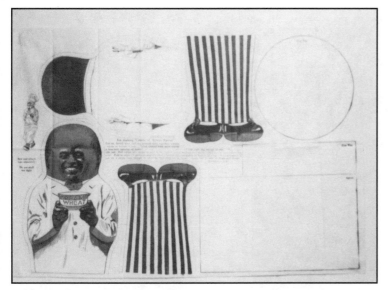

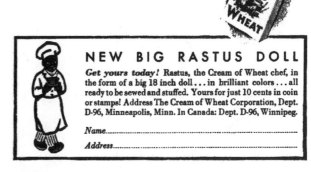

Plate 301: Cloth cut out and sew "Rastus," Cream of Wheat doll. This doll is different from the two "Rastus" dolls shown in earlier book by the author. This Rastus has black and white striped pants. The other dolls wore red and white striped pants in one version and brown and black striped pants in the other. $225.00.

Plate 302: Advertisement for Cream of Wheat "Rastus Doll." In the color ad, Rastus has on the red and white striped pants and is 18" tall. Magazine ad appeared in 1936.

CREAM OF WHEAT COMPANY

MINNEAPOLIS, MINN.

GEO B CLIFFORD, PRESIDENT
J WALKER SMITH, VICE PRESIDENT

D. F. BULL, TREAS AND GEN MANAGER
G. V. THOMSON, SEC AND ASST. MGR.

Dear Friend:

We are very glad to send you the Rastus Doll, ready to be sewed and stuffed, and feel sure his lovable, familiar figure will find a hearty welcome from the little folks.

You know school health authorities have found by actual test that the child who eats a Hot Cooked Cereal Breakfast does a better morning's work.

So fully is this proved that the U. S. Bureau of Education makes this statement to mothers: "A well-cooked cereal is an essential part of a child's breakfast."

For thirty years nutrition specialists have recommended Cream of Wheat as the ideal Hot Cooked Cereal for children of all ages, from babies up through high school age.

It contains a wonderful store of rich energy--and children need a never-failing supply! Its simple form is quickly, easily digested, with the least possible effort. It contains none of the indigestible parts of the wheat.

We are enclosing a leaflet which gives a number of recipes for delicious energy dishes which are easy and economical to prepare. Remember, one big box of Cream of Wheat gives forty generous servings. This leaflet also refers to our booklet, "The Important Business of Feeding Children", which we will gladly send you on request.

Hoping Rastus will mean many happy play hours for the children, we are,

Yours very truly,

CREAM OF WHEAT COMPANY

Plate 303: Letter from Cream of Wheat Company, manufacturers of Cream of Wheat, Minneapolis, Minnesota. The letter was sent along with the previous doll, probably in the 1950's.

Plate 304: Handmade cloth doll from the 1950's. Embroidered features. The shoes are integrated into the legs and match the material on the skirt. Collection of and photograph courtesy of Joyce A. Wilkinson. $135.00.

MIRANDA AND SAMBO

1068

Miranda and Sambo are made for each other, and for youngsters who love cuddly dolls. In the sewing basket there are sure to be leftover pieces to make the soft bodies and gay clothes of a pair of these likable playmates (1068).

Buy patterns from McCall dealers or by mail, prepaid, from McCall Corporation, Dayton, O., at prices and sizes listed on the last page.

Plate 306: 1943 advertisement for cloth dolls "Miranda and Sambo" from McCall Corporation, a pattern company.

Plate 307: Hand crocheted potholder doll. 17½" long. Button eyes and nose, red yarn mouth. Head unbuttons at neck and body is used as a potholder. Made in early 1990's. Collection of Cheryl Perkins. $20.00.

Above Center: Plate 305: Early 1900's handmade Jamaican souvenir doll. Painted features, brown cloth body, jointed limbs. $95.00.

Plate 308: Printed cloth cut out and sew doll. 14" tall. Dress is brown print. Printed on apron is another brown print, printed on apron strings in back. Unmarked. Black sewn on yarn hair. Collection of Joan Banks. $100.00.

Plate 309: Advertisement for transfer pattern for cloth doll "Little Brown Koko" and cloth dog "Shoog-pup." Also mentioned in the ad was a contest for naming the doll. Completed doll would be 16". Advertisement is dated 1940.

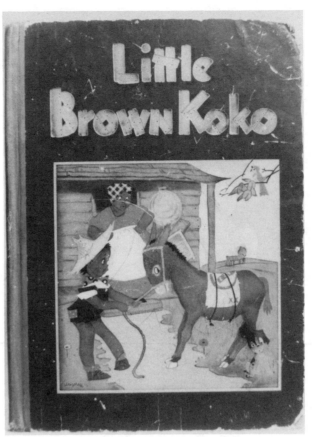

Plate 311: Children's book *Stories of Little Brown Koko* by Blanche Seale Hunt, illustrated by Dorothy Wagstaff, published by American Colortype Company, 1940. Previous doll was based on character "Little Brown Koko" in this book. Other books were also written about Koko's adventures. $50.00.

Plate 310: "Little Brown Koko." 16" tall. Cloth with cotton stuffing. Courtesy of Susan Girardot. $275.00.

Plate 312: "Little Brown Koko." 25" tall. Mask face head, black yarn wig, painted eyes and mouth, cloth body with jointed legs. Sewn on red gingham socks and red felt shoes form the feet. Unmarked. All original. $250.00.

Plate 313: Global. "Charlie Ragg," #AW701. 23" tall. All cloth with black looped yarn hair, painted features. Originally dressed in red pants and cap, green shirt, white bowtie. Hangtag has photograph of actress Esther Rolle holding Charlie Ragg and a girl doll named "Annie Ragg" with the statement "I give you love/Esther Rolle," printed in the corner. The two dolls were conceived and designed by black artist Ann Miller Woodford. Tag sewn to body: E & A GLOBAL ENTERPRISES/LOS ANGELES, CA. $50.00.

Left — Plate 314: Commonwealth Toy & Novelty Co. "Softhearted Friends." 27½" tall. All cloth with brown yarn hair, lithographed features, sewn on clothing. Tagged body. $15.00.

Right — Plate 315: Cloth doll by Jean Sipes. 1970's. 30" tall. Embroidered features, stitched on wig. All original in yellow dress and booties. Collection of and photo courtesy of Etta Houston. No price available.

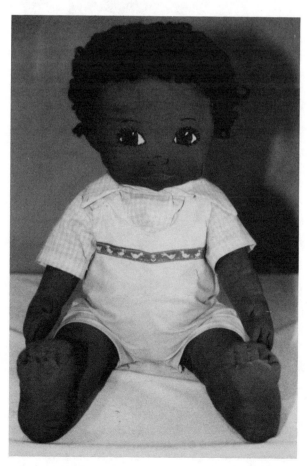

Left — Plate 316: Boy cloth doll by Jean Sipes. 30" tall. Embroidered features, yarn wig, original yellow outfit. Unmarked. 1970's. Collection of and photo courtesy of Etta Houston. No price available.

Right — Plate 317: Brown felt, applied felt eyes and mouth, felt clothing with elaborate beadwork. Doll is carrying a tiny baby on its back. 1980–90. Collection of Michael Wolk-Laniewski. Approximately 12". $65.00.

Plate 319: Rainbow Classics. Cloth doll 17½" tall. Painted features, black yarn hair sewn under bonnet, removable purple print dress, sewn on bonnet and shoes. Doll had no name when marketed. Tag sewn to body is marked RAINBOW CLASSICS. $12.00.

Plate 318: Pair of handmade cloth dolls. 10½" tall. Black yarn hair, painted features, attached goldtone earrings, bead necklaces. 1960's. Collection of Michael Wolk-Laniewski. $90.00 pair.

Plate 320: Collection of "Voodoo Dolls" purchased in New Orleans, 1993. Dolls are 7" to 10" tall. Doll on the right was made by New Orleans Mystic Arts Centre. According to information accompanying doll, the doll was made by New Orleans Practitioners and are defined as follows: "VooDoo dolls are most commonly used to influence another person or to help change a situation. The doll is the means by which thought transference is successful because the doll is used as a medium." $12.00 each.

Plate 321: 24" tall. All cloth, embroidered mouth, sewn on nose, felt eyes, sewn on ears, black yarn hair, handmade. Dressed in off white footed romper outfit with matching yellow bib. Marketed by Dolls in Hobby Hill, SC. Collection of the Museum of African American History (Detroit). $35.00.

Plate 322: Avon. "Joyce Marie," a Rose Garden Tea Set doll. 25" tall. All cloth, painted features, black yarn hair, sewn on clothing. Tag sewn to body: ...©AVON 1991 — ALL RIGHTS RESERVED/REG. NO. PA. 940. $20.00.

Plate 323: Troys Toys. "Robin's Pals" ©1991. Cloth doll with printed on features, brown yarn hair, pink and green sewn on dress, yellow legs, sewn on pink shoes. 10½" tall. Tag sewn to body: TROYS/TOYS/©1991 CHATHAM, NJ 07928. $6.00.

Plate 324: Knickerbocker. Cloth girl with printed features, glued on black yarn hair, brown cloth body. 12" tall. All original in tagged print and checked dress that can be shortened to knee length or dropped to ankle length. It is not certain whether she ever had shoes. Doll is unmarked. $45.00.

Left — Plate 325: Kenner. "Bubbles" from the "Hugga Bunch" collection. 17" tall. All cloth soft plush pile, rooted brown hair, stationary blue glassine eyes with lashes, seam jointed limbs. All original in three piece orange print outfit. Tag attached to left arm: BUBBLES/HUGGA BUNCH. Tag sewn to body: KENNER/CINCINNATI, OHIO 45202/HUGGA BUNCH COLLECTION/BUBBLES/©1985 HALLMARK CARDS INC./75100 HN/MADE IN CHINA. $25.00.

Right — Plate 326: Kenner. "Tweaker" with her baby form the "Hugga Bunch Collection." 17". Rooted dark brown hair, amber eyes with lashes, attached nose and ears, embroidered mouth. All original. Tagged body. 1985. Collection of Valerie Burbank-Pugh. $30.00.

Left — Plate 327: Imagination Factory. "Club Kids." 1990. 17" tall. All cloth, clothing forms the body, embroidered features, tuft of brown yarn for hair. Body tagged: PETER G. BLANK & THE IMAGINATION FACTORY LTD. MINNEAPOLIS, MINN. Collection of Valerie Burbank-Pugh. $25.00.

Right — Plate 328: Pringle. "Phyllis Fairchild." 20½" tall. Original cloth doll by artist Helen Pringle. One-of-a-kind sculptured cloth doll, hand painted features, applied ears. All original in burgundy checkered dress, blue print bonnet, burgundy and gold striped stockings, black plastic shoes. Hang tag: FAIR CHILDREN/ NEW ENGLAND RAG DOLLS©/BY HELEN PRINGLE/11-30-92. Courtesy of Patricia Whittler Martin. $600.00.

Plate 329: T.J. Tots. "Felisha." 16½" tall. Soft sculpture cloth doll. Edition three, number 6,822 of 18,000 dolls. Janet Waters, designer. Papers that accompany doll state that the doll was born on Hooker Hollow Road in the mountains of West Virginia. Painted eyes, black yarn hair styled in cornrows with white eyelet rompers, white shoes, pink socks. Courtesy of Clara Phillips Hill. $125.00.

Plate 330: Determined Products. "Peter." 11½" tall. Pressed face cloth doll based on author Ezra Jack Keats' stories about a character named Peter. Glued on black yarn-like hair, painted features, applied ears, brown cloth body. All original in red and white print shirt, blue shorts, red socks, blue shoes, large gray felt hat. ©1992. Available in 1993. $18.00.

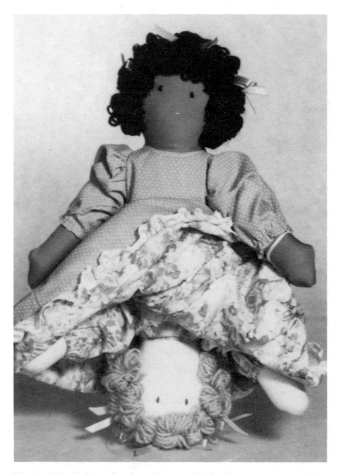

Plate 331: Delton Product Corp. 13" cloth topsy-turvy. 1991. Yarn hair, embroidery stitches for eyes. Dolls do not have any other facial features. All original in mauve dotted dress on black doll, matching hairbows; floral print dress on white doll, pink hairbows. Stickers stuck on back of each dress: DELTON PRODUCT CORP./MADE IN TAIWAN ROC. $25.00.

Plate 332: Dolls by Christina. "Jazzabelle." 20". All cloth doll with machine embroidered features, black yarn hair. All original. Tag sewn to apron: DOLLS BY CHRISTINA/©1992/ALL RIGHTS RESERVED. Second tag attached to apron: 100% HANDMADE IN/NEW ORLEANS/LOUISIANA — U.S.A. (second tag is handwritten.) Collection of Tina Burbank. $40.00.

Plate 333: "Harriet Tubman," an original cloth doll by the great-great grandniece of Harriet Tubman, Joyce Stokes Jones of Syracuse, N.Y. The face of the doll is patterned after Joyces' daughter who bore a striking resemblance to their "Aunt Harriet." Her daughter died at age 25. The doll's face is printed on brown vinyl fabric with black and brown braided yarn for hair. The body and limbs are brown cloth. 18" tall. Tag sewn to body: HARRIET TUBMAN/AN ORIGINAL BY/GR.GREAT GRANDNIECE/JOYCE STOKES JONES. Cloth body is hand-signed on the back: JOYCE STOKES JONES/3 9 91. $75.00.

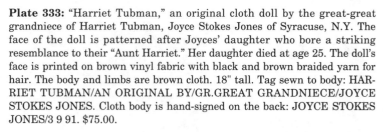

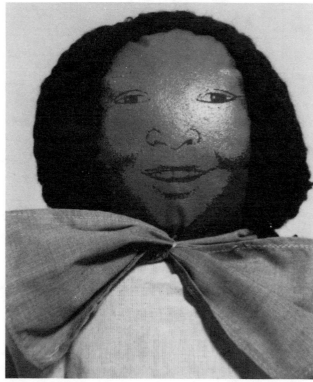

Plate 334: Hallmark Cards. "Beloved Belindy," 1974. 5½". All cloth, black yarn hair, printed black and white eyes, red nose and mouth, black feet. Redressed. $40.00.

Plate 335: Avon. Cloth doll. 10". 1986. Printed facial features, brown yarn hair, sewn on yellow and white dress and matching cap. Part of the clothing forms the body. Body is tagged. $30.00.

Plate 336: Playskool. "Busy Dressy Bessy." All cloth doll with five learn to dress activities: zipper, snap, button, buckle, and tie. 14" tall. Sewn on clothing, brown yarn hair, painted features. Marks: BUSY DRESSY BESSY/456/©1990 PLAYSKOOL, INC..., tag sewn to body. Collection of Leanne Nicole Johnson. $15.00.

Plate 337: Simplicity. "Pickaninny Dolls." Pattern #7329 from Simplicity Pattern Co., Inc. ©1947 for "Pickaninny Dolls." Pattern cost fifteen cents when issued new. Included in the package were transfer designs for doll's clothes, and complete sewing and embroidery instruction sheet. $125.00.

Plate 338: "Pickaninny Dolls" made from the previous Simplicity pattern, #7329. Dolls are 17" tall. Eyes are embroidered in the satin stitch. Outline stitching around the eyes, nose, mouth, and toes is embroidered in the chain stitch. Both dolls have black yarn hair. All original. Circa 1950. $175.00.

Plate 339: McCall Corporation. Pattern #894, ©1941, to make a sock doll. Black doll, in the upper right corner would be 9" when completed. $45.00.

Plate 340: Simplicity Pattern Co. Pattern #9137, ©1970. Pattern to make rag dolls that teach children how to tie, button, count, zip, and basic shapes. Completed dolls are 24" tall. Pattern includes transfers. Black boy and girl dolls are pictured on the right. $10.00.

Plate 341: Simplicity Pattern Co. Pattern #7247, ©1975. Pattern to make two black cloth dolls, a boy and a girl, shown on the left in above pattern. Completed dolls are approx. 20" tall and are shown in author's previous book, *Black Dolls, 1820–1991*, plates 217 and 218. $10.00.

Plate 342: Simplicity. ©1972. Pattern #5378. Pattern to make set of rag dolls. Two of the dolls shown on the pattern cover are black. Completed dolls would be 13". Transfers are included for seven different facial expressions. $10.00.

Plate 343: "Big Dolls Teach Children to Zip, Button, Tie." 24". Free instructions for making the dolls could be ordered from magazine *Family Circle*, August, 1973. Dolls were designed by Frances Gutman. $15.00.

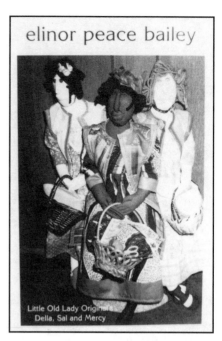

Plate 344: McCall Pattern Co. Pattern #5740, ©1977 to make a set of cloth dolls. Completed dolls would be 37½" tall and 16" tall. Materials required are felt for the face and facial features, embroidery thread for the eyebrows and eyelashes, rug yarn for the hair, cotton cloth for the body and clothing. $10.00.

Plate 345: Donna Gallagher, Creative Neele-Arts, Inc. "Mammy and Friends." Pattern for making cloth dolls Mammy, Lisbet, and Etsie. Mammy and Etsie are the black dolls, 12" and 9" tall when completed. Pattern #845 from the "Home Folk" series. Completed dolls are jointed with covered buttons. ©1985. $5.00.

Plate 346: Bailey. Pattern for making cloth doll "Della" from the "Little Old Ladies" by cloth doll artist Elinor Peace Bailey. ©1985. $6.00.

Plate 347: McCall Pattern Co., pattern #5796, ©1977. Pattern to make a 16" baby doll, sleeping or awake. $12.00.

Plate 348: McCall Pattern Co., pattern #7352, ©1980. Pattern to make a 19" cloth doll. $5.00.

Plate 349: Simplicity. "Lillian August Collection." ©1987. Pattern to make cloth dolls 22½" and 14½" tall. $10.00.

Plate 350: Butterick. "The Fun Has Just Begun." Butterick pattern #4252. 1989. Pattern was designed by Rachel Wallis. Completed dolls are approximately 26" tall. $10.00.

Plate 351: McCall Pattern Company. "Ethnic Doll" from the "Country Chums" pattern #5990, ©1992. Included in pattern are directions for 21" tall ethnic doll with braided hair and clothes. $8.00.

Plate 352: McCall Pattern Company. "Aggie Whipple and Argus Whipple" from the "Attic Babies," views C and A, designed by Marty Maschino, ©1991, pattern 5695. The pattern was sold for individual home use only and not for commercial or manufacturing purposes. Completed dolls would be 17½" tall. $8.00.

Plate 353: 13" two sided yarn doll. Yarn covers foam ball for head, felt features. One side has a cheerful smile, the other a sleeping face. All original. Collection of Emma Ransom Hayward. $85.00.

Plate 354: Commercially made cloth doll. 16" tall. Black yarn hair, blue gingham body. Dressed in original red felt dress trimmed with rickrack. Untagged. $35.00.

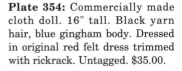

Plate 355: Rainbow Classics. "Talking Rag Doll." 23" tall. Painted features, very dark brown yarn hair, removable lilac print dress with matching sewn on bonnet, sewn on lilac shoes, talking pull string in back. Doll says the following: "I'm so sleepy now," "May I have a cookie?" "You're my best friend," "Please give me a piggyback ride," "I'd like to go outside," "Let's play hide and seek." Doll was available in Sears Christmas catalog, 1991. Marks: RAINBOW CLASSICS INC. Tag sewn to body. $20.00.

Plate 356: Calico Critters. "I'm Amanda." 14" tall. All cloth, printed facial features, glued on brown yarn hair, sewn on green print dress forms the body and arms, sewn on white pantaloons form the legs, removable matching green print skirt. Tag sewn to body: CALICO CRITTERS/ P.O. BOX 707, PINEBROOK N.J. 07058/ALL NEW MATERIALS — SHREDDED CLIPPINGS/ OH.7686, PA 337 (N.J.) MADE IN U.S.A. Collection of the Museum of African American History (Detroit). $35.00.

Left — Plate 357: Determined Productions. "Tina," USA girl, 1993. 13". From the "Opt 4 Kids" collection. All cloth, printed features, black yarn hair, applied ears, removable clothing, tagged body. Booklet attached to arm of doll states that a portion of sales from the dolls will be donated to international children's organizations. $20.00.

Right — Plate 358: Determined Productions, Inc. "Moza" from the "UNICEF Kids" collection. "Moza" represents the country of Tanzania in Africa. All cloth doll with glued on black yarn hair and painted features. 13" tall. Doll was marketed and distributed by European Toy Collection. The purchase of the doll benefits the U.S. Committee for UNICEF. Tag sewn to body: U.S. COMMITTEE FOR UNICEF/EUROPEAN TOY COLLECTION/PORTAGE, IN 46368/©1991 DETERMINED PRODUCTIONS, INC. $25.00.

Plate 359: Determined Productions, "Laurie," U.S.A. Girl II from "UNICEF Kids" collection, #8690–9, ©1992. 12" tall. All cloth with painted features, black yarn hair, removable clothing. $20.00.

Plate 360: Dolly Mine. 15" cloth doll. Black yarn hair, painted features, sewn on pink and yellow outfit with sewn on pink dotted shoes. Marks: DOLLY MINE.../...©1987..., tag sewn on body. $10.00.

Plate 362: Dinner bell doll. Circa 1980. Head is made of string, body is a dinner bell. Dressed in red and white polka dotted dress, red headpiece and white apron with Charleston, S.C. printed at tail. Collection of the Museum of African History (Detroit.) $15.00.

Plate 361: Russ Berri & Co. 4" cloth doll. Black yarn hair in two pigtails and bangs, felt eyes and nose, embroidered mouth. Sewn on pink bonnet, removable pink tagged dress. Collection of the Museum of African American History (Detroit). Also available in a lavender dress and bonnet. $10.00.

Plate 364: Soft Things, Inc. 24" tall. Cloth doll with lithographed face, black yarn hair, sewn on clothing forms the body and head, tiny floral print dress and bonnet, red and white striped legs, black cloth sewn on shoes, attached red apron with green felt trim. 1980's. Tagged on body. $25.00.

Plate 363: Sankyo. "Musical Movements." Musical clown who plays "You Light Up My Life" and moves head and limbs, key wound. Stockinette face, felt eyes and mouth, red button nose, black fake fur hair, blue and white costume. 8" tall in sitting position. Marks: MUSICAL MOVEMENTS/FROM/SANKYO JAPAN, on key. $10.00.

Left — Plate 365: YDC. "Sandy," 1991. Cloth doll with printed facial features, baby blue yarn hair attached at five points around her face, sewn on blue gingham dress, blue bonnet and shoes. 14½" tall. Doll's name is machine embroidered on bib of dress. $10.00.

Right — Plate 366: Eegee. "Odessa — Black is Beautiful," #k4504 from the "Kisses" series. 9½" tall. All cloth, acrylic yarn hair, printed on facial features, sewn on clothing forms the body. Tag sewn to body: EG KISSES!/ ©C VIVIAN GREEN INC./ ALL NEW MATERIALS/ COTTON AND SYNTHETIC FIBERS; reverse side of tag: EG/GOLDBERGER DOLL MFG. CO. INC./BROOKLYN, N.Y. 11237/MADE IN TAIWAN, REPUBLIC OF CHINA. $45.00.

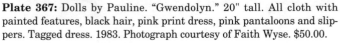

Plate 367: Dolls by Pauline. "Gwendolyn." 20" tall. All cloth with painted features, black hair, pink print dress, pink pantaloons and slippers. Tagged dress. 1983. Photograph courtesy of Faith Wyse. $50.00.

Plate 368: "Blackeyed Susan." 1973. Printed cloth doll to be cut out and sewn at home. 19½" tall. Dress is red, white, and blue, red nose and mouth, red hearts on cheeks and dress pocket. Unmarked. $65.00.

Plate 369: Ace Novelty Co. "Magic Johnson" from the "M.V.P. Sports Stars" series. Series includes the following black dolls: "Randall Cunningham" and "Warren Moon" from the "Tackling Dummies"; "Ken Griffey Jr." from the "Super Sluggers," "Magic Johnson" and "Patrick Ewing" from "Hoopster Heroes" series. 22" tall. Lithographed cloth. $30.00.

Plate 370 Ace Novelty Co. "Randall Cunningham" from the "Tackling Dummies" series of "M.V.P. Sport Stars," #29405. 22" tall. Lithographed cloth. $30.00.

Plate 371: Ace Novelty Co. Inc. "Patrick Ewing" from the "Hoopster Heroes" series. 24" tall. $25.00.

Left — Plate 372: Ace Novelty Co., Inc. "Warren Moon" from the "Tackling Dummies" series. 23" tall. $25.00.

Right — Plate 373: Ace Novelty Co. Inc. "Ken Griffey, Jr." from the "Super Sluggers" series. 22" tall. $25.00.

This chapter covers dolls made of composition (wood pulp), rubber, celluloid and wood. The great majority of them were made between 1900 and 1950. Following are descriptions of dolls falling in this category where photographs were not available.

Averill Manufacturing Co. introduced "Dolly Dingle" and "Rufus" in 1928. Dolls had composition head and arms, cloth bodies and legs, painted side-glancing eyes, closed mouths, Dolly Dingle had three tufts of yarn hair. Rufus had painted hair. Dolls were designed by Grace Drayton. Dolls are sometimes seen with ink stamped identification on torso. Wholesale cost in 1929, was $39.00 per dozen.

"Whistling Rufus," 13" tall, made by Madame Hendren, was offered at auction May 2, 1993, by Cobb's Doll Auction in Columbus, Ohio. Doll had composition head and arms, cloth body and was in his original outfit, overalls, a shirt, and cap. Doll wore his original "Whistling Rufus" button with his picture. Doll sold for $750.00.

Black Nun doll was made around 1930, 22" tall. Doll had composition shoulder head, hands and forearms, open mouth with two upper teeth, metal and glass eyes, cloth body. Dressed in 1930 by nuns in an all black convent in New York City. For photograph, see *The Warner Collector's Guide* by Jean Bach, page 180.

A jointed celluloid baby doll was made in the 1930's by Pupee Nobel. Doll is marked FRANCE/(SNF in a diamond frame.) Doll is 11¾" tall and has molded hair.

"Kinky," 10" tall, is an all composition baby doll with painted hair, three holes drilled in head for yarn pigtails, painted side-glancing eyes. Doll was shown on page 204 of a Chicago catalog called *Chicago Mail Order Company*. The doll had movable arms and legs and was dressed in printed rompers and socks. The cost in 1931 was forty-nine cents. In the same catalog, on page 205, a black all composition baby doll, 9½" tall was shown. She had painted hair without the three tufts of yarn hair and was twenty-five cents. She had movable arms and legs and was dressed in a trimmed chemise.

"Snowball," sometimes referred to as "Black Grumpy" (not to be confused with later "Baby

Plate 374: November 1924 *Good Housekeeping* advertisement for gifts showing "Whistling Rastus." Cost in 1924 was 60¢.

A QUEER DEVICE.
Home-made doll which
a firm is now manu-
facturing.

Plate 375: Black doll pictured in the article "Where Santa Claus Buys His Dolls" from "Leslie's Illustrated weekly Newspaper," December 5, 1912, page 580.

Grumpy" by Effanbee) was made by Effanbee Doll Co. circa 1915. Doll was 12" tall with composition head and hands, molded hair, painted side-glancing eyes, closed mouth, cloth body, cloth legs in red, tan, and green striped material with black cloth for feet or shoes. Marks: 172, on head.

Also around 1915, Effanbee made "Aunt Dinah." She was 15" tall, composition head and hands, molded hair with curl hanging down on forehead, painted eyes, open-closed mouth, ground cork-stuffed cloth body, tan, red, and green striped material for legs, sewn on black shoes. Marks: 106 (shown reversed,) on neck.

Effanbee Doll Co. made a black composition doll named "Rosemary" in the 1920's. She had a composition shoulder head, composition arms and legs, a white cloth body, black shoulder length wig, sleeping brown metal eyes, real hair eyelashes, and an open-mouth with four teeth. She was marked: EFFANBEE/ROSEMARY/WALK/TALK/SLEEP/MADE IN USA, on back of her shoulder head.

Effanbee also made "Patsy Joan." She is composition with molded hair, socket head, and jointed composition body.

Around 1925, Effanbee Doll Co. made "Baby Grumpy." She had a composition shoulder head, full composition arms, toddler composition legs, cloth body. Doll is 12" tall. Marks: EFFANBEE/DOLLS/WALK TALK/SLEEP, in oval on back of shoulder head. A similar doll was made by Effanbee that has three holes in head for string hair, has brown cloth legs, and is 11" tall. Doll has the same marks and is shown on plate 427.

Effanbee made a doll named "Bubbles" that is extremely rare in a black version. It is composition and is 19" tall.

All composition doll "Baby Grumpkins" was made by Effanbee during the early 1930's. Doll was 12½" tall with three holes in head for tufts of yarn hair, side-glancing painted eyes, closed mouth, jointed at neck, shoulders, and hips. Doll was issued in a red polka-dotted dress. Marks: EFFANBEE, on back.

Also during this same period, Effanbee made "Skippy," a 14" all composition boy jointed at neck, shoulders, and hips with painted side-glancing eyes, and black molded hair. Doll is marked: PATSY/PAT./PENDING, on body.

The Gem Doll Corporation made a 9½" all composition doll "Topsy" in the late 1920's. Doll has molded hair with holes for three tufts of black floss hair, painted side-glancing eyes, closed mouth. Doll is marked "Gem" on back.

In 1926, "Honey Child" was copyrighted by the American Doll Company. Doll had a composition shoulder head, side-glancing, painted brown eyes, closed mouth, molded black hair, brown cloth body stuffed with straw with black shoes stitched on to form the feet, and composition arms. Doll was 26" tall and was dressed in a red cotton shirt with black cotton checkered overalls. Marks: HONEY CHILD, incised on front of the chest; AM DOLL CO. ©1926, incised on back of the shoulder. In 1930, Montgomery Ward & Co. advertised "Topsy and Eva" babies as follows: "An adorable pair — a mischievous pickaninny and a dear little white baby — both the same size, 9½" tall. All composition, painted eyes, hair, and features. They're cunning together if you want both. Often sell for 50¢ each. We Pay Postage.

48 E 2503 — White doll...29¢

18 E 2502 — Pickaninny doll...29¢"

A "Little Black Sambo" doll was made by WPA (Works Progress Administration) Handicraft Project in Milwaukee, Wisconsin, in the 1930's. The back doll was said to be popular with black women who made the dolls as well as black children in the schools and nurseries. WPA dolls were made by black and white women working side by side making black and white dolls. The Works Progress Administration was started by Franklin D. Roosevelt as part of his New Deal program to give unemployed people a chance to earn money during the depression. It is not known what size the dolls were or what material was used to make them.

In 1947, Noma Toy Co. marketed a "Walking Mammy" doll 10" tall pushing a baby buggy with a white baby. Mammy has a composition head with painted hair and features, papier-maché walker body. Doll wore a dotted dress and headwrap and is unmarked.

In *The Crisis,* March, 1928, page 82, a little girl is photographed as a first place winner of a baby contest. She appears to be approximately five years old and is holding a black doll. The child's name is listed as Nancy Hopes from Newport, R.I.

Is there anything a boy loves more than a pen-knife? If so it's a train, and here is an engine with the knife and a soldier-box container, $1

How to Order

Articles on these two pages may be purchased through Good Housekeeping Shopping Service, shipping charges prepaid. See page 40 for detailed instructions

Boy Scout Creed, $1

Also for the rainy day is the raft of Robinson Crusoe (above). It will sail in the bath-tub with as much efficiency as in the lake, and with much more safety! $1

Boys and Girls

Plate 376: November, 1924 *Good House-keeping* toy page advertisement for black doll "Harmonica Joe." Doll was probably made of composition and sold for $1.88. $175.00 for doll.

Dainty as a little girl herself, is the painted mirror above, $1.25 and also the tiny per-fume container below it, about 3″ high, $1.25

A bubble set is a life-saver for rainy days, and solves the problem of what to do. This set with jumping-rope below, $1.50

Small daughter may keep her important addresses in the notebook above, $2; and as the knife is enameled it will also please her, $2

Tommy Tumble for the small baby is of water-proof painted wood, and always popular, $1

A decorated jumping-rope is al-ways more interesting than the or-dinary variety; with bubble set, $1.50

Harmonica Joe has a charm all his own and must be seen to be appreciated, $1.88

This little book (shown in center below) will teach the children in an amusing way to save their pennies, $1

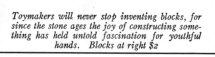

Children love to play Mah Jong in their own par-ticular way, and a cardboard set is indispensable if one wishes to keep the best ivory set intact. Complete set, $1

Toymakers will never stop inventing blocks, for since the stone ages the joy of constructing some-thing has held untold fascination for youthful hands. Blocks at right $2

These
Jigsaw Plant Boxes
Are Easy to Make

With a jig or coping saw and some plywood pieces, you can easily make these clever little indoor boxes to hold plants and flowerpots. We will send you a transfer pattern that will include directions for making the hen and rooster pair, the donkey, dog, and the boy and girl, all well-known characters in the Little Brown Koko stories which have appeared regularly in Household Magazine during the past six years.

Send in your own one-year new or renewal subscription to Household Magazine with 50c and we will send you FREE, transfer pattern C9399. Send your subscription with remittance to the address below and be sure and mention pattern C9399.
THE HOUSEHOLD MAGAZINE, Topeka, Kansas

Plate 377: December, 1941, advertisement from *The Household Magazine* for pattern for making plantboxes with characters "Little Brown Koko and Snooky" from the popular series of Little Brown Koko stories. Snooky is the girl and Little Brown Koko is the boy.

American Stuffed Novelty Co.

Reproduced here is a photograph of "Aunt Jemima" which is made in three sizes, namely, 15″, 18″ and 27″, and coming with assorted dresses of latest style prints. The number retails from $1.00 to $5.00, and is one of the "Life-Like Line" which embraces a full line of mama and baby dolls, and art dolls of a very fine type, coming in pastel shades.

Plate 378: Advertisement for "Aunt Jemima" from the American Stuffed Novelty Co. Ad was in *Playthings,* March, 1930, page 120.

Plate 379: Advertisement for unbreakable "colored" dolls, probably made of composition, by Berry & Ross Mfg. Co., Inc., New York, N.Y. Quoting from the ad: "So far as we know this is the only Negro Doll Factory in the World." The ad was placed in *The Crisis* magazine, September, October, and November of 1919.

Plate 380: Advertisement for "Rachel," black doll on the right, from *Playthings,* December, 1924, page 287. Rachel was a character from a comic strip by Frank O. King.

Colored Dolls for Your Children

Teach your children pride of race and appreciation of race. Early impressions are lasting. These beautifully dressed, unbreakable, brown skin dolls designed and made by colored girls in a factory owned and controlled entirely by colored people. These are not the old time, black face, red lip aunt Jemima colored dolls but dolls well made and truly representative of the race in hair and features.

16 inches with long flowing curls, beautifully dressed $3.50

16 inches with marcel wave, nicely dressed 3.00

16 inches Buster Brown style hair, very neat 2.50

Soldier boy in full uniform............ 1.50

So far as we know this is the only Negro doll factory in the world.

BERRY & ROSS, Inc.

Factory: 36-38 W. 135th St.
NEW YORK CITY

H. S. Boulin, President,
Dr. E. Rawlins, Vice President,
Counsellor P. Ifield, General Manager,
S. Reid, Business & Sales Manager.

AGENTS WANTED   WRITE FOR TERMS

Only those who mean business need write us.

Plate 381: Advertisement for "colored" dolls from Berry & Ross, Inc., New York City. According to the ad, the factory was owned and operated entirely by colored people. Dolls were probably composition as they were described as unbreakable. Advertisement was placed in *The Crisis,* February, 1919, page 202. The same ad also appeared in the March, April, May, and June, 1919, issues of *The Crisis.*

COLORED DOLLS

Berry's Famous Unbreakable Brown Skin Dolls

Send for Catalog

Berry & Ross Mfg. Co., Inc.
Factory, 36-38 West 135th St.
New York, N. Y.

Plate 382: Advertisement for unbreakable dolls from Berry & Ross Mfg. Co., Inc., New York, N.Y. The most popular unbreakable dolls during the period were dolls made of composition. Ad appeared in December, 1919 issue of *The Crisis,* page 94.

5000 AGENTS and DEALERS WANTED

Unbreakable Walking and Talking Dolls. Light Brown Skin with Long Curls and Beautiful Dresses.
Size 19 inches $2.98
$25 Dozen
Also lots of other Dolls and Novelties. Photo Medallions, Photo Jewelry, Toys, Negro Post Cards, Negro Religious Pictures, Photo enlargements.
We copy from Photo. We return all Photos. Prompt Shipments. Free Catalog.

BELL MFG. CO., Box 103, Jamaica, N. Y.

Plate 383: Advertisement for agents and dealers for unbreakable walking, talking dolls from the Bell Mfg. co. Ad appeared in *The Crisis,* April, 1924, page 285.

COLORED DOLLS AND NOVELTIES

Pretty Light-Brown and Mulatto Dolls with Real Human Hair Curls. They Sleep, Walk, Talk and Cry. Sizes 14 to 30 inches. 15 different styles. 100 other novelties. Free Catalog.

19 inches, $5.50 each, $42. doz.
23 inches, $7.50 each, $49. doz.
30 inches, $11.98 each, $88. doz.

AGENTS WANTED

BETHEL MFG. CO.
Dept. C. 97 South St.   JAMAICA, N. Y.

Plate 384: Advertisement from the Bethel Mfg. Co. for colored dolls. Ad appeared in *The Crisis* from February, 1927 to June, 1927, and November, 1927 to December, 1928.

Dolls with beautiful Brown Skin— Walk and Cry

While they last we are selling our regular $3.00, 14 inch walking and crying colored dolls at $2.23.
Postage prepaid.

O-K COLORED DOLL COMPANY
2293 SEVENTH AVENUE, NEW YORK, N. Y.

Plate 385: Advertisement for "Dolls with beautiful Brown Skin" appeared in *The Crisis,* April, 1923, page 238. Company placing the ad was the O-K Colored Doll Company, New York, New York. Dolls were described as 14" walking and crying dolls and sold for $2.23.

COLORED DOLLS
21 in. tall—Cry—Sleep
Only $3.50
Write to . . . . . . THE CRISIS

Plate 386: Advertisement for "Colored Dolls" for $3.50 from *The Crisis,* February, 1939, page 37.

Justus, Joseph and Leta Davis, p. 342

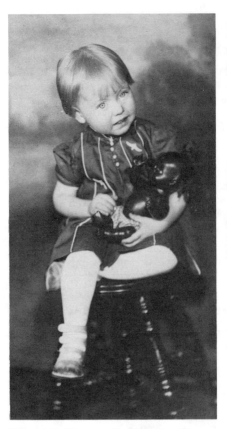

Plate 387: Photograph of Justus, Joseph, and Leta Davis from *The Crisis,* October, 1928, page 345. The girl is holding a black doll that was advertised in *The Crisis* the previous year. As reported in *The Crisis,* Justus, Joseph, and Mae Davis were agents for the magazine in Phoenix, Arizona. Besides being energetic agents, the children were amateur Jubilee Singers. It is not clear from the information given whether the girl's correct name was named "Leta" or "Mae."

Plate 388: Photograph of Sandra Fishburn Larry with her black doll. Picture was taken in the early 1950s in Summerville, South Carolina. Most of Sandra Larry's childhood dolls were black. They were probably purchased in Charleston, South Carolina.

Plate 389: Photograph of Marilyn Thomas at age 3 in 1938. This was one of her favorite dolls. The photographer went door to door with his camera and backdrops taking photographs of children in their homes. Photograph courtesy of Michele Bady.

Plate 390: Advertisement for Negro dolls from the Art Novelty Co., New York City. Ad appeared in *The Crisis,* December, 1933, page 298 and January, 1934, page 22.

Plate 391: Advertisement from the Art Novelty Co., New York City for Negro Dolls. Ad appeared in February and March issues of *The Crisis* in 1932, pages 70 and 106 respectively.

Plate 392: Advertisement for "Fine Art Negro Dolls" from the Art Novelty Co., New York City. Ad appeared in *The Crisis,* a monthly magazine, from April, 1932, to November, 1932. Ad differs slightly from previous ad placed by the same company.

Plate 393: Advertisement for pretty Negro dolls that walk, talk, and cry from the Art Novelty Co. Dolls were probably made of composition. Ad was placed in *The Crisis,* August, 1931, page 280.

COLORED DOLLS

LITTLE LOU

The cutest and cuddliest 27-inch brownskin baby. She sleeps, cries, and has such a soft cotton body. Also has a petticoat, rubber panties, imitation leather moccasins, stockings, and the sweetest organdy dress trimmed with lace; baby hat to match.

Our attractive catalogue contains a large selection of moderately priced dolls. Catalogue FREE on request.

Santone Mfg. Sales Co.

P. O. Box No. 1, Station A.
NEW YORK, N. Y.

A. T. Barnes, Jr.   *J. Jacksier*

AGENTS WANTED
We are manufacturers. Dolls sold wholesale and retail.

Plate 394: Advertisement for a mama doll "Little Lou" from Santone Mfg. Sales Co. Doll was 27" tall, sleeps and cries. Doll was probably made of composition. Ad was run in *The Crisis,* December, 1934, page 371.

Colored Boudoir Dolls

At *Popular* Prices

FREE Catalogue on Request

We wish our many patrons and friends a Merry Christmas and a Happy New Year.

SANTONE MFG. SALES CO.

P. O. Box No. 1, Station A.
New York, N. Y.

A. T. Barnes, Jr.   J. Jacksier

Plate 395: Advertisement for "Colored Boudoir Dolls" from the Santone Mfg. Sales Co. Advertisement was placed in *The Crisis,* January, 1935, page 29.

Colored Boudoir Dolls

At *Popular* Prices

FREE Catalogue on Request

AGENTS WANTED
We are manufacturers. Dolls sold wholesale and retail.

SANTONE MFG. SALES CO.

P. O. Box No. 1, Station A.
New York, N. Y.

A. T. Barnes, Jr.   J. Jacksier

Plate 396: Ad for boudoir dolls by the Santone Mfg. Sales Co., New York, N.Y. Ad was placed in *The Crisis,* February and March, 1935 issues, pages 61 and 94 respectively. Ad is slightly different from Santone ad above.

NEGRO DOLLS!

Special Sale! Every home should have a Colored Doll. We offer in this sale two flashy numbers with hair, moving eyes, voice, nicely dressed. Price $4.98; large size, $5.98. If C.O.D. postage extra. Agents wanted. Write NATIONAL CO., 254 W. 135th St., New York 30, N. Y.

Plate 397: Advertisement for "Negro Dolls" from *The Crisis,* July, 1944, page 237. The same ad also appeared in the October, 1944, issue, page 333. Ad was placed by the National Co., New York, N.Y.

Plate 398: Advertisement for dolls with hair and moving eyes from the National Company. Ad is from *The Crisis,* October, 1945, page 301. The same ad appeared in the November, 1945 issue, page 333.

Negro Dolls

With Hair, Moving Eyes, Shoes, Stockings. Nicely Dressed. Price $4.98 and $6.59 (if C.O.D., postage extra).

Agents—Dealers Wanted. Write

NATIONAL COMPANY

254 W. 135th St., New York 30, N. Y.

COLORED DOLLS

Write in
For
Catalogue
No Charge

•

Many lovely
Styles

•

All Types
of Doll
Accessories
Obtainable

•

Also
Exquisite
Boudoir
Dolls

LULU BELLE

This is a reproduction of one of the many lovely styles we are offering at exceptional prices. We carry white dolls. Write

VICTORIA DOLL CO.

Dept. M

18 W. 21st St.   New York City

Plate 399: Ad for "Lulu Belle" from the Victoria Doll Co. Doll is made of composition. Ad was placed in *The Crisis,* May, 1936, page 157 and June, 1936, page 189.

FREE!
THIS BEAUTIFUL BROWN DOLL

It Is Nearly 2 Feet Tall

It Cries

It Sleeps

It Has a Pretty Dress, Shoes and Cap

It Retails for $3.00

It Is Durable

It Will Be Sent Absolutely FREE with Only 4 Yearly Subscriptions to THE CRISIS

Race Appreciation Must be Taught EARLY What better time than in CHILDHOOD

Any little girl will love this BIG BEAUTIFUL BROWN DOLL What better CHRISTMAS or BIRTHDAY present could you give?

For Your Library Table

Your Library Table is known by its magazines.

When your guests look over your magazines they judge YOUR mind by what you read.

THE CRISIS on your library table immediately places you in the *civilized minority*.

Its presence there indicates that you appreciate and understand the better things your people are doing and have a vital interest in their future.

It places you in the same category as the libraries at 300 great universities that regularly subscribe for *THE CRISIS*.

THE CRISIS is authoritative, courageous and provocative of thought.

To be one of its readers is a distinction.

HERE'S WHAT YOU DO

1. Send us *four* yearly subscriptions at $1.50 each, or $6.00 in all.

2. Send us the names and addresses of the subscribers, *printed* in ink or typewritten, and enclose money order.

3. Tell us to whom the big beautiful brown doll is to be sent.

4. Send in your remittance before Dec. 15, 1938. *That's All.*

THE CRISIS

69 FIFTH AVENUE **NEW YORK, N. Y.**

Plate 400: Advertisement for "Free Beautiful Brown Doll" in exchange for four yearly subscriptions to *The Crisis*. The same ad appeared in November and December, 1938 issues of the magazine, pages 360 and 392 respectively.

Plate 401: Advertisement from Calumet Baking Powder showing Kate Smith's Mammy Doll. Ad was shown in *Country Gentleman*, November, 1939, page 58.

Top Right — Plate 402: Advertisement for "Negro" dolls from the N.V. Sales Company, New York. Ad is from *The Crisis*, November, 1945, page 333.

Center Right — Plate 403: Slightly different ad from the N.V. Sales Company. Ad is from *The Crisis*, August, 1946, page 254.

Bottom Right — Plate 404: Another different ad from the N.V. Sales Company for Negro dolls. Ad is from the November, 1946, issue of *The Crisis*, page 348.

Plate 405: Averill Manufacturing Co. "U-Shab-Ti." 18" tall. 1923. Doll was made to celebrate the discovery in 1922, of the tomb of Tutankhamen, king of ancient Egypt from about 1347 to 1339 B.C. Tutankhamon was only eight or nine years old when he became king and his reign continued for only eight or nine years. Dolls found in ancient Egyptian tombs were primarily used for religious purposes and are referred to as "Ushabti." However, dolls used as playthings were found in tombs dating back to the year 2000 B.C. Possibly "King Tut" as he is commonly referred to, would have had a Ushabti doll as he was also nicknamed "Boy King." This doll is a real collector's find as it is all original (right shoe missing) and still has its tag attached with the original ornate brass pin. Doll has composition head and hands, brown cloth arms, legs, and body, painted eyes, molded painted brown hair, open-closed mouth with painted teeth. Doll is unmarked. Original tag reads: THIS IS A GENUINE/TUT-ANAH-AMEN/TRADE MARK REG./U-SHAB-TI/ INSPIRED BY THE RECENT/DISCOVERY IN LUXOR,/EGYPT. $650.00.
Right — Close up of original tag.

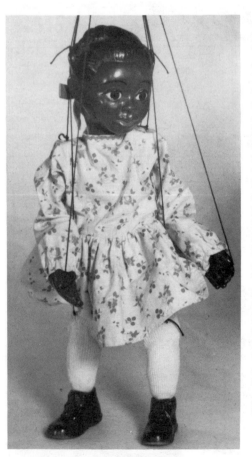

Plate 406: Effanbee. "Liza Lee." 13" tall. Marionette designed in the 1930's by Virginia Austin. Composition head, hands, and shoes, jointed wood and cloth body, painted Negroid features, hair is molded into three sections into pigtails. Doll was originally marketed by Virginia Austin under the business name of her husband, Curtis Craft. Rights to the doll were later transferred to Effanbee and marketed along with a boy doll "Lucifer," shown in my earlier book, and a clown doll "Clippo." Head on Emily is unmarked. Both feet are marked: CLIPPO PUPPETS/MADE IN/ USA/CURTIS CRAFT. Collection of Donald N. Thurber. All original in yellow print dress. $800.00.

Plate 407: Effanbee. "Jambo the Jiver." 14". Marionette from the "Talen-Toy" collection. Head, body, and limbs are made of hardwoods with joints pinned, stapled, or jointed with eyelets. All original. Collection of and photograph courtesy of Virginia Kiley. $225.00.

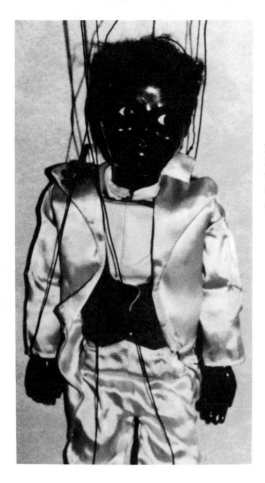

Plate 408: Hazelle. "Tap Dancer" marionette. 20" tall. 1952. #203 in the 500 series. Collection of Virginia Kiley. $300.00.

Plate 409: Hazelle. "Uncle Tom." 1941. 14" tall. Mohair wool crepe hair. Tenite head, hands, hand carves shoes. Marionette is pictured in 1941 *Children's Activities* magazine. Collection of Virginia Kiley. $300.00.

Plate 410: Advertisement for "Topsy and Sambo," 14" marionettes from Hazelle's Marionettes. 1945.

117

Plate 411: Pelham. "Minstrial Man." 14" tall. marionette with wooden head. All original in red and white striped jacket, blue pants, red and yellow hat, red wooden shoes. Collection of and photograph courtesy of Virginia Kiley. $250.00.

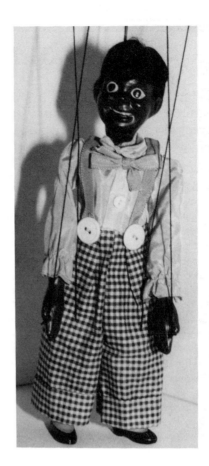

Plate 412: Sarg. "Sambo." Approximately 11" tall. Marionette made by Tony Sarg/ Madame Alexander in the mid 1930's. Head is molded composition, painted features, upper arms and legs are made from pieces of cloth (slack, not stuffed,) lower arms and legs are composition with painted shoes. This one of two black marionettes made by Tony Sarg. The other one, "Bones," is shown following. Marks: TONY SARG/ ALEXANDER, on torso; TONY SARG, on head. From collection of and photograph courtesy of Pat and Bill Biskie. $350.00.

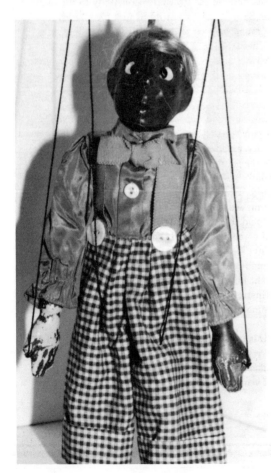

Plate 413: Sarg. "Bones." Approximately 11" tall. Doll is of identical construction as previous Tony Sarg marionette. Marks are also the same. Collection of and photograph courtesy of Pat and Bill Biskie. $350.00.

Tony Sarg wrote a play for the two black marionettes and a white marionette named "Interlocutor." The play is called "Dixieland Minstrels" and is printed as follows, courtesy of Pat & Bill Biskie from an original copy of the play:

THE DIXIELAND MINSTRELS

This play is arranged for two negro minstrels and a white interlocutor. However, while three characters would be better, it is possible to dispense with one of the negro minstrels and in this event give 'Bones' all the jokes. At the rise of the curtain the whole cast is on the stage. They bow very low; then the interlocutor steps forward.

Interlocutor: (Bowing again) Ladies and Gentleman, allow me to present The Dixieland Minstrel Boys!

(All bow again, the others come forward)

All: (Singing to tune of 'Oh, Susanna') Oh, we've come to make you happy — yes we've come to make you gay;
Oh, we hope that we're successful and we drive your cares away
We are happy, for we are always that way —
But we'll feel a great deal better if you clap for us today.

(All step to rear of stage but Interlocutor)

Interlocutor: Good morning, Mr. Bones.

Bones: (Stepping forward) Good morning, sah, it's a fine afternoon dis evening, ain't it?

Interlocutor: (Lifting his hand to his head) Oh, stop that. But jokin aside, it is a fine day.

Sambo: (Stepping forward as Bones steps back) Yas, sah, it's a great day fo' de race!

Interlocutor: I didn't know there was any race today. What race do you mean?

Sambo: The human race! (They all laugh, waving their hands and slapping their knees)

Interlocutor: By the way, Sambo, I hear that you left your job at the garage. What was the matter?

Sambo: Oh, jes' a little sumpin' de boss said de other day.

Interlocutor: You shouldn't get insulted so easily. What did he say?

Sambo: He said, "Sambo, you're fired'" (All laugh — same business as before)

Interlocutor: (Turning to Bones) By the way, Mr. Bones, how is your pa?

Bones: He's fine, thank you, he is.

Interlocutor: And your ma?

Bones: She's fine, thank you, she is.

Interlocutor: And your sister?

Bones: She's fine, thanks, she is.

Interlocutor: And that stingy landlord of yours?

Bones: He's daid, thanks, he is.

Interlocutor: I'm sorry to hear that. What was the complaint?

Bones: There wasn't no complaint. Everybody's satisfied. (All laugh — wave hands, etc.)

Interlocutor: Say, Sambo, how is your farm coming along?

Sambo: Oh, it's comin' alon fine. Ah won a prize th' other day!

Interlocutor: That's good. What did you win it for?

Sambo: Ah entered de contest for de largest lemon. But when de jedges saw mah lemon, it was so large dey made a mistake.

Interlocutor: Well, what happened?

Sambo: Dey gave my lemon de prize fo' de largest grapefruit. (All laugh)

Interlocutor: Do you expect me to believe that?

Sambo: 'Cos ah does. What's mo', ah'll show you de prize to prove it.

Interlocutor: What is the prize, Mr. Sambo?

Sambo: Ten dollars — and ah'll show it to you anytime! (All laugh. Pause) Say, Mr. Interlocutor, ah feels a song comin' on. Kin ah please sing it?

Interlocutor: Why certainly you may. (Bowing to audience) Ladies and Gentlemen, our mellow-voiced Mr. Sambo will now render 'Oh, Susanna.'

(Sambo sings and tap-dances. All join in chorus and when he has finished all applaud.)

Interlocutor: Thank you, Mr. Sambo, thank you. (Turning to Bones, who steps forward) How is it that you are so cheerful today, Mr. Bones.

Bones: Yo' see, ah just came from de dentist...

Interlocutor: Well, that's nothing to be happy about.

Bones: Oh, yes it am! You see, he was away and he won't be back for three days. (All laugh)

Bones: Say, Mr. Interlocutor, how's your son, William?

Interlocutor: He's fine, thank you, Mr. Bones.

Sambo: Ah saw William de other day at the Barber Shop where ah works now. An' ah made up a poem about what he said to the barber. (All crowd around him and ask to hear the poem)

Sambo: Here goes: "Please cut my hair," said Willy to the man in the Barber Shop. "And I want it cut just like Daddy's — With a little round hole on the top" (All laugh, pointing at Interlocutor's head)

Interlocutor: (A little angry) Making fun of my bald spot, are you? Well, I have a good mind to stop this show right now!

Bones: Before you stops it, ah'd like to ask you something.

Interlocutor: What is it?

Sambo: You always says you can talk English good, don't you?

Interlocutor: I can speak the English tongue with quite a degree of facility, excellence and beauty. Why do you interrogate me upon the point?

Sambo: What's dat?

Interlocutor: I said, "I do speak well. Why do you ask?"

Sambo: Well, let me see you say dis —

If a woodchuck could chop wood, how much wood would a woodchuck chop, if a woodchuck could chop wood?"

Interlocutor: That's easy. (He tries, but stumbles over the words. All laugh but Interlocutor) That is all, enough, the end, the finish! In other words, ladies and gentlemen, the Dixieland Minstrels will now sing their parting song. (All sing to the tune of 'Oh, Susanna' and all but Interlocutor dance)

All: Oh we're finished and we hope that you liked our little show; And if you have, dear audience, we wish you'd let us know — So please tell us, before we have to go, By clapping very loudly if you think you've liked our show. (All bow very low)

Curtain

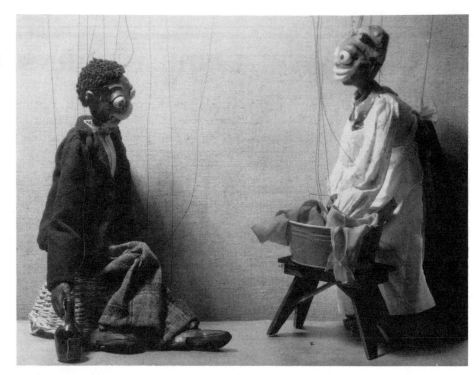

Plate 415: Unidentified marionettes with exaggerated features. Photograph courtesy of Virginia Kiley. $800.00.

Plate 414: Two marionettes, one white, the other black. The black one is in the lower right in photo. Unidentified. Photograph courtesy of Virginia Kiley. $800.00.

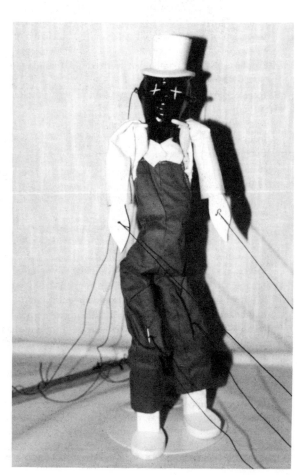

Left — Plate 416: Another unidentified marionette. Photograph courtesy of Virginia Kiley. $800.00.

Right — Plate 417: All original black marionette. Photograph courtesy of Susan Girardot. $100.00.

Plate 418: 14" marionette with composition head and hands, wooden feet, painted features. All original. Unmarked. $75.00.

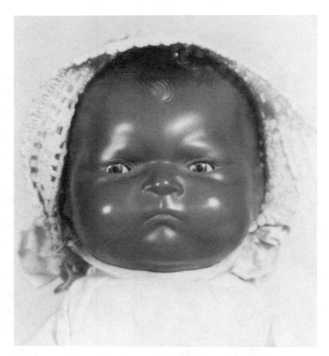

Plate 419: Acme Toy Co. 15" tall. Grumpy-type character face. Composition head, molded painted hair, amber sleep eyes, closed mouth, composition hands, white cloth body and legs, with cry box, 1920's. Marks: ACME/TOY CO., on head. $300.00.

Plate 420: Alexander. "Rumbero and Rumbera" of Cuba. 9" tall. 1942–43. Composition heads, painted eyes, black mohair wigs, jointed composition heads, painted eyes, black mohair wigs, jointed composition straight leg bodies. All original. Marked on back. In 1937, a dark complected 9" Hawaiian doll was made by Alexander. She was wearing a grass skirt. $300.00 each.

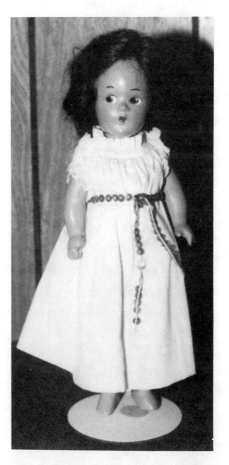

Plate 421: Alexander. "Egyptian." 9" 1936. Jointed composition, painted features, black wig. Doll is made from the "Little Betty" mold. Photograph courtesy of Susan Girardot. $300.00.

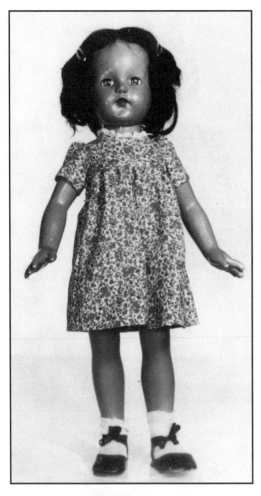

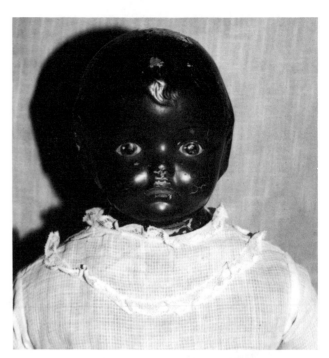

Plate 422: Effanbee. "Anne Shirley." 21" tall. Composition head, jointed composition body, amber sleep eyes with lashes, closed mouth, brown wig. Redressed. Shoes and socks could be original. Marks: EFFANBEE/ANNE SHIRLEY, on back. $900.00.

Plate 423: Effanbee. 20" tall. Doll is marked with early script marking on shoulder-plate. Photograph courtesy of Susan Girardot. $300.00.

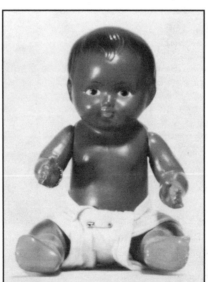

Plate 425: Effanbee. "Baby Huggins." Circa 1913. 9". One piece composition head and body, jointed arms and legs, molded-painted black hair, painted eyes, closed mouth. Marks: EFFANBEE, on back. $300.00.

Plate 424: Effanbee. "Suzette." Composition head, painted brown eyes, closed mouth, jointed composition body. 11" tall. All original in long grass skirt, orange bra top, orange and yellow lei. Marks: SUZETTE/EFFANBEE, on head; SUZETTE/EFFANBEE/MADE IN/USA, on back. Doll won Honorable Mention in United Federation of Doll Clubs 38th Annual Exhibit, 1987, Boston, Massachusetts. $350.00.

Plate 426: Effanbee. ©1912. 10½". Composition shoulder head and arms, white cloth body, brown cloth legs. Jointed at shoulders and hips. Painted eyes, mohair wig. A previous owner had doll treated with a sealer to prevent crazing. Marks: EFFANBEE, on back shoulder. $175.00.

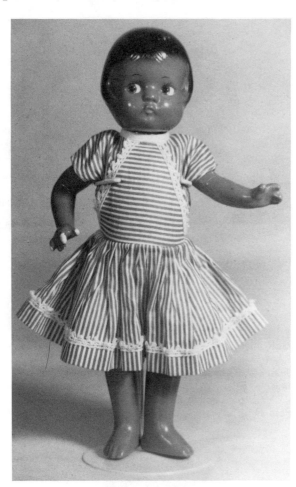

Left — Plate 427: Effanbee. "Baby Grumpy." 11". Composition shoulder head, movable composition arms, brown cloth body, jointed brown cloth legs and feet, painted eyes, molded hair with three holes drilled for tufts of black string hair. Marks: EFFANBEE/DOLLS/WALK/TALK/SLEEP, embossed inside an oval on back shoulderplate. $300.00.

Right — Plate 428: Effanbee. "Patsyette." 9" tall. Composition head, molded painted black hair, painted eyes, jointed composition body with paint chipping on right hand. Redressed by a previous owner. Marks: EFFANBEE/PATSYETTE/DOLL, on back. $750.00.

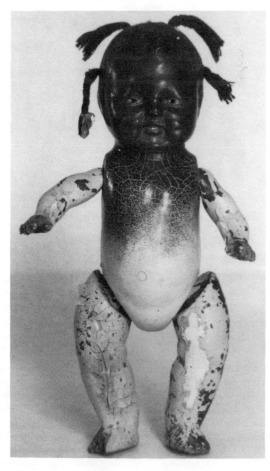

Left — Plate 429: Effanbee. "Patsykins (Patsy, Jr.) 11" tall. 1930–40. All composition, jointed at neck, shoulders and hips, molded hair with bangs and three holes for tufts of black string hair, molded headband, curved right arm, straight left arm, painted eyes, closed mouth. All original in red dotted dress with white collar, white socks with pink trim, black shoes. Marks: EFFANBEE/PATSY JR./DOLL, on back. $600.00.

Right — Plate 430: Golberger. 13" tall. 1922. Composition one piece head and body, spring jointed arms and legs, four tufts of black string hair, painted eyes, open-closed mouth with two painted teeth, dimpled cheeks. Almost all of the brown paint has flaked off limbs, legs badly crazed. Body was only painted to the chest. Lower body was never painted. Doll was probably originally dressed to cover the body. Marks: GOLBERGER, on back. This doll could possibly have been made by "Goldberger" and the "d" was accidentally left out when marking the doll. Collection of J.D. Carmichael. $100.00.

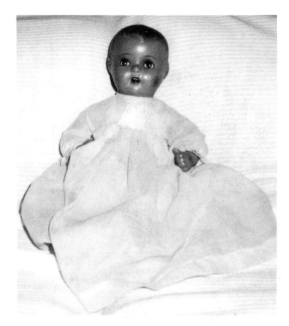

Plate 431: Hendren. "Sis" from the "Dolly Dingle" series. 14" tall. Composition and cloth doll designed by G.G. Drayton who also designed the famous Campbell Kids. Composition shoulder head and lower arms, cloth body, upper arms, legs, and feet, painted hair with five holes drilled for tufts of black pigtails, painted features. Marks: G G DRAYTON, on back of shoulder-plate. From collection of and photograph courtesy of Lynn Shay. $400.00.

Plate 432: Estrella. 13" tall. Composition head, arms, and legs, cloth body, painted hair, blue eyes (unusual for a black doll), open mouth with upper teeth. Marks: ESTRELLA, on back of head. Estrella in Portuguese means "star." Collection of and photograph courtesy of Joyce A. Wilkinson. $300.00.

Plate 433: Ideal. "Shirley Temple" doll as "Marama" from the movie *Hurricane.* 18" tall. Composition head, painted side-glancing eyes, open-closed mouth with four painted upper teeth, black yarn hair, jointed composition body. All original in ecru hula skirt made of string with gold felt waistband, two paper leis around the neck, orange flower in hair. Marks: SHIRLEY TEMPLE/18, on head; 18, on back. Doll was also available in 8", 13", and 15" sizes. $1,300.00.

Plate 434: Ideal. "Snow White." 16½". 1938. Jointed composition. Swivel head, molded hair with center part with molded red bow, painted eyes, jointed straight leg body. Doll is wearing a red and white dress that is appropriate with the period and could be original. Unmarked. $600.00.

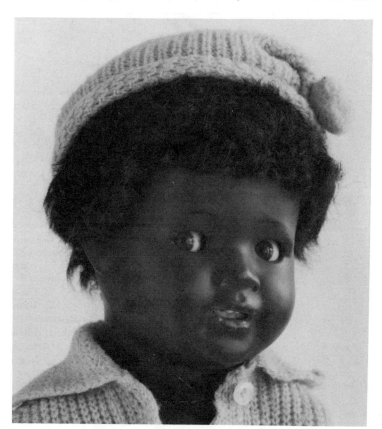

Plate 436: Hermann Steiner, Germany. 20" boy doll, circa 1930. All composition with glass flirty eyes. Mold #134. Collection of and photograph courtesy of the Rosalie Whyel Museum of Doll Art. $1,500.00+.

Plate 435: Mollye. 7". Composition swivel head, jointed bent-leg composition baby body, three tufts of back string hair tied with yellow ribbons, slightly molded hair, side glancing painted eyes, closed mouth. All original in yellow organdy dress, white booties tied with yellow ribbons. Doll is unmarked. Dress is tagged: COSTUME DESIGN/BY/MOLLYE/REG. U.S. PAT. (A small portion of the tag is sewn into dress seam and cannot be read.) $175.00.

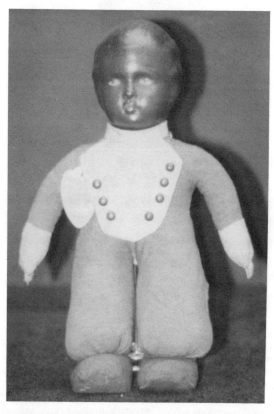

Plate 437: Trion Toy Co. 10½" tall. Early 1900's. Composition head and arms, cloth body and legs stuffed with straw, molded painted hair, painted eyes, open-closed mouth. Marks: ©/TRION TOY CO., on head. $125.00.

Plate 438: Unica. "Hassan." 11" tall. Composition or papier-maché boy, cloth body, painted face. Dressed in blue pantaloons, white bib and gloves, brown shoes. Doll was made by Unica, Courtray, Belgium. Photograph courtesy of Faith Wyse. $150.00.

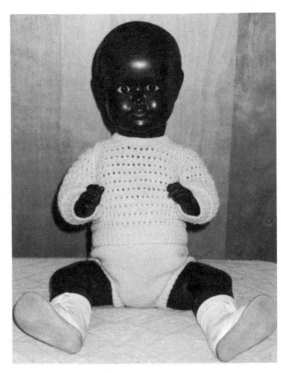

Plate 439: Wellings. 7". Made in England. Composition head, painted side glancing eyes, painted smiling mouth with teeth, black mohair wig with goldtone hoop earrings attached, brown velvet body. All original in grass skirt, beads around neck, bracelet around ankle and top of right arm appear to be made of a bone-like material. Unmarked. Attributed to Norah Wellings. $200.00.

Plate 440: Hugo Weigand, Germany. 24". All composition baby doll, molded and painted curly hair, glass sleep eyes, closed mouth. Photograph courtesy of Phyllis Schlatter. $1,000.00+.

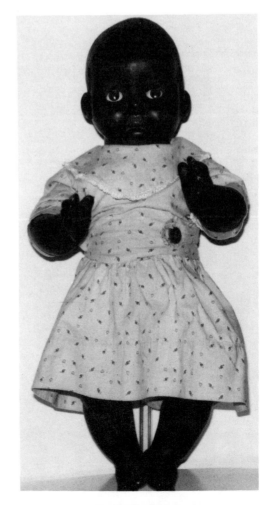

Plate 442: 18" transition doll with composition bent-leg baby body and hard plastic head. Sleep eyes, closed mouth. Redressed. Head is marked: MADE IN ENGLAND. PAT. NO. 535811 & FOREIGN PATENTS. Photograph courtesy of Connie Parsons. $250.00.

Plate 441: Topsy-turvy. 7½" tall. Composition head, shared composition body, painted eyes, molded painted hair, closed mouths. Black head is movable, white head is attached to the body. All original in burgundy dress with white dots on the black doll, attached navy dress with white dots on the white doll. A similar doll is shown in authors earlier book, *Black Dolls 1820–1991*, plate 251, except this doll does not have the holes for tufts on hair on the black end. Unmarked. $200.00.

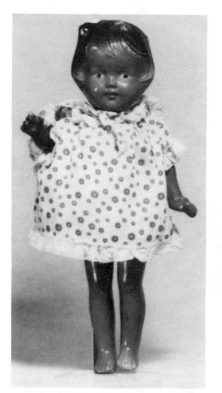

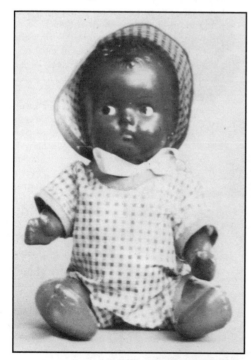

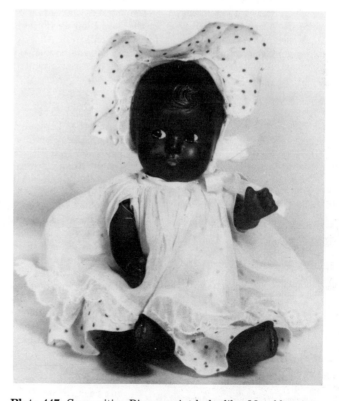

Plate 445: Composition topsy-type baby doll, painted eyes looking to the left, closed panted mouth, three tufts of mohair stapled to the head. Most doll of this type had holes drilled into the head and hair was inserted. Head and body are one piece with jointed arms and legs. Unmarked. Dolls of this type were generally sold wearing only a diaper. 1920's to 1930's. $125.00.

Plate 443: Patsy-type composition doll. 14" tall. 1930's. Molded loop in her black molded and painted hair, painted features, open-closed mouth, swivel head on a five piece strung body. Body and right arms look like old replacements as the finish is a darker brown. Value $250.00.

Plate 444: Souvenir doll from the Virgin Islands. 9". Movable composition head, molded hair painted black with three holes for tufts of black string hair, painted eyes, jointed five piece composition bent-leg body. All original in taped on native type outfit in multi-colored raffia type material over diapers. Unmarked. Original store tag is still attached. One side shows a woman with a tray of fruit on her head. Bottom of tag reads: VIRGIN ISLANDS/NATIVE PRODUCTS. Reverse side of tag: HANDMADE BY NATIVES/IN THE VIRGIN ISLANDS/OF THE UNITED STATES/OF AMERICA FOR/THE COOPERATIVES/STOCK NO. 662 (stock no. is written in pencil.) Doll was probably dressed in the Virgin Islands but not made there. $100.00.

Plate 446: Composition baby doll. 8" tall. One piece head and body, movable arms and legs, side glancing painted eyes, closed mouth, molded painted black hair without holes drilled into head for tufts of hair. All original in blue gingham romper suit and matching bonnet. Unmarked. $95.00.

Plate 447: Composition Dionne quint look-alike. Movable composition socket head, side glancing painted eyes, closed mouth, molded hair, jointed composition baby body. Dressed in white organdy dress with red dot, matching bonnet, white organdy overlay. Clothing is said to be original. Unmarked. 7½" tall. $100.00.

127

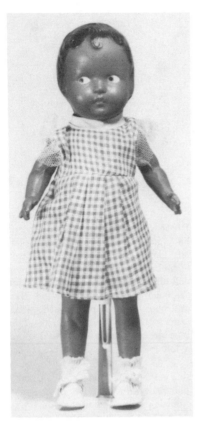

Plate 448: All original composition doll, Circa 1930. 15". Head and body are one piece, molded painted side glancing eyes, closed mouth, movable composition arms and legs. All original in purple gingham dress with matching panties, white shoes and socks. Doll is old store stock used by the Goodfellows, a charitable organization, for Christmas gifts. Unmarked. $195.00.

Plate 449: 15" tall. Another all original unmarked composition doll used by the Goodfellow for Christmas gifts for needy children. All original in pale pink hat and bonnet. Collection of Michael Wolk-Laniewski. $195.00.

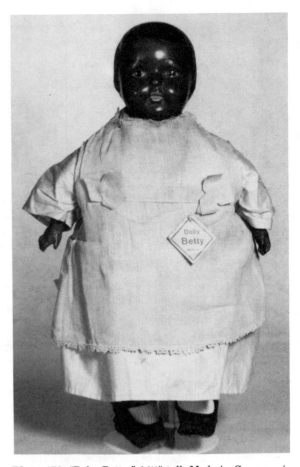

Plate 450: "Baby Betty." 14½" tall. Made in Germany in the early 1900's. Composition shoulder head, molded straight hair, painted eyes, open-closed mouth, composition hands, brown cloth body, upper arms, legs, and feet. All original, including shoes and socks. Dress is pink cotton with white cotton pinafore, white socks, black button shoes. Doll is rare in that it still has the original paper name tag tacked onto the dress. Tag reads: BABY/ BETTY/GERMANY. Doll is unmarked. $350.00.

Plate 451: Unusually large "Aunt Jemima," 1920's. 25" tall. Composition head, molded painted black hair, painted eyes and upper eyelashes, red dots in nostrils, closed mouth painted red, composition hands and lower arms (repaired,) white cloth body stuffed with straw, brown cloth legs and feet. Clothing could be original. Aunt Jemima was one of the most highly advertised black dolls in the 1920's, usually in the 14" size as shown in authors previous book, *Black Dolls, 1820–1991.* Unmarked. $350.00.

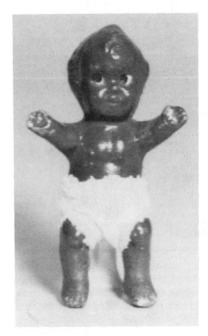

Plate 452: Composition novelty doll. 3" tall. Doll is all one piece, head and body, painted side glancing eyes with the portion that is usually white painted blue, molded hair. Unmarked. $25.00.

Plate 453: Composition. 21" tall. Composition head, arms, and legs, cloth body, molded hair, amber sleep eyes with lashes, open mouth with two upper teeth, red tongue. Original clothing, replaced shoes. $250.00.

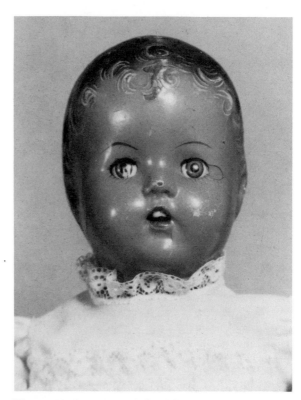

Plate 454: Composition baby doll. 1940's. 18". Composition head, molded hair, brown tin sleep eyes with upper lashes, open mouth with two upper teeth, stuffed rubber arms and legs, white cloth body. Marks: O, on back of head. $85.00.

Plate 455: "Ma-Ma" doll. 22½" tall. Composition movable shoulder head, composition arms and legs, amber sleep eyes with lashes, black wig, open-mouth with four upper teeth, cloth body with cry box. Doll was purchased in 1952, in Detroit, Michigan, for Melven Baines. Redressed. Marks: M, on head. Even though doll was sold in the early 1950's, it was probably manufactured in the 1940's. Collection of Melven Baines Jolley. $250.00.

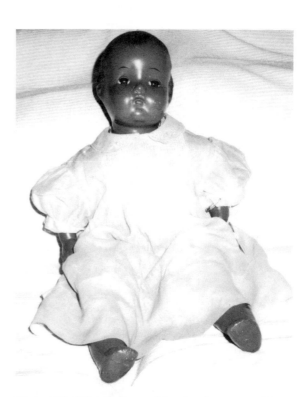

Plate 456: 21" tall. Composition head, arms, and legs, cloth body, brown sleep eyes, closed mouth, molded hair. Unmarked. Collection of Wood photograph courtesy of Joyce A. Wilkinson. $200.00.

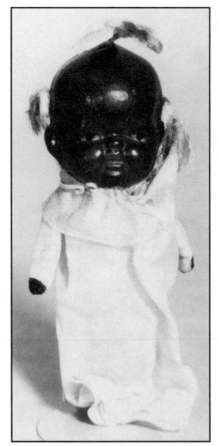

Plate 457: Gerber-type baby. 11". Composition head, molded painted hair with two holes for tufts of black yarn hair, painted side-glancing eyes, open-closed mouth. Head and torso are one piece with jointed composition limbs. Unmarked. $350.00.

Plate 458: Baby with composition flanged neck head, three holes in head for tufts of hair tied with ribbons, painted facial features. Cloth body and arms. Doll is dressed in sewn on pink acetate bunting, body forms the bunting and is marked: JAPAN, on the hemline. 4" tall. All original. $45.00.

Plate 459: Souvenir type doll. 12". Head is hard composition-like material, shoulder head, painted side glancing eyes, molded hair, brown cloth body and arms, legs covered in leather, sewn on clothing. Doll was probably imported to Haiti to be dressed and sold to the tourist trade. Photograph courtesy of Lin Murphy. $100.00.

Plate 460: Grace Drayton-type composition dolls. 6¾". One piece composition head, body, and legs with movable arms. Molded hair in a "bob" style popular in the 1920's, painted side-glancing eyes, painted closed mouth. All original in brown print cotton dresses. Unmarked. $75.00 each.

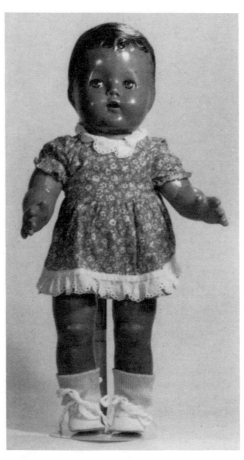

Plate 461: Composition toddler doll. 16½" tall. Molded painted black hair, tin sleep eyes with brown eyelashes, open mouth with two upper teeth and felt tongue, five-piece jointed toddler body. Redressed by a previous owner. Unmarked. Back of head looks like it was repaired as well as parts of the body and limbs. $200.00.

Plate 462: 23" baby doll. Composition head, arms and legs, black mohair wig, amber sleep eyes, open mouth with two upper teeth, red felt tongue, white cloth body. Clothing is said to be all original, including shoes and socks. Unmarked. $250.00.

Plate 464: Composition "Mardi Gras King." Souvenir type doll. 1930's. Approximately 22". All original in grass skirt and accessories. Painted features and molded hair. $225.00.

Plate 463: German composition dolls with googlie eyes. 20" tall. Photograph courtesy of Frasher's Auctions. No price available.

Plate 466: 30" tall. Composition head with flange neck, painted eyes, cloth body stuffed with cork, arms and legs straw stuffed with metal disc hinge. Redressed a long time ago by a previous owner. Doll is unmarked. Doll was a blue ribbon winner and judges choice at a doll show in 1990. Photograph and doll from the collection of Jane Cameron. $450.00.

Plate 467: Composition creche figure. 22" tall. Painted features. $450.00.

Plate 465: "Can't Break 'Em" boy doll, 12". Material used for the head is said to be called "biskaline," a material that is supposed to be unbreakable. Painted eyes, bald head, open mouth with molded teeth, composition hands, cloth gauntlet arms, white cloth stuffed body, cloth legs and feet. All original in long sleeve red cotton shirt with off white muslin trousers. $300.00.

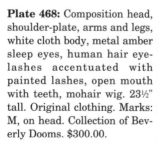

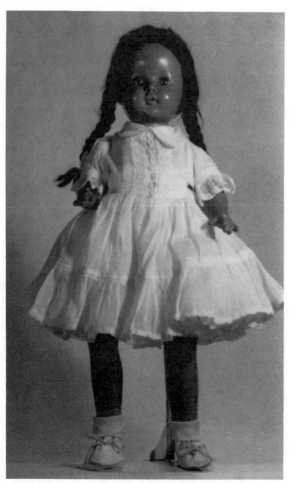

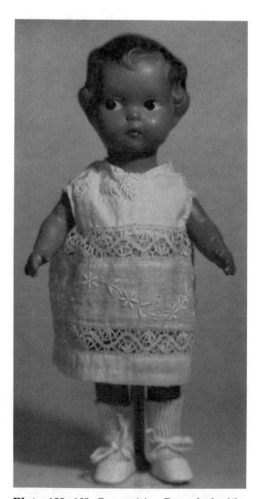

Plate 468: Composition head, shoulder-plate, arms and legs, white cloth body, metal amber sleep eyes, human hair eyelashes accentuated with painted lashes, open mouth with teeth, mohair wig. 23½" tall. Original clothing. Marks: M, on head. Collection of Beverly Dooms. $300.00.

Plate 469: 12". Composition Patsy look-alike with molded hair, molded red bow on left side near part in hair, painted italigo eyes, closed mouth, jointed composition arms and legs. Body is one piece with the head. Unmarked. Redressed. 1920–30. A marked Effanbee doll has the same molded hair. $150.00.

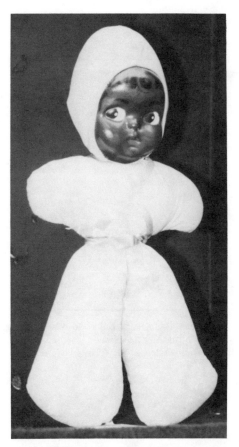

Plate 470: 18" tall. Celluloid face, stuffed cloth body. Dressed in orange top, blue and orange printed pants, bright orange cap. Photograph courtesy of Faith Wyse. $40.00.

Plate 471: Celluloid caricature doll, movable head, arms, and legs, pierced ears with gold tone hoop earrings, open-closed mouth, stationary eyes that appear to open and shut when doll is tilted. 10" tall. Marks: HONG KONG, on back. $65.00.

Plate 472: Schildkrot Puppen. Made in Western Germany, 1950's. Jointed celluloid toddler doll. Molded black curly hair, stationary brown celluloid eyes, closed mouth, pierced ears with round coin-like earrings. 13" tall. All original in green, yellow, and red grass skirt and multi-colored plastic beads around the neck. Hang tag on arms pictures a white turtle on a blue background. Marks: (pictures of a turtle inside a diamond)/34, on head; the identical marks are on the body. Original yellow cardboard box has pictures of children from around the world on the sides and top. Printed on the box: SCHILDKROT/PUPPEN/(TURTLE LOGO)/IN ALLER WELT. STOCK #4793/34/27, MADE IN WESTERN GERMANY. $250.00.

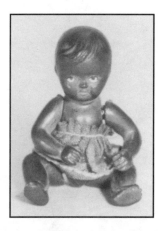

Plate 474: 7" celluloid doll. Painted features, molded painted hair, painted clothing, movable arms. Made in Japan. Photograph courtesy of Faith Wyse. $65.00.

Plate 473: Celluloid boy and girl dolls with movable heads and hands, molded hair, stationary eyes, closed painted mouths. All original in red and white outfits and red celluloid shoes. Both dolls are 9" tall and are identical except for molded hair styles. Marks: HONG KONG, on head. $80.00.

Plate 475: Celluloid baby. 2¾" long. Molded hair, painted eyes, painted closed mouth, jointed arms and legs. Head is one piece with the body. All original in glued on red skirt in synthetic fabric. Marks: E.S., on body. $30.00.

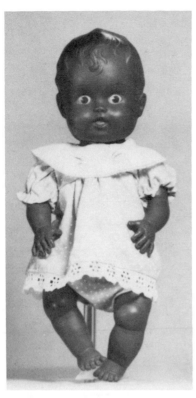

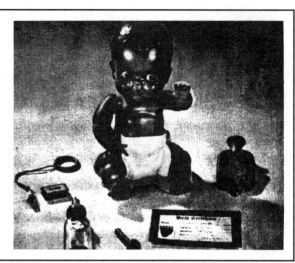

Plate 477: Advertisement for the "Amosandra" doll, the Amos 'n Andy Baby. Ad was in *Life* magazine, 1949. Ad was a part of a page of toy ads promoting American-made toys sponsored by members of the Toy Manufactures U.S.A. The Amosandra doll is shown in previous book by the author, *Black Dolls, 1820–1991,* page 94.

Plate 476: Rubber doll. Circa 1950. 10". Movable head, painted eyes, open-closed mouth, molded hair, one piece body and limbs. Unmarked. Redressed. $45.00.

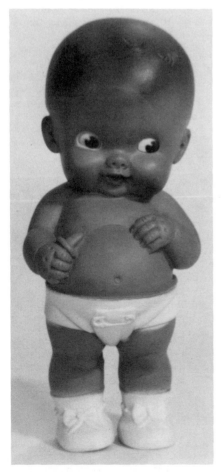

Plate 478: Sun Rubber. "Tod-L-Tyke." 8" tall. One piece rubber doll with squeaker inside body. Doll has molded on white diapers, shoes, and socks. Marks: ©RUTH E. NEWTON/THE SUN RUBBER CO., on back. $65.00.

Plate 479: Sun Rubber. "Sun-Dee." 1956. 18" tall. Rubber head, molded hair, sleeping brown eyes with lashes, nursing mouth, jointed rubber bent-leg baby body. All original in pink and white two-piece knitted outfits. Marks: SUN-DEE/©SUN RUBBER 1956, on head; MFG. BY/THE SUN RUBBER CO./BARBERTON, OHIO U.S.A., on body. Dolls were purchased in the mid 1950's in the Detroit area as Christmas gifts for sisters Rocquelle Turner and Yolande Turner Williams. Collection of Reevah Turner. $125.00.

Plate 480: Copy of package label from the previous Tod-L-Tyke doll by the Sun Rubber Co. Doll was $3.00 when issued in the mid 1900's.

Left — Plate 481: Approximately 8". Flexible rubber dolls similar in construction to the Flagg dolls. Dolls have wire armature inside of body and limbs for posing. Painted features. All original. Collection of Emma Ransom Hayward. $45.00 each.

Right — Plate 482: Combex. Squeak doll. 11" tall. One piece rubber doll with molded on clothing, painted features, molded hair. Marks: COMBEX/MADE IN ENGLAND/4085, on bottom of feet. Collection of Michele Bady. $350.00.

Plate 483: 16½" doll made from what appears to be tree bark. Doll has no legs or hair, molded nose, painted mouth, shell or button painted eyes. Clothing is also made from bark. Head and arms are painted black. Private collection. $100.00.

Plate 484: "Ramp Walker." 4½" tall. Wooden with carved face. Made in United States. There are also ramp walkers made in Japan, however, the faces are painted on and not carved into the wood. Photograph courtesy of Jean Turner. $100.00.

Plate 485: 4½" wooden ramp walker. This one has a lithographed face, wooden hands and feet. Torso is a thick cardboard spool. Original clothes and kerchief. Unmarked. Photograph courtesy of Connie Parsons. $100.00.

Plate 486: "Wilson Walkie," Mammy ramp walker. Wooden spool head, decal face, (thread) cone body. All original. Photograph courtesy of Susan Girardot. $100.00.

Plate 487: Wooden dollhouse dolls. Circa 1900. Hand carved heads, painted facial features, hand carved limbs, wooden block bodies. Man is 4¼" tall. Woman is 3½" tall in a sitting position. Sewn on clothing is very old and could be original. Unmarked. $100.00.

Plate 488: Dinner Bell Doll. 6½" tall. One piece wooden head and straight body, painted features, glued on wig is missing, wire arms with black cloth wrapped around the ends for hands. Wooden body is the handle for the dinner bell. All original in sewn on blue dotted dress, white apron, and white shawl. Unmarked. $50.00.

Plate 489: Authentic Models. "Nesting Santas." Five wooden nesting Santas varying in height from 5½" to 1¾". Made in China. On the market in 1992. $20.00.

Plate 490: Russian Gift ITC. "Nesting Dolls." 5" to 1". 1993. Dolls represent jazz players. Sticker on bottom reads: HAND-MADE IN RUSSIA/RUSSIAN/GIFT ITC. Handwritten on bottom: AЪ OPOHUHA/MADE IN RUSSIA. $60.00.

Plate 491: "Nesting Mummies." Four wooden nesting dolls that represent the mummy of Nes-mut-aat-neru, dating to 700–675 B.C. from the Egyptian collection of the Museum of Fine Arts, Boston. The largest mummy doll has the design seen on Nes-mut-aat-neru's wooden outer anthropoid sarcophagus. The second doll is painted with the colorful design that decorates the lid of cartonnage of her inner sarcophagus. The third doll shows her liner shroud adorned by beads. The smallest doll bears the image of the mummy. Largest doll is 7" tall. $30.00.

Left — Plate 492: Wooden clothes brush doll. Approximately 8" tall. $65.00.

Right — Plate 493: Schoenhut "Negro Dude," early 1900's. 9" tall, including attached hat. All wood, painted eyes, painted mouth with slight smile. All original in felt jacket and vest, checked cotton pants, white shirt. This is not the native head without a smile as is shown in my earlier book *Black Dolls, 1820–1991.* Courtesy of Kitty Dade. $450.00.

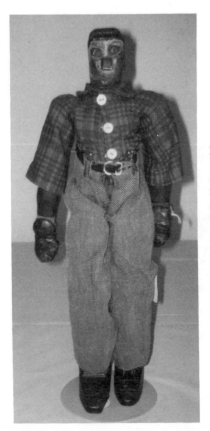

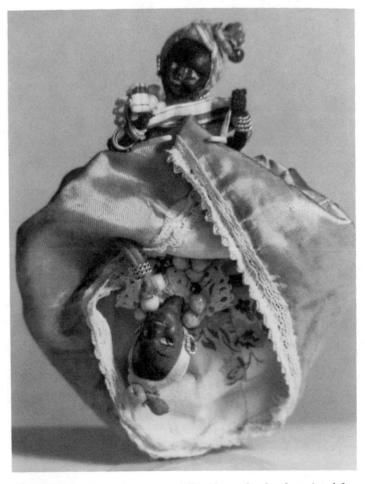

Plate 494: "Boxer." 16½". Hand carved articulated wooden man, carved boxing gloves, jointed at neck, wrists, elbows, shoulders, hips, and knees, painted features, nose not carved completely. Collection of Emma Ransom Hayward. $200.00.

Plate 495: Brazilian topsy-turvy doll with wooden heads, painted features. One head is dark brown, the other a little lighter shade of brown. Approx. 8" tall. Collection of Reevah Turner. $35.00.

Plate 496: 5½" tall. "Rev. Crow" and "Mrs. Crow." Early cornhusk dolls with nut heads. Collection of Reevah Turner. $50.00 each.

Plate 497: Coconut doll. 11" tall. Coconut head and body, rope legs and arms, wood feet, shells for facial features. Probably sold as a souvenir doll. Collection of Emma Ransom Hayward. $150.00.

Plate 498: Rope doll. 26" tall. Foam ball covered with rope forms head, twisted rope arms and legs, glued on felt and paper eyes, felt lips. Collection of Emma Ransom Hayward. $35.00.

Plate 499: Tobacco leaf doll. 9" tall. pecan head with painted features, body made of layers of tobacco leaves, cotton hair attached to pecan head. Collection of Emma Ransom Hayward. $45.00.

Plate 500: Nut head dolls. Left — chestnut head, female doll, 4" tall, painted features, wire limbs wrapped with paper, torso stuffed, no legs, body attached to stick, hair is cotton batting, shawl, apron, dress, and cotton bandanna. Center — pecan head doll, 5½", painted features, wire wrapped arms, cotton dress and bandanna, starched muslin shawl-type apron with "New Orleans" printed on hem, stuffed pincushion-type body. Right — pecan head, female doll, 5½", painted features, wire wrapped arms, upper torso is a wrapped stick, no legs, cotton and checked dress, apron printed "Souvenir of Dixieland." Collection of Emma Ransom Hayward. $45.00 each.

CHAPTER 5
VINYL AND PLASTIC DOLLS,
MID 1900'S TO PRESENT

Following is a list of vinyl collectible dolls, with their descriptions, where photographs were unavailable. Identifying marks, if known, are also included.

Gotz. "Lotta" #44061 from the "Admired Children" collection, 1992. Vinyl head, arms, and legs, cloth body. 18" tall. Dressed in white eyelet with matching bonnet. Also available from the same collection was "Lonnie" #44062. She had a vinyl head, arms, and legs, cloth body. 18" tall. Dressed in yellow and white knit outfit with bear appliqué on the front and matching headband. "Gladys" #77887 from "Fanouche and Her Friends" collection, 1992. She is 15" tall, jointed vinyl, rooted hair, painted eyes, and closed mouth. Gladys is dressed in a red dotted dress with white collar and pocket trim, white shoes and socks. "Cherry" #85884 was also in the collection. She is a 14" tall, jointed vinyl baby, dressed in a black and white checked dress with white dotted trim and matching hat.

Hasbro made "Baby Uh-oh," a drink and wet doll. When you give the doll a drink, she soils her diaper. When you dip her "dirty" diaper in water, it's clean again. Available in 1990.

Pedigree of England made a 10½" black hard plastic doll with black wig and closed mouth. Pedigree also had black twins included in their "Saucy Walkers" collection in 1952. Dolls were named "Mandy Lou" and "Dixie." Pedigree walkers were advertised as having "roving eyes" and could say "mama."

Totsy. "Major Gil Jones." 12". Vinyl action figure was advertised in *Playthings* magazine, February, 1993, page 96.

Uneeda. "Debbie." 11½". Jointed vinyl fashion doll, rooted saran hair, painted eyes, high-heeled feet. Early 1960's. Marks: U, on head.

Uneeda. "Posy Pixie." 17" Doll had a pixie looking face, vinyl head and hands, rooted hair, glassine sleep eyes, closed mouth in a pixie grin, cloth body. Marks: UNEEDA/DOLL CO./INC./1964.

Vogue Dolls made "Pat," Ginny doll #31 from the Kindergarten School Series, 1953. Original clothes were a yellow dress and large yellow bow in her hair. In 1968, Vogue made "Africa." She had black hair in an upsweep with two headbands, a band around her arm, and one around her leg. She had goldtone earrings and necklace. Outfit was red with gold print. Both dolls were 8" tall.

Plate 501: November 1971 advertisement for dolls advertised on T.V. Included are "Soul" by Hasbro, "Rock Flower Rosemary" by Mattel and "Dale" by Hasbro. Full description of these dolls is included in my earlier book *Black Dolls, 1820–1991*.

Plate 502: Advertisement from *Travel* magazine, 1957, for six imported dolls in a basket. Included with the six dolls is one black doll. The dolls are about 12" tall with no mention as to where they were imported from. The bodies, arms, and legs are made of cloth, painted eyes and closed mouth. The heads are probably made of some type of plastic or vinyl as the ad says that they are unbreakable.

Left — Plate 503: Aces. Jointed vinyl doll. 7¼" tall. Painted eyes, rooted brown hair, closed mouth. All original in long floral print dress over green Hawaiian skirt and print bra top. Marks: ACES (inside diamond)/MADE IN/HONG KONG, on body. $20.00.

Right — Plate 504: A&H Doll Co. "Bride," 1950's. Hard plastic doll jointed at neck and shoulders, amber sleep eyes, black glued on mohair wig, closed mouth. All original in white bridal outfit that is stapled onto doll and black slipper shoes. 7" tall. Doll came in plastic bell. Doll is unmarked. Marks on cardboard on bottom of the bell: MADE IN USA/A&H DOLL/WOODSIDE, N.Y. 11377. $40.00.

Plate 505: A&H Doll Co. "Mammy." 7½". Hard plastic head, amber sleep eyes with one-piece eyelashes and painted eyelashes, closed mouth, jointed hard plastic body with molded on black shoes. All original in long red gingham skirt, matching headwrap, dotted white bodice and apron, pink shawl, carrying a red gingham handkerchief, stapled on goldtone hoop earrings. Doll came in clear plastic bell. Doll is unmarked. Cardboard base of bell is marked: MADE IN U.S.A./WOODSIDE 77, N.Y., incised on base; THIS IS A/MASOM DOLLS/MAMMY, stamped on base. $40.00.

Plate 506: A&H Doll. "Bell Doll." 15" tall. Designed for "Telephone Pioneers of America." Vinyl head, rooted black hair, sleeping brown eyes with lashes, closed mouth, jointed vinyl body. All original blue jacket, jeans, white shirt, and white plastic hardhat. Marks: A&H DOLL/N.Y./1981, on head. $50.00.

Plate 507: A & H Doll. Another "bell" doll from 1950–60. 7½" tall. Hard plastic head, black mohair wig, amber sleep eyes, closed mouth, hard plastic jointed body. All original in striped taffeta dress. Dolls are commonly referred to as "bell" dolls because they were sold inside a clear plastic bell. Unmarked. $40.00.

Left — Plate 508: Alexander. "Cynthia." 18" tall. Hard plastic head, jointed hard plastic body, black saran wig, brown sleep eyes with lashes. All original in tagged dress. Courtesy of Susan Girardot. $800.00.

Right — Plate 509: Alexander. "Ebony," ©1991 by Hildegard Gunzel. Vinyl head and breastplate, stationary brown eyes with eyelashes, long black wig, closed mouth, hard vinyl arms and legs, brown cloth body. 24" tall. All original in cotton print dress trimmed in ecru lace, ecru pinafore, slip, and pantaloons, white stockings and shoes, natural straw hat with rust velvet ribbon. Made in U.S.A. Marks: HILDEGARD/GUNZEL/1991, on head; HILDEGARD GUNZEL/©1991, on breastplate. $360.00.

Plate 510: Alexander. "Charlene," ©1991, #8035. Vinyl head, black sleep eyes, rooted dark brown hair, mouth with lips slightly parted, vinyl arms and legs, brown cloth body. 18" tall. All original in pink cotton dress and matching bloomers. Marks: MADAME/ALEXANDER/©1991, on head. $160.00.

Plate 511: Alexander. "Blanca" from the Hildegard Gunzel collection, 1991. 16" tall. Vinyl head, vinyl shoulder-plate, black curly wig, brown plastic stationary eyes, closed mouth, vinyl arms and legs, brown cloth body. All original in pink cotton dress with pink taffeta accessories, white lace tights, white patent shoes. Marks: HILDEGARD/GUNZEL/ALEXANDER DOLL CO.,/MADE IN USA, on back of shoulder-plate. $175.00.

Left — Plate 512: Alexander. "Leslie," ballerina with Polly face. Vinyl head, rooted dark brown hair with cut bangs, closed mouth, sleeping amber eyes, pierced ears with pearl earrings, hard vinyl jointed body and limbs. All original in pink ballerina outfit with matching flowered hair accessory. 17" tall. Marks: ©ALEXANDER DOLL CO., INC./1965, on head. $475.00.

Right — Plate 513: Alexander. "Leslie." 17" tall. Vinyl head, jointed hard vinyl body, rooted brown hair, sleeping brown eyes, closed mouth, pierced ears with drop pearl earrings, ring on left hand. All original in yellow net gown with rhinestones on bodice and sleeves, yellow satin shoes, and yellow velvet hairbow. Marks: ©ALEXANDER DOLL CO. INC./1965. $500.00.

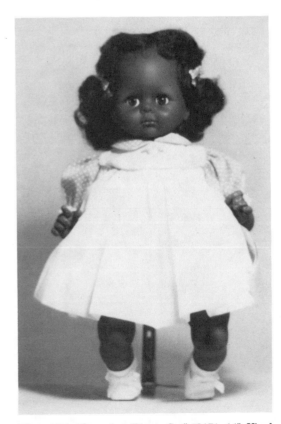

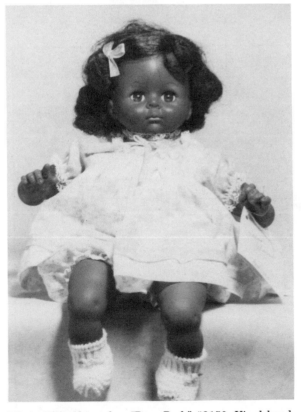

Plate 514: Alexander. "Pussy Cat" #3171. 14". Vinyl head, arms, and legs, brown cloth body, rooted dark brown hair, sleeping brown eyes, closed mouth, cry box inside body. All original in tagged white cotton dress with pink dotted sleeves and collar, white bloomers, socks, and plastic shoes. Marks: ALEXANDER/19©77, on head. $80.00.

Plate 515: Alexander. "Rose Bud," #3150. Vinyl head, sleeping amber eyes, rooted brown hair, closed mouth, vinyl arms and legs, brown cloth body. 14" tall. All original in pink print cotton dress with matching bloomers and white knitted booties. Marks: ALEXANDER/19©77, on head, Doll looks like "Pussy Cat." $85.00.

Plate 516: Alexander. "Flower Girl," #334-1, from the "Americana Collection," 1992. 8" tall. Vinyl head, rooted black hair, black sleep eyes, closed mouth, jointed hard vinyl body. All original in pink organdy dress trimmed with pink lace and pearls with pearl and flower head piece. Marks: ALEXANDER, on body. Discontinued after 1992. $45.00.

Plate 517: Alexander. "Cheerleader," #324-1, from the "Americana Collection," 1992. 8" tall. Vinyl head, black wig. All original in blue and gold cheerleader outfit with the letters "M" and "A" on the sweater, blue and white saddle shoes. Marks: ALEXANDER, on body. $45.00.

Left — Plate 518: Alexander. "Happy Birthday," #325-1 from the "Americana Collection," 1992. Hard vinyl head, black glued on wig, black sleep eyes with one piece lash, closed mouth, jointed hard vinyl body. 8" tall. All original in tiny floral print dress with pink plaid pinafore. Doll is carrying four balloons, a wrapped present, and is wearing a birthday hat. Marks: ALEXANDER, on back. $55.00.

Right — Plate 519: Alexander. "Happy Birthday Billy," #345-1. 8". From the "Americana Collection." Vinyl head, brown wig, sleeping dark eyes, freckles on cheeks, jointed vinyl body. All original in tagged clothing. Marks: ALEXANDER, on back. $55.00.

Left — Plate 520: Alexander. "Ballerina," #331-1 from the "Americana Collection," 1992. Hard vinyl head and jointed body, black sleep eyes, black wig styled in braided coils at ears, closed mouth. All original in pink ballet outfit. 8" tall. Marks: ALEXANDER, on back. $60.00.

Right — Plate 521: Alexander. "My Little Sweetheart." 8" tall. Limited edition doll made only for "A Child At Heart" in Arlington, TX. Total edition of the dolls, black and white, was 4,500. Black edition was limited to 500 dolls. Jointed vinyl, black hair, brown eyes. All original in red and white outfit. Marked ALEXANDER, on the body. $150.00.

Plate 522: Alexander. "Welcome Home 1991," girl. 8" tall. Honoring those who served in Operation Desert Storm. Hard vinyl head, black sleep eyes with one-piece lashes, closed mouth, long dark brown hair parted in the center and pulled back, hard vinyl jointed body. All original in army jumpsuit. Doll comes with an American flag. Marks: ALEXANDER, on body. Clothing is marked: "WELCOME HOME" 1991 — EXCLUSIVE/©BY MADAME ALEXANDER/MADE IN U.S.A. $60.00.

Plate 523: Alexander. "Welcome Home 1991," boy. Identical to girl except for short curly black wig. $60.00.

Plate 524: Alexander. "Prissy," #637 for the "Scarlett" series, 1992. Hard vinyl head, black wig, black sleep eyes with one piece lashes, closed mouth, jointed hard vinyl body. 8" tall. All original in burgundy print dress, tan print headscarf and carrying a pail. $60.00.

Plate 525: Alexander. "Easter Sunday." 7¾" tall. From the "Americana Collection," 1993. Hard vinyl head, dark brown straight bobbed hair with bangs, black sleep eyes with molded lashes, closed mouth, jointed hard vinyl body. All original in tagged pink faille dress, slippers, and straw bonnet. Marks: ALEXANDER, on body. $60.00.

Plate 527: Amanda Jane Limited. "Amanda Jane." Beautifully made doll from England. Vinyl head, rooted black hair, painted eyes, closed mouth, jointed hard vinyl body. 7". All original in yellow print cotton dress with yellow plastic shoes. Additional clothing and accessories sold separately. Marks: HONG KONG, on head; AMANDA JANE/REGISTERED/4065/MADE IN/HONG KONG, on body. $40.00.

Plate 526: Alexander. "Anna," #9707 from the "Let's Play Dolls" collection by Alice Darling. Vinyl head and jointed body, black wig, painted eyes. All original in floral print dress. Marks: ©1992/ALEXANDER DOLL CO., on head. $95.00.

Plate 528: Amanda Jane Limited. "Amanda Jane Baby." Vinyl head, rooted black hair, painted eyes, closed mouth, hard vinyl body and movable arms, movable soft vinyl bent legs. All original in deep pink gingham dress and white terrycloth diapers. 6" tall. Marks: 18/1273/HONG KONG, on head; AMANDA JANE/BABY/4064/MADE IN/HONG KONG, on body. $40.00.

Plate 529: American Trading Inc. "Wear-A-Doll." 1983. 3½" tall. Vinyl head, rooted black hair, painted features, cloth body and limbs, removable red skirt. Doll attaches with Velcro® to your clothing. Skirt is tagged "WEAR-A-DOLL." Made in Hong Kong. $10.00.

Plate 530: Anabas. "General Hawk," Rambo's partner in *Rambo Part IV*. All vinyl jointed action figure, molded painted hair, molded on yellow shirt, brown pants, and boots. 6¾" tall. Marks: ©1985 1986 ANABAS/INVESTMENTS. N.V./PAT PEND MADE IN CHINA, on right leg. $20.00.

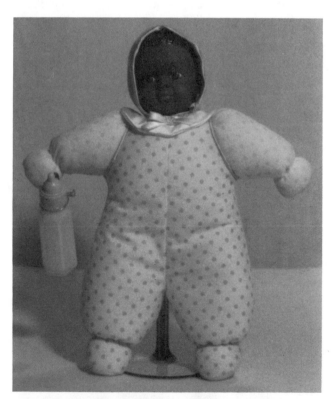

Plate 531: Avon. "Be My Baby." Vinyl head, painted brown eyes, molded painted dark brown hair, cloth body and limbs with sewn on white dotted clothing, removable pale pink bonnet. 11½" tall. Doll comes with bottles with disappearing "milk." Tag sewn to body: CREATED EXCLUSIVELY FOR AVON IN CHINA...: Reverse side of tag: AVON PRODUCTS, INC. DISTR. NEW YORK, N.Y. 10019/©AVON 1991 — ALL RIGHTS RESERVED... $12.00.

Plate 532: Avon. "Amber," bride doll. 11½" fashion doll. Vinyl head, painted eyes, open-closed mouth with painted teeth, rooted long dark brown hair. All original in bridal gown. Unmarked. Made in China. ©1992. $20.00.

Plate 534: Avon. "Small World" cologne bottle doll. 4" tall. Marks on bottom: AVON/SMALL/WORLD/COLOGNE/2 FL. OZ./AVON PRODUCTS INC. NEW YORK, N.Y. 10020. $25.00.

Plate 533: Avon. "Brandon," groom doll. 12" fashion doll. Vinyl head, molded black hair, painted eyes, open-closed mouth with painted teeth, jointed vinyl body. All original in black tuxedo. Made in China. Unmarked. ©1992. $20.00.

Plate 535: BBI Toys. "Coca-Cola" fashion doll, 1987. Brown painted eyes, black rooted hair, all vinyl. Photograph courtesy of Stephanie Lisoski. $35.00.

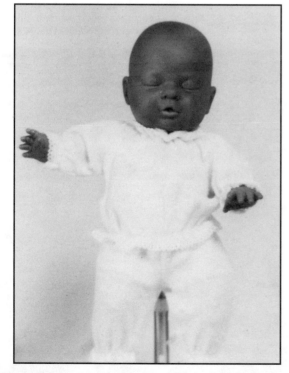

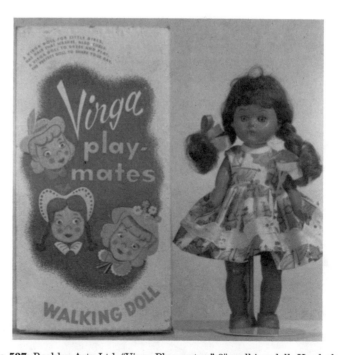

Plate 536: Barval. "La Baby," sleeping. 11". Vinyl head, closed eyes, open-closed mouth, bald head, vinyl arms and legs, white cloth body. All original in 2 piece pink pajamas. Marks: BERJUSA, on head. Made in Spain. $20.00.

Plate 537: Beehler Arts Ltd. "Virga Play-mates." 8" walking doll. Hard plastic head and jointed walking body, brown wig in braids and bangs, sleeping amber eyes, closed mouth, molded on t-strap shoes under orange vinyl shoes. All original in print dress with matching underpants. Original box is shown next to the doll. An identical doll was marketed by Fortune Toys and was named "Pam." See plate 671 for a photograph of Pam. Both dolls are unmarked. $125.00.

Plate 538: Belcam Inc. "Bubble Bath Bottle Doll." 10" tall. Molded on long blue gown is the bottle, vinyl head is the top. Rooted black hair, painted eyes, closed mouth. Marks: ©BELCAM INC. 1989/MADE IN CHINA, on bottom of the bottle. $25.00.

Plate 539: Benamy. "Black Girl," #12007. This doll appears to have been made from the Shindana mold "Zuri." Vinyl head is identical except that hole for nursing mouth is slightly larger than that of Zuri and rooted black hair has been added over the sculptured hair. Doll was ordered from Kaplan School Supply Corp., supplier of materials for preschool and elementary schools. 12" tall. Marks: (faint trace of part of the word "SHINDANA" is on doll's head). Doll is all original in red and white romper outfit. $15.00.

Plate 540: Benamy. "Black Boy," #12006. Identical to previous girl except for short black wig and original outfit in red, yellow, and blue. $15.00.

Plate 542: Berjusa. "Minene." 28" vinyl and cloth mechanical baby made in Spain. Open-closed mouth, sleep eyes, bald head. Battery operated, moving head. Photograph courtesy of Phyllis Schlatter. $75.00.

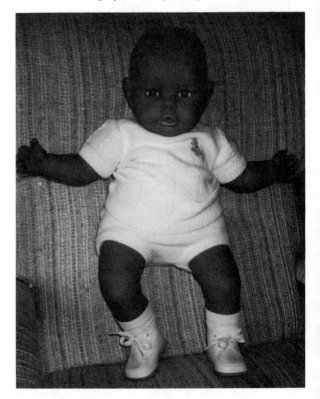

Plate 541: Berjusa. "Girl." 18" tall. Vinyl head, hands, and feet, cloth body, amber sleep eyes, rooted light brown hair. All original. Marks: BERJUSA, on head. Courtesy of Xzena Moore of the Cubbyhole. $125.00.

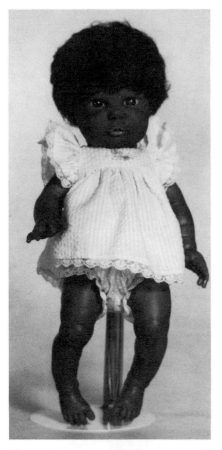

Plate 543: Berjusa. 12" tall. Anatomically correct vinyl baby girl. Rooted curly black hair, stationary brown eyes, open-closed mouth with molded tongue, jointed body. All original in pink dress and matching panties. Marks: BERJUSA©, on head. $35.00.

Plate 544: Bradley Dolls. 16" vinyl dolls from the "Teri Collection," 1993. Dolls are, from left, "Porgy" #17530B, in white dress with blue trim; "Porgy" #17530P, in pink dress; "Peggy" #17547P dressed in pink; and "Peggy" #17547W in a white dress. Other black dolls shown in the 1993 catalog were three 18" vinyl dolls from the "Teri Collection" named "Poly." All three wore similar print dresses with headbands and collar trim in different colors. Also shown in the catalog were two more 18" vinyl dolls in striped outfits. They were both named "Nera." Photograph courtesy of Bradley Dolls. $40.00.

Left — Plate 545: Blue Box. "Hugga Buds." Vinyl bald head, painted eyes, closed mouth with dimples in each cheek, cloth body and limbs with sewn on aqua clothing, removable matching hat. Marks: BLUE BOX, on head. $10.00.

Right — Plate 546: Berkeley Design. "Cuddle Kidz™." Musical doll sitting in a wooden rocking chair. Doll plays "Play-mates" and rocks in the chair. Doll and chair are 10" tall. Stockinette face, brown yarn hair, black button eyes, painted mouth, cloth body. $20.00.

Plate 548: Cameo Doll Products. "Kewpie Sleeper." Circa 1970. Designed by Rose O'Neill. Style #6191. All soft vinyl with movable head and one piece body, molded hair in famous top-curl, painted eyes, closed mouth in mischievous smile. 10½" tall. All original in red and white striped flannel one piece sleepers with feet. Marks: 733 (slash) 1 CAMEO/©JLK, on head; ©/CAMEO, on body. $125.00.

The following poem was printed on the back of the original box:

THE KEWPIE DOLL
You ask why we are hurrying so,
We're going to be Dolls, you know.
Rose O'Neill has shown us how;
Look inside and see one now.

For Children Dear, we've always known
Need Kewpies of their very own;
So, really, the best way with them
Is just to come and play with them,
Turn into Dolls and stay with them.

From Kewpie you'll not wish to part,
But when you've learned its smile by heart,
Just give that little smile away
To everybody, everyday
And with each smile I hope you'll feel
The Kewpish love of Rose O'Neill.

Plate 547: Burger King Corporation. 4" tall. "Jaws." Vinyl action figure from Burger King Kids Club meal. Molded on green and blue clothes, black and green hi-top sneakers. Jointed at neck, shoulders, and hips. Marks: ©1990/BURGER KING CORP/CHINA AP GC 23, on back. Designed and manufactured by Alcone Promotions. $6.00.

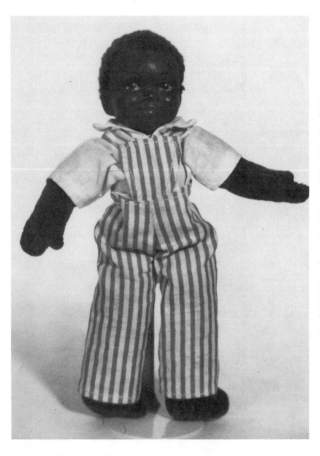

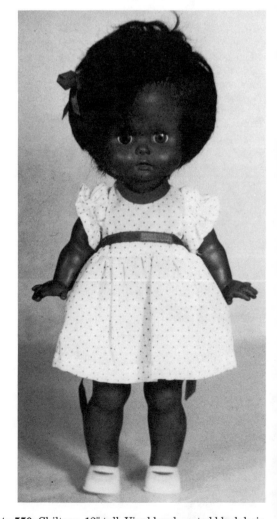

Plate 549: Chad Valley. 6½" tall. Hard plastic head, curly brown synthetic wig, painted eyes, closed mouth, brown felt body and limbs. All original in red and white striped cotton bibbed pants, white cotton shirt. Tag sewn to pants: HYGIENIC TOYS/ MADE IN ENGLAND BY/CHAD VALLEY CO. LTD. $95.00.

Plate 550: Chiltern. 12" tall. Vinyl head, rooted black hair, brown sleep eyes with lashes, jointed vinyl body. Marks: CHILTERN/MADE IN ENGLAND, on head. $45.00.

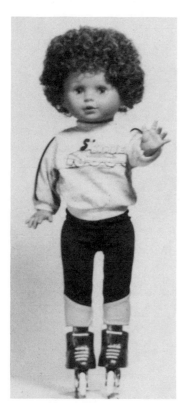

Left — Plate 551: Cititoy. "Skatie" #64470, ©1990, in-line skates doll. 17" tall. Vinyl head, rooted curly brown hair, sleeping brown eyes, closed mouth, jointed vinyl body. All original in sweatshirt with name machine embroidered on and black pants trimmed in hot pink. Skates are black and yellow. Marks: T516/©1989 CITITOY/GP002 CHINA, on head; MADE IN CHINA, on body. $20.00.

Right — Plate 552: Cititoy. "Sweet Susan Layette" #69880. 14" tall. Vinyl head with sculpted hair, sleeping brown eyes with lashes, nursing mouth, vinyl arms and legs, brown cloth body. All original in pink heart print dress with sewn on white bib, pink headband, white panties and booties. Doll came with two extra dresses, designer diapers, and plastic toys. Marks: ©1989 CITITOY/6813A CHINA/TS16, on head. $20.00.

Plate 553: Cititoy. "Trica's Fashion Ensemble." 14". Vinyl head, rooted black hair, amber sleep eyes with lashes, closed mouth, vinyl arms and legs, brown cloth body. All original in red, yellow, and blue two-piece pant outfit. Doll comes with four extra outfits. Marks: TS (slash) 4/MADE IN CHINA/©1988 CITITOY, on head. $30.00.

Plate 554: Coleco. "Cabbage Patch Kid" with freckles. 16". Vinyl head, rooted brown cut loop yarn hair, eight freckles on each cheek, dimples in each cheek, closed mouth, brown cloth body and limbs. Dressed in Cabbage Patch Kids clothing. Marks: ©COPY R. 1978 1982/ORIGINAL APPALACHIAN ART WORKS INC./MANUFACTURED BY COLECO IND. INC./2, incised on head; 39, embossed on head. "O.K." on tagged body. Brown signature. $200.00.

Plate 555: "Cabbage Patch Kids" houseshoes for girls. Rooted black yarn looped hair, painted eyes, dimpled cheeks. Slippers are yellow. Tagged on the inside: CABBAGE PATCH KIDS/©1984 ORIGINAL APPALACHIAN/ART WORKS, INC./ALL RIGHTS RESERVED; reverse side of tag: MFG. FOR BARRY CORP./.../MADE IN KOREA. $40.00.

Plate 556: Coleco. "Cabbage Patch Kids All Stars," 1986, dressed in Chicago Cubs uniform. $65.00.

Plate 557: College Bound Dolls. "Cammie Goes to College." 11½" vinyl fashion doll. Painted eyes, rooted black hair, closed mouth, jointed body with bendable knees and swivel waist. All original in blue suit with dotted blue blouse. Gray sweatsuit imprinted "College Bound" also came with the doll. Cammie doll is endorsed by The United Negro College Fund with their slogan "A mind is a terrible thing to waste!" imprinted on the box. A percentage of doll sales is donated to the UNCF. Doll is very similar to an earlier doll by Tanline, a doll company in Michigan. Marks: CHINA, on head; MADE IN/CHINA, on body. $20.00.

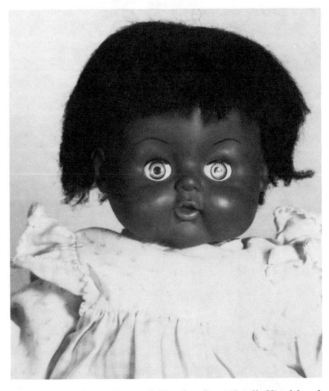

Plate 558: Collette Toy and Novelty Co. 16" tall. Vinyl head, arms and legs, white cloth body, rooted black hair, sleeping amber eyes, open-closed mouth. Marks: COLLETTE/K18TME 15EYE/MADE IN TAIWAN, on head. Tagged body. $25.00.

Left — Plate 559: Corolle. "Betsy." 11" tall. Vinyl head, rooted black hair, black sleep eyes with one-piece eyelashes, open-closed mouth, jointed vinyl body. All original in blue print dress, white socks, black strap shoes. Doll was available in several outfits, all with "Corolle" embroidered on collar. Made in France. Marks: ©1992/COROLLE, on head. Manufactured for Timeless Creations The Collectible Specialty Doll Division of Mattel, Inc., on sticker printed on box. $35.00.

Right — Plate 560: Corolle. 15" tall. Vinyl doll with chocolate scent. No. 1302/83, on tag, signed by Catherine Refabet. Collection of Reevah Turner. $150.00.

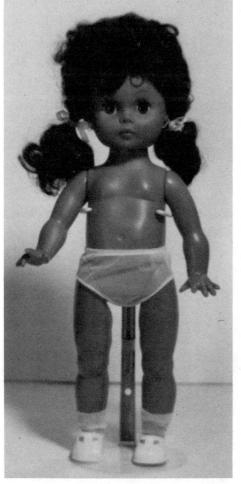

Plate 561: CST. "Dolls for the Dressmaker." Vinyl head, brown sleep eyes, rooted black hair, closed mouth, jointed vinyl body. 16" tall. Doll came dressed in white underpants, socks and shoes. Marks: CST ©1989/116/MADE IN CHINA, on head; CST 116/MADE IN CHINA, on body. $10.00.

Plate 562: CST. "Dolls for the Dressmaker." Vinyl head, brown sleep eyes, rooted black hair, closed mouth, jointed hard vinyl body. 13" tall. Doll was sold for dressing in white panties, white shoes and socks. Marks: CST 1989/113/MADE IN CHINA, on head; CST — 113/MADE IN CHINA, on body. Redressed in red striped shirt and blue dotted romper. $10.00.

Above — Plate 563: Creata. "The Magical Mermaid" ©1991. Vinyl head, long rooted black hair, painted brown eyes, closed mouth, jointed vinyl body with swivel waist. 11½" tall. All original in pink mermaid outfit. Marks: ©CREATA/1988, on head; CREATA 1986/MADE IN/CHINA, on body. $8.00.

Above Center — Plate 564: Creata. "The Magical Mermaid," ©1991. 6½" tall. Available in black only at Walmart. Vinyl head, rooted long dark brown hair with bangs, painted eyes, closed mouth, jointed vinyl body with swivel waist. All original in two piece pink mermaid costume. Doll came in 18 different outfits: mermaid — in pink, red, or blue; clowns — Binkie, Rebo, or Joco; costume — hula, wire-walker, or leopard; ballerina — swan, bluebird, or firebird; circus kids — animal tamer, high-flyer, or ringmistress; musical kids — singer, guitarist, or pianist. Marks: ©CREATA/1985, on head; ©CREATA/1991/CHINA, on body. $20.00.

Above Right — Plate 565: Creata. "Flower Princess Ballerina Leeanna." 1984. 11½" tall. All vinyl, brown painted eyes, brown streaked rooted hair, jointed at waist. All original. Marks: CREATA 1982, on head. Photograph courtesy of Stephanie Lisoski. $35.00.

Plate 566: Cosmopolitan. "Ginger." 7½". Hard plastic head and jointed body, center stitched black saran wig, brown sleep eyes with molded lashes, closed mouth. All original Hawaiian outfit, green grass skirt, orange lei, pink bra, and panties. Unmarked. Doll is shown with original box. $225.00.

Plate 567: DVP. "Dan Dolls." Native man and woman vinyl dolls. She has a baby boy on her back in a sling type holder. He has a rooted beard, both have rooted hair and painted eyes. All original. Wrist tag reads: "DAN DOLL DVP GARANTI 2 AR. Marks on neck: DVP DENMARK. Photograph courtesy of Etta Houston. $300.00 set.

Plate 568: Darice. "Doll Parts." #550018C. Vinyl doll head with hands, sold in craft shops for making your own doll. Rooted black yarn hair, painted black eyes, painted red nose, freckles, painted mouth. Head is 4" in height. Marks: HONG KONG, on head. $10.00.

Plate 569: Darice. Similar to previous doll except for size and hair. This one has rooted orange yarn hair, painted features. 3" height. Marks: HONG KONG, on head. $10.00.

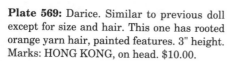

Plate 570: Darice. "Coconut Kids." 3½". Vinyl head and hands kit for making a doll. Black looped yarn hair, painted eyes. Marks: HONG KONG, on back of head; ©COPYRIGHT DARICE INC., on base of head (this will be hidden once doll is made up). $5.00.

Plate 572: Canadian postcard with "Calypso Jill," on left, made by Dee & Cee, 1960. The same photograph was also on a Canadian postal stamp. Doll is shown in author's previous book *Black Dolls, 1820–1991*, plate 403. $5.00 for postcard only.

Plate 571: DKP. "Orchid." 6" tall. Jointed vinyl, painted eyes, rooted dark brown hair, molded on green tights, painted on purple shoes. All original in white and purple outfit. Made by David Kirschner. Marks: A.53/©DKP/1984, on head; ©D.K.P. 1984, at back waist. $25.00.

Plate 573: Elsie Denney. "Hawaiian Doll Set." 6". Hard plastic head and jointed body, sleeping amber eyes, black mohair wig, molded on unpainted shoes. All original in a print "pau," a wrap around skirt, under a green grass skirt and lei. Unmarked. From information sheet enclosed with doll, the doll was distributed by Elsie Denney, Box 2809, Honolulu, Hawaii. $20.00.

Plate 574: Eegee (Goldberger). "Life Size Walking Pretty," available on the market in 1992. Vinyl head, short curly rooted black hair, sleeping brown eyes, closed mouth, jointed hard vinyl body and limbs. All original in white dotted dress trimmed in blue and yellow, white tights, yellow socks, black vinyl t-strap shoes. Dress has "Walking Annette," the name of an earlier Eegee doll, on the front of the dress. 31" tall. Marks: ©EEGEE CO/31E/4, on head. $35.00.

Left — Plate 575: Eegee (Goldberger). "Patti Cake" ©1991. She claps her hands or hugs you when you press her tummy. No batteries required. Vinyl head, rooted black hair, sleeping brown eyes, open-closed mouth with two bottom teeth, vinyl arms and legs, brown cloth body. 16" tall. All original in pink and blue dress, white tights and shoes. Marks: ©EEGEE CO 1983/217 16YT/MADE IN CHINA, on head. $25.00.

Right — Plate 576: Eegee (Goldberger). "Cute Looks," 1991. One of a series of three character toddler dolls. Vinyl head, closed pouty mouth, sleeping brown eyes with lashes, rooted black hair, dimpled chin, vinyl hands, cloth body and legs. All original in yellow and pink print blouse and yellow pants with feet. 15" tall. Marks ©EEGEE CO./16 DT, on head. $20.00.

Plate 577: Eegee. "Cute Looks," 1991. The second in a series of three character toddler dolls. Vinyl head, open laughing mouth with two lower teeth, sleeping brown eyes, rooted black hair, cloth body. All original in the same dress as the previous "Cute Looks" doll. Marks: ©EEGEE CO 1983/217 16YT/MADE IN CHINA, on head. 15" tall. $20.00.

Plate 578: Eegee. "Cute Looks," 1991. The third in a series of three character toddler dolls called "Cute Looks." Vinyl head, smiling mouth with tongue sticking between her lips, faintly dimpled cheeks, sleeping brown eyes, rooted straight black hair, vinyl hands, brown cloth body. 15" tall. All original in blue dotted pants with feet and pink striped top with blue dotted sleeves. Marks: 16 NT/©EEGEE CO., on head. $20.00.

Plate 579: Eegee. "Bundle of Joy." Vinyl head, molded sleep eyes, closed mouth, vinyl hands, cloth sewn on pink pajamas. 12" tall. Machine washable and dryable. Marks: 40021280/1990 EEGEE CO./MADE IN CHINA, on head. $10.00.

Plate 580: Eegee. "Bundle of Joy," awake. 12". Vinyl head and arms, painted eyes, closed mouth, molded hair. Dressed in blue bunny sleeper that forms the body. Marks: (top line is unreadable)/©1990 EEGEE CO./MADE IN CHINA, on head. $10.00.

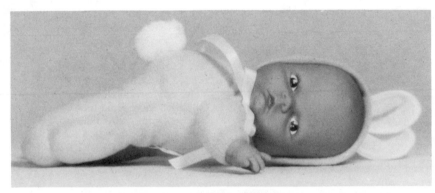

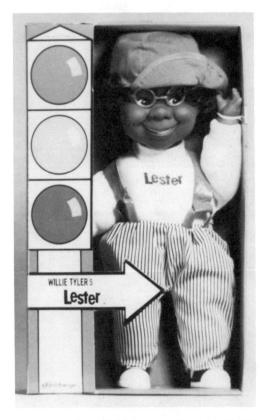

Plate 581: Eegee (Goldberger). "Lester," #3149. 12" tall. Vinyl head and hands, painted eyes, rooted black hair, painted smiling mouth with teeth, yellow cloth body that doubles as a sweatshirt, black and white vinyl sneakers for feet, removable blue and white striped pants, red plastic suspenders, red cotton hat, removable plastic glasses. Similar doll is shown in author's previous book, *Black Dolls, 1820–1991,* page 124. Marks: EEGEE CO./NO. 3149, on head. $15.00.

Plate 582: Eegee. "Gemette." 15" tall. Vinyl head, rooted black hair, sleeping brown eyes with one-piece lashes, closed mouth, vinyl teenage body. All original in long pink sateen gown with lace ruffles and matching hat. Marks: ©EEGEE/1963, on head; ©1963/EEGEE CO., on body. $75.00.

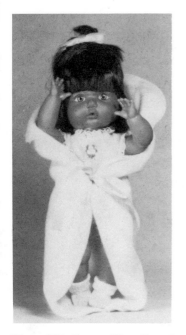

Plate 583: Eegee. "Just Born." 13" tall. Vinyl head, rooted black hair, stationary amber eyes, vinyl jointed bent-leg baby body, nursing mouth. All original in pink fleece romper, wrapped in pastel colored blanket. Doll came with pink and white crocheted layette. Marks: ©EEGEE CO/15VS, on head. Made in China. $25.00.

Plate 584: Eegee. "Sweet Kandi," #1510. 14". Drink and wet doll, vinyl head, rooted black hair, sleeping brown eyes with lashes, nursing mouth, vinyl jointed body. All original in striped dress, white shoes and socks. Marks: MADE IN HONG KONG/©EEGEE CO./14 BA/NF, on head. $25.00.

Plate 585: Eegee. "Razzle Dazzle Dolly." You can decorate her clothes with her 3-D paint. Paint is washable before drying, permanent after drying. Additional outfits complete with Scribbles 3-D paint are sold separately. Vinyl head, rooted black hair, sleeping brown eyes, jointed vinyl body. 14". All original in blue, pink, and yellow dress with pink pants. Marks: 14FLCM/©EEGEE/MADE IN CHINA, on head; EG/MADE IN CHINA/F (sideways), on body. $30.00.

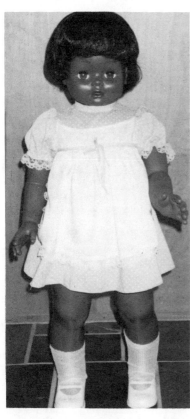

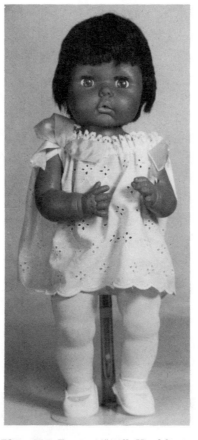

Plate 586: Eegee. "Baby Two Year Old." 32". Vinyl and hard plastic, open-closed mouth, sleep eyes, rooted black hair. Photograph courtesy of Phyllis Schlatter. $75.00.

Plate 587: Eegee. 16" tall. Vinyl bent-leg baby doll. Rooted black hair, sleeping amber eyes, nursing mouth. All original in white eyelet smock trimmed with pink bows, white tights, and white plastic shoes. Marks: 17/©EEGEE CO./16 US, on head. $40.00.

Plate 588: Eegee. "Softina." 1974. 15½". Vinyl head, rooted black hair, sleeping amber/brown eyes, nursing mouth, one piece stuffed vinyl body with hole in bottom for "wetting." Marks: EEGEE CO./19©74, on head; 105/DUBLON/PAT NOS. 3,432,581/3 (followed by unreadable digit)/56,046/OTHER PAT'S PEND/EG/SOFTINA/GOLDBERGER DOLL MFG. CO. INC./BROOKLYN, NEW YORK, N.Y., on body. $35.00.

Left — Plate 589: Effanbee. 16" tall. Baby doll with vinyl head, sculpted hair, sleeping amber eyes with lashes, nursing mouth, jointed vinyl baby body. Redressed. Marks: EFFANBEE/ 19©68, on head. Collection of the Museum of African American History (Detroit). $80.00.

Right — Plate 590: Effanbee. "Peaches & Cream," 1981, from the "Grand Dames" collection. 11" tall. Fully jointed vinyl doll, sleeping brown eyes, rooted long brown hair, closed mouth. All original in peach organdy dress with tucks and lace and matching hat. This doll was one of four Limited Edition Grande Dames made for Treasure Trove, a company that distributes collector dolls. The set was limited to 125 dolls. The other dolls in the set were "Francoise," "Saratoga" and "Lady Ascot." Marks: EFFANBEE/1975/1176, on head; EFF & BEE, on body. $95.00.

Plate 591: Effanbee. "Atlanta" from the "Pride of the South Collection," ©1983. 13" tall. All vinyl doll, rooted brown hair, sleeping eyes with one piece lashes, closed mouth. All original in lavender print dress and natural straw hat. Marks: EFFANBEE/ 1381/1981, on head; EFFANBEE, on body. Collection of Beverly Dooms. Black "Pride of the South Collection" is a limited edition of 100 sets. $95.00.

Plate 592: Effanbee. "Charleston" from the "Pride of the South Collection." Her description is the same as "Atlanta." All original in blue print dress with a cameo at the neck and white straw hat. Collection of Beverly Dooms. $95.00.

Plate 594: Effanbee. "Dallas" from the "Pride of the South Collection," 1983. She is the same basic doll as "Atlanta." All original in floral print gown and white straw bonnet. Collection of Beverly Dooms. $95.00.

Plate 593: Effanbee. "Mobile" from the "Pride of the South Collection." Her description is the same as "Atlanta." All original in pink cotton dress trimmed with white lace. Collection of Beverly Dooms. $95.00.

Plate 595: Effanbee. "Richmond," ©1983, from "Pride of the South Collection." The description is the same as "Atlanta." All original in ecru with burgundy print dress trimmed with burgundy ribbon and a natural straw hat with burgundy ribbon. Collection of Beverly Dooms. $95.00.

Plate 596: Effanbee. "Olivia," limited edition of 50 dolls, from the "Grande Dames Collection." Vinyl head, sleeping brown eyes with lashes, closed mouth, jointed vinyl body. All original in dotted satin ivory gown with ivory striped underskirt and matching hat. 15" tall. Marks: EFFANBEE/19©78/1578, on head. $125.00.

Plate 597: Effanbee. "Dolly Shopper," 1983. 11". Numbered limited edition of 1200 dolls made exclusively for Meyer's by Effanbee to commemorate Meyer's 70th year in business. This is doll #586. The doll is dressed in a typical 1914 shoppers costume, the year Meyer's was established. All vinyl jointed doll with sleeping brown eyes, rooted brown hair, closed mouth. A straw shopping bag with a little white baby came with the doll. Marks: EFFANBEE/©1975/1176, on head; EFF & BEE, on body. $125.00.

Plate 598: Effanbee. "Amelia," #1548 from the "Grandes Dames Collection," 1984. 15" tall. Vinyl head, sleeping amber eyes with real lashes, dark brown hair with center part, closed mouth, jointed hard vinyl body. All original in ivory satin gown trimmed with brown velvet ribbon and lace, matching hat, pearl choker at neck. Marks: EFFANBEE/19©78/1578, on head. $125.00.

Plate 599: Effanbee. "Absolutely Abigale Recital Time." #8 of limited edition of 125 dolls made for Treasure Trove. $100.00.

Left — Plate 600: Effanbee. "Carolyn," #1242, antique bride from the "Keepsake Collection," 1979. Vinyl head, sleeping amber eyes, dark brown rooted hair parted in the center and pulled back, closed mouth, jointed hard vinyl body and limbs. 11½" tall. All original in ecru lace bridal gown with rows of ruffled lace on skirt bottom and matching bridal bonnet. Bridal bouquet has one blue rose. Marks: EFFANBEE/©1976/1176, on head. $85.00.

Right — Plate 601: Effanbee. "Absolutely Abigale Sunday Best." #8 in limited edition of 125 dolls made for Treasure Trove. 1982. $100.00.

Plate 602: Effanbee. "The Skaters" from the "Currier & Ives Collection," #1252 (girl) and #1251 (boy). These dolls are #92 in a special limited edition of 100 sets made for Treasure Trove. 11" tall. Dolls are jointed vinyl, rooted brown hair, sleeping brown eyes with molded lashes, closed mouth, girl has painted lips, boy does not. Girl is all original in blue velvet jacket and matching hat, lavender pleated skirt. Boy is all original in blue velvet jacket and cap with black velvet pants. Marks on both: EFFANBEE/©1975/1176, on head; EFF & BEE, on back. The author has another set, #27, identical to this set except that the girl has a long sky blue skirt. The boxes for this set are marked #1232 Black for the girl and #1231 Black for the boy. This set also states that the dolls were made for Treasure Trove. $225.00.

Plate 603: Effanbee. "Jacqueline," #1147 from the "Grandes Dames" series, 1984. Vinyl head, sleeping amber eyes, short rooted brown hair, closed mouth, jointed vinyl body. 11" tall. All original in long off-white organdy gown with gold headband with sequins and rhinestones. Marks: EFFANBEE/©1975/1176, on head; EFF & BEE, on body. $80.00.

Left — Plate 604: Effanbee. "Suzanne" #1158 from the "Grandes Dames Collection," 1983. Vinyl head, sleeping amber eyes, rooted short brown hair, closed mouth, jointed vinyl body. 11" tall. All original in pink taffeta dress trimmed with a green ribbon at waist and a white straw hat. Marks: EFFANBEE/©1975/1176, on head; EFF & BEE, on body. $80.00.

Right — Plate 605: Effanbee. "Francoise" from the "Grandes Dames" series, 1981, No. 1156, from a limited edition of 125 dolls made for Treasure Trove, a mail order doll company. All original in mauve gown with matching hat. $125.00.

Left — Plate 606: Effanbee. "Saratoga" from the "Grandes Dames" series, 1981, No. 1159, from limited edition made for Treasure Trove. This is number 25 of 125 sets made. All original in black and white striped outfit with matching bonnet. $125.00.

Right — Plate 607: Effanbee. "Lady Ascot" from the "Grandes Dames" series, 1981, No. 1157. Limited edition of 125 sets of four Grandes Dames made for Treasure Trove. This doll is from set number 25. 11" tall. All original in white cotton batiste dress with burgundy bodice and satin burgundy dotted overskirt, white straw hat with burgundy matching ribbon. $125.00.

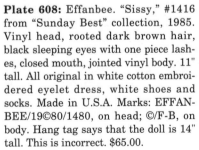

Plate 608: Effanbee. "Sissy," #1416 from "Sunday Best" collection, 1985. Vinyl head, rooted dark brown hair, black sleeping eyes with one piece lashes, closed mouth, jointed vinyl body. 11" tall. All original in white cotton embroidered eyelet dress, white shoes and socks. Made in U.S.A. Marks: EFFANBEE/19©80/1480, on head; ©/F-B, on body. Hang tag says that the doll is 14" tall. This is incorrect. $65.00.

Plate 609: Effanbee. "Sam," #1415 from the "Sunday Best" collection, 1985. Identical to previous Sissy except for shorter hair and clothing. All original in one piece outfit with white shirt and blue pants, white shoes and socks. Marks are the same as those on Sissy. $65.00.

Plate 610: Effanbee. "Miss India," #1119 from the "International" collection. 11". Vinyl head, long black hair, white dot on forehead, sleeping amber eyes, closed mouth, jointed hard vinyl body. All original in aqua and white sari trimmed in gold and navy blue braid, rhinestone headband. Marks: EFFANBEE/©1975/1176, on head; EFF & BEE, on body. $70.00.

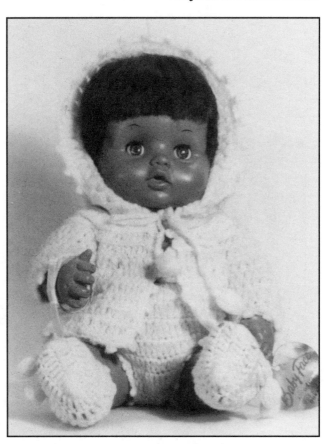

Left — Plate 611: Effanbee. "Pocahontas" #1157 from the "Historical Collection," 1977–1978. Vinyl head, rooted long brown hair, sleeping amber eyes, closed mouth, jointed hard vinyl body. All original in brown suede-like dress with matching mocassins and headband. 11". Marks: EFFANBEE/©1975/1176, on head; EFF & BEE, on body. $85.00.

Right — Plate 612: Effanbee. "Baby Face." 12" tall. Vinyl head, sleeping amber eyes with lashes, nursing mouth, rooted brown hair, jointed vinyl body and limbs. All original in pink hand crocheted hooded jacket, panties, and booties. Marks: EFFANBEE/1969, on head. Collection of the Museum of African American History (Detroit). $85.00.

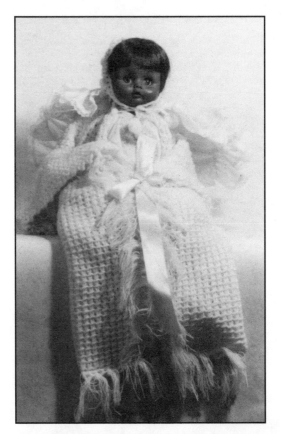

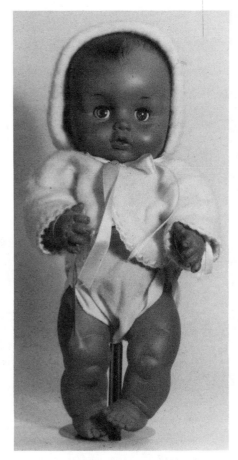

Plate 614: Effanbee. "Butterball." 12" vinyl doll, movable head, arms and legs, sculpted hair, sleeping amber eyes with lashes, nursing mouth. All original in white flannel jacket trimmed with pink embroidery, matching bonnet, white flannel diapers. Marks: EFFANBEE/1969/6569, on head; EFFANBEE/1969/6569, on body. Collection of the Museum of African American History (Detroit). $75.00.

Plate 613: Effanbee. "Baby Winkie." 14" tall. Vinyl head, rooted brown hair, sleeping amber eyes with lashes, nursing mouth, jointed vinyl baby body. All original in long white gown with floral embroidery down the front, pale pink hand crocheted long coat with matching bonnet, hand crocheted pale pink sack blanket, and cotton pink pillow trimmed with white ruffles. Marks: EFFANBEE/1971/6171, on head; EFFANBEE 2400, on body. Collection of the Museum of African American History (Detroit). $65.00.

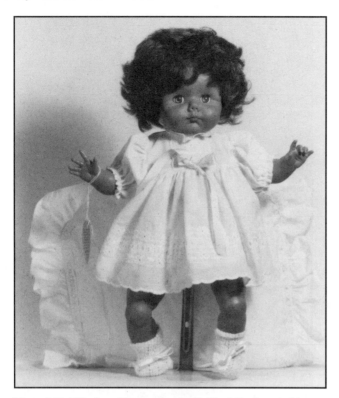

Plate 615: Effanbee. "Butter Cup." 14". Vinyl head, rooted brown hair, sleeping amber eyes with lashes, closed mouth, vinyl arms and legs, brown cloth body. All original in white eyelet dress trimmed with pink ribbon, white booties, white snap-on diaper. Doll came with a white ruffled pillow. Marks: 13/EFFANBEE/ 19©77/8377, on head. Collection of the Museum of African American History (Detroit). $75.00.

Plate 616: Effanbee. "Chipper Bride." 1980's. 14" tall. All original in white cotton gown with net overskirt trimmed in lace, removable lace bodice. Jointed vinyl with light brown sleeping eyes, brown hair, closed mouth. Marks: EFFANBEE/19©79/1579, on head. $125.00.

Plate 617: Effanbee. "Chipper Bride," No. 1512 from the 1979 "Bridal Suite Collection." Vinyl head, brown rooted hair, sleeping amber eyes, jointed hard vinyl body and limbs. 15" tall. Marks: EFFANBEE/19©66, on head. Ecru bodice of bridal gown is attached to the slip with an ecru bridal gown overskirt. $125.00.

Plate 618: Effanbee. "Bride, Chipper," from the "Bridal Suite Collection," early 1980's. Vinyl head, sleeping brown eyes, rooted brown hair, closed mouth, jointed vinyl body. 15" tall. All original in embroidered net gown with lace and net headpiece. Marks: EFFANBEE/19©78/1578, on head. $125.00.

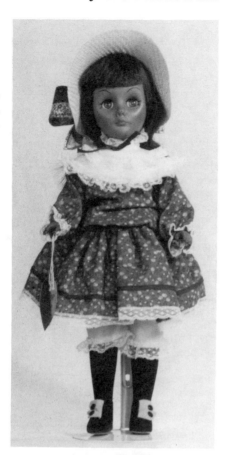

Left — Plate 619: Effanbee. "Chipper," 1979, #1548 from the "American Beauty Collection." Vinyl head, sleeping amber eyes, rooted brown hair, closed mouth, jointed vinyl body. 15" tall. All original in burgundy velveteen dress with white pin tucked organdy apron overpiece trimmed in lace. Marks: EFFANBEE/19©66, on head. $125.00.

Right — Plate 620: Effanbee. "Chipper," #1582B, 1983 from "Granny's Corner Collection." 15". All original in mauve cotton print dress trimmed with white lace, white pantaloons, black stockings, old-fashioned shoes, natural straw hat with mauve print band in different print from dress. $125.00.

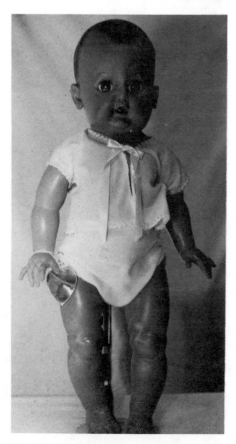

Plate 621: Effanbee. "Chipper," 1982 from the "Enchanted Garden Collection." 15" tall. All jointed vinyl doll, sleeping brown eyes with lashes, rooted brown hair, closed mouth. All original in blue print gown with white organdy overskirt. Marks: EFFANBEE/19©78/1578, on head. $95.00.

Plate 622: Effanbee. "DyDee Baby." 21". 1950's. All original vinyl doll. Used as Red Cross training doll. Marks: EFFANBEE, on neck; EFFANBEE DY DEE BABY, on shoulders. Photograph courtesy of Etta Houston. $275.00.

Plate 623: Effanbee. "Dy Dee Baby." 17" tall. Jointed vinyl baby doll, rooted brown hair, sleeping amber eyes, nursing mouth. All original in print pajamas holding teddy bear marked "Trudy Toys." Marks on doll: ©EFFANBEE/5671, on head; EFFANBEE/1967, on body. The same doll is listed in the 1977, 1978, and 1979 Effanbee catalogs from the "Sweet Dreams Collection." (See author's previous book for another all original DyDee Baby holding a different teddy bear named "Bashful" by Russ.) Collection of the Museum of African American History (Detroit). $120.00.

Plate 624: Effanbee. "Little Lovums" from the "Crochet Classics" collection, 1977. 14" tall. Vinyl head, arms and legs, brown cloth body, sculpted hair, sleeping amber eyes, closed mouth. All original in white cotton dress and panties, pink hand-crocheted hooded sweater and booties. Marks: 13/EFFANBEE/19©77/8377, on head. Collection of the Museum of African American History (Detroit). $70.00.

Plate 625: Effanbee. "Little Luv." 14". Vinyl head, rooted brown hair, sleeping amber eyes with lashes, open-closed mouth, vinyl arms and legs, brown cloth body. All original in red gingham dress with print patches, white panties and white knit booties. Marks: 10/EFFANBEE/19©70/9370, on head; ALL NEW MATERIAL/EFFANBEE DOLL/CORPORATION/NEW YORK, N.Y., tag sewn to body. Collection of the Museum of African American History (Detroit). $70.00.

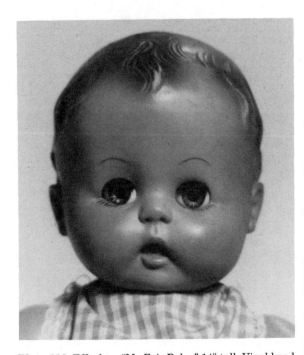

Plate 626: Effanbee. "My Fair Baby." 14" tall. Vinyl head, sleeping brown eyes with lashes, nursing mouth, molded hair, jointed vinyl baby body. Marks: EFFANBEE/©1959, on head; EFFANBEE/19©64, on body. Redressed. $95.00.

Left — Plate 627: Effanbee. "Pun'kin" #1344B from "A Touch of Velvet Collection," 1978. 11" tall. Vinyl head, rooted brown hair, sleeping amber eyes, open-closed mouth, jointed vinyl body. All original in burgundy velveteen and white eyelet dress. Marks: EFFANBEE/19©66, on head. $70.00.

Right — Plate 628: Effanbee. "Pun'kin" #1382B from the "Granny's Corner Collection," 1983. 11" tall. Vinyl head, rooted brown curly hair, sleeping amber eyes, jointed vinyl body. All original in old-fashioned cotton patchwork print in mauve shades, natural straw hat with band matching dress, white pantaloons, black stockings, black and tan suede shoes. Marks: EFFANBEE/19©66, on head; ©/F-B, on body. $70.00.

Plate 629: Effanbee. "Pun'kin." 11". Vinyl head, body, and limbs, rooted brown hair, sleeping amber eyes with one-piece lashes, closed mouth. All original in long floral print gown trimmed with lace, matching panties and bonnet. Marks: EFFANBEE/19©66, on head. Collection of the Museum of African History (Detroit). $70.00.

Plate 630: Effanbee. "Pun'kin" #1328 from "Over the Rainbow Collection," 1981. Vinyl head, sleeping amber eyes, open-closed mouth, rooted brown hair, jointed vinyl body. All original in a long dress of pastel gingham and white trimmed with gingham bows, white pantaloons, and white slipper shoes. 11" tall. Marks: EFFANBEE/ 19©66, on head; ©/F-B, on body. $70.00.

Plate 631: Effanbee. "Pun'kin" #1351, from the "Heart to Heart Collection," 1980. The fabric pattern is hearts and flowers with the Effanbee signature in the background. Vinyl head, sleeping amber eyes, rooted brown hair, open-closed mouth, jointed vinyl body. All original in short print dress with white tights. 11" tall. Marks: EFFANBEE/ 19©66, on head. $70.00.

Left — Plate 632: Effanbee. "Sara." 16" tall. 1985. All vinyl, brown sleep eyes, rooted curly dark brown hair, closed mouth. All original in white dress with an eyelet skirt and eyelet trim on bodice, at neck, and on sleeves. Pink sash with flowers attached on one side. Velvet Mary Jane white shoes with rosebud trim, four pink bows in hair. Marks: EFFANBEE/19©67/2600, on head. Wrist tag says "SUNDAY BEST COLLECTION." Collection of and photo courtesy of Maureen Braeden. $95.00.

Right — Plate 633: Effanbee. "Sweetie Pie," 1976, #9421 from the "Baby Classics Collection." Vinyl head, rooted curly brown hair, sleeping amber eyes, closed mouth, vinyl arms and legs, brown cloth body. All original in white organdy dress trimmed with white lace and pink ribbon with white knitted booties. 18" long. Marks: 14/©EFFANBEE/1969/9469, on head. $100.00.

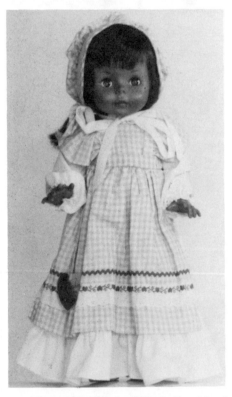

Plate 634: Effanbee. "Suzie Sunshine," 18". Vinyl head, rooted reddish brown hair, sleeping brown eyes, closed mouth, freckles, jointed vinyl toddler body. All original in patchwork red checked dress with white bodice. Marks: EFFANBEE/©1961, on head. $125.00.

Plate 635: Effanbee. "Suzie Sunshine." 18". Toddler doll. Vinyl head, rooted brown hair, sleeping amber eyes with lashes, freckled face, closed mouth, jointed vinyl body. All original in old fashioned white eyelet dress trimmed with pink ribbon, white stockings, black velvet shoes with white spats, natural straw brimmed hat. Marks: EFFANBEE/©1961, on head. Collection of the Museum of African American History (Detroit). $125.00.

Plate 636: Effanbee. "Suzie Sunshine," #1867B from the "American '76 Collection," 1976. 18" tall. Vinyl head, rooted brown hair, sleeping amber eyes with lashes, freckles, jointed vinyl toddler body. All original in blue gingham apron sewn onto a white cotton dress, matching bonnet. Marks: EFFANBEE/©1961, on head. $125.00.

Left — Plate 637: Effanbee. "Suzie Sunshine" #1844B from "A Touch of Velvet Collection," 1977. 18" tall. Vinyl jointed toddler doll, rooted long brown hair, sleeping brown eyes with lashes, closed mouth, freckles. All original burgundy velveteen and white cotton dress trimmed in white eyelet. Marks: EFFANBEE/©1961, on head. $125.00.

Right — Plate 638: Effanbee. "Suzie Sunshine" from "Granny's Corner Collection," 1975–76 #1866. Vinyl head, sleeping brown eyes, freckles, closed mouth, jointed vinyl toddler body. 19" tall. All original in long print dress with burgundy velveteen trim and matching bonnet. Marks: EFFANBEE/©1961, on head. $125.00.

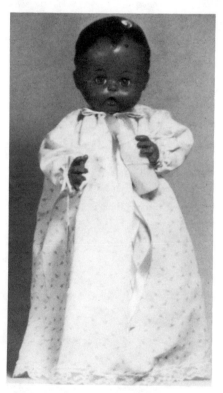

Plate 639: Effanbee. "Suzie Sunshine," #1811B. 18" tall. Jointed vinyl, rooted long brown hair, freckled face, sleeping amber/brown eyes with lashes. All original in pink print and white dress with embroidered skirt. Marks: EFFANBEE/1961©, on head. $125.00.

Plate 640: Effanbee. "Twinkie," 1981–82, from the "Heart to Heart Collection," #2559. All original in cotton gown in the hearts and flowers pattern with the Effanbee signature in the background. Jointed vinyl doll, sleeping amber eyes with lashes, molded painted hair, nursing mouth. 14" tall. Marks: 14/EFFANBEE 19©68/2500, on head; EFFANBEE/19©68/2808, on body. $55.00.

Plate 641: Effanbee. "Twinkle." 17" tall. Vinyl head, arms and legs, brown cloth body, rooted brown hair, sleeping amber eyes, nursing mouth. All original in ecru cotton eyelet dress trimmed with pink ribbon, white booties. Originally came with her own pillow. Marks: 14/EFFANBEE/ 19©68/2500, on head. Collection of the Museum of African American History (Detroit). $85.00.

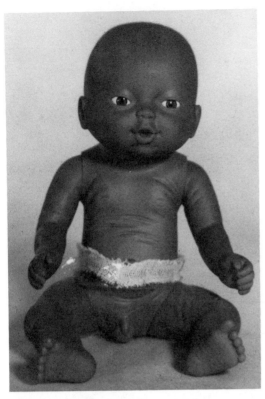

Plate 642: Emson. 8" tall. Jointed vinyl, brown stationary glassine eyes, open-closed mouth, bald, anatomically correct boy. Marks: ©EMSON/CHINA, on body. Collection of Valerie Burbank-Pugh. $35.00.

Plate 643: Emson. "Newborn Baby Doll." Doll comes with newborn baby doll certification of birth registration that the child fills in with name you are giving your doll, sex of the doll, birthdate and family name. All vinyl with jointed arms and legs, inset amber glassine eyes, molded hair, open mouth with pacifier. 18" tall. All original in white romper outfit. Marks: ©EMSON 1988/MADE IN CHINA, on head; ©EMSON/MADE IN CHINA, on body. $30.00.

Plate 644: Eugene. "Bitter Sweet Sugar 'n Spice and Everything Nice," style #771370. Vinyl head, rooted black hair, painted eyes, open mouth with two molded teeth, freckles, fat jointed toddler body. 13" tall. All original in red cotton dress with red plaid attached apron front, red bonnet, red plastic shoes, and white socks. Marks: 713(slash)TP/MADE IN TAIWAN/LORRIE DOLL CO./©1974/11, on head. $45.00.

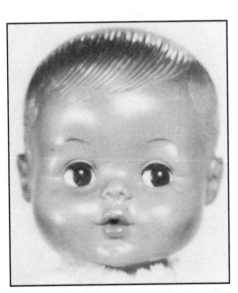

Plate 645: Eugene. Hard vinyl head, molded hair painted black, sleeping black eyes with real lashes looking to the left, dimpled chin, one piece hard vinyl body with hole for wetting. Redressed in blue baby dress. 13" tall. Marks: LORRIE DOLL/19©73, on head. Some dolls marketed by Eugene Doll Co. are marked LORRIE on the head. $45.00.

Plate 646: Eugene. "Satin 'n Lace," ©1987, style #46187. Vinyl head, sleeping amber eyes with lashes, rooted curly black hair, closed mouth, pierced ears with orange earrings, vinyl arms and legs, white cloth body. All original in white satin like dress with cotton print trim and white satin panties. Original black shoes are marked: IDEAL TOY CORP./MADE IN U.S.A. Doll is 18" tall. Marks: MADE IN CHINA/FOR THE: EUGENE DOLL CO./NEW YORK, N.Y./..., tag sewn to body. $40.00.

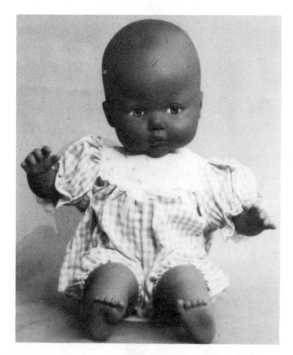

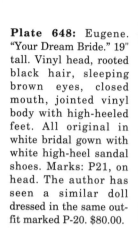

Plate 648: Eugene. "Your Dream Bride." 19" tall. Vinyl head, rooted black hair, sleeping brown eyes, closed mouth, jointed vinyl body with high-heeled feet. All original in white bridal gown with white high-heel sandal shoes. Marks: P21, on head. The author has seen a similar doll dressed in the same outfit marked P-20. $80.00.

Plate 647: Eugene. "Just Born Baby," ©1989. 16" tall. Vinyl head, stationary amber eyes, sculptured hair, open-closed mouth, vinyl arms and legs, brown cloth stuffed body. All original in pink gingham rompers. Marks: ©EEGEE CO./ 17VSBE, on head; ...GOLDBERGER DOLL MFG. CO. INC./..., tag sewn to body. Made in China. $20.00.

Plate 649: Eugene. 13". Vinyl head, rooted curly black hair, sleeping brown eyes with lashes, closed mouth, vinyl arms and legs, white cloth body. All original in pink sateen dress trimmed with white lace. Original white socks are missing. Marks: ©1987 EUGENE DOLL CO., on head. Made in China. Courtesy of Xzena Moore of the Cubbyhole. $30.00.

Plate 650: Eugene. "Kiss Me Baby." 15" tall. Vinyl head, rooted black hair, sleeping amber eyes with lashes, nursing mouth, vinyl arms and legs, white cloth body. Doll really kisses, no batteries required. All original in pink dress with white attached apron front, pink bonnet and panties, white shoes and socks. Marks: 1/©EUGENE DOLL/1977, on head. Collection of the Museum of African American History (Detroit). $45.00.

175

Plate 652: Eugene. "Hug 'n Love Baby." 11" tall. Vinyl head, rooted bangs for hair, head bald in back, painted eyes, open-closed mouth, cloth body and limbs with sewn on clothing, removable hat. Marks: 29/ ©1987 EUGENE DOLL, on head. $13.00.

Plate 651: Eugene. "Hug n' Love Baby." 9" tall. Vinyl head, bald, painted eyes, pacifier attached to mouth, cloth body and limbs with sewn on clothing, removable cap. Marks: EUGENE DOLL CO./©1984/19, on head. Tagged body. $13.00.

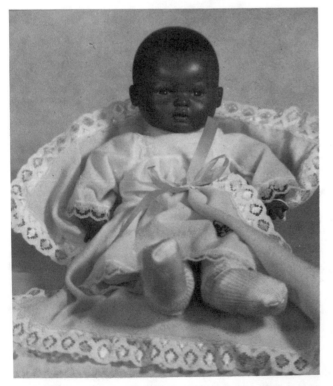

Plate 654: Eugene. "Sherbet." 13" tall. Fruit scented vinyl doll, rooted yellow hair, painted eyes, closed mouth, jointed body. All original in yellow dress. Marks: EUGENE DOLL/19© 76, on head. Box is marked ©MCMXXI. Doll is also available with blue hair. $40.00.

Plate 653: Eugene. "Li'l Just Born." 14". Vinyl head and arms, white cloth body and legs, molded painted black hair, painted eyes, open-closed mouth. All original in white gown and pink blanket, both lace trimmed. Marks: 17©EUGENE DOLL/1975, on head. Box is marked ©1981. $25.00.

Plate 655: Eugene. 12½" tall. Vinyl head and jointed body, rooted black hair, painted eyes, closed mouth, freckles. All original in green and yellow striped pants and hat, floral print shirt. Marks: LORRIE DOLL CO./©1974/713 CF/MADE IN TAIWAN 22, on head. $55.00.

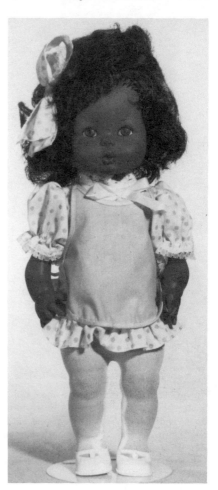

Plate 656: Eugene. "Color My Dress Pretty," #45149. 1989. Doll comes with a special wand to draw designs on dress. Vinyl head and jointed body, rooted black hair, painted eyes, open-closed mouth. All original in white and pink dotted dress with special pink apron for drawing on. Marks: 8/EUGENE DOLL/ 19©77, on head. $16.00.

Left — Plate 657: Eugene. 11½" tall. Vinyl head, rooted short black hair, sleeping amber eyes with molded lash, closed mouth, jointed vinyl body. Original green and white striped dress. Marks: ©LORRIE DOLL/11, on head; MADE IN/HONG KONG, on back. Probably from the 1970's. $30.00.

Right — Plate 658: Eugene. Baby Doll, 14". Vinyl head, nursing mouth, rooted black hair, sleeping amber eyes with lashes, bent-leg vinyl body. Dressed in pink with tam. Marks: 1260/LORRIE DOLL/19©63, on head. Courtesy of Linda Boulware of Dolls of Color, Inc. $75.00.

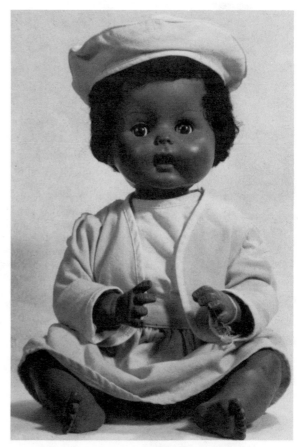

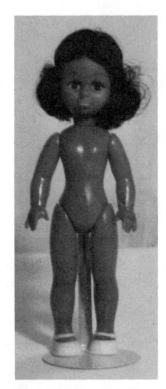

Plate 659: Fibre Craft. "Black Angel Doll," made for dressmaking. Sold dressed in white panties, shoes, and socks. Vinyl head, rooted black hair, sleeping brown eyes, closed mouth, jointed vinyl body. 13" tall. Marks: MADE IN CHINA, on body. Redressed in blue dotted shirt with yellow striped short overalls with one shoulder strap. $5.00.

Plate 660: Fibre Craft. "Music Box Doll" No. 3178B. Vinyl head light brown in coloring, rooted black curly hair, sleeping brown eyes, closed mouth, jointed vinyl body with music box inserted in doll's back. Music box is activated by pressing button and plays "Silent Night." Doll came dressed in white underpants, shoes, and socks. 13" tall. Marks: ©1988 FIBRE CRAFT/MATERIALS CORP./MADE IN CHINA, on body. $5.00.

Plate 661: Fibre Craft. "Angel Doll," made for dressmaking. 9½" tall. Vinyl head, rooted black hair, painted eyes, closed mouth, jointed inexpensive vinyl body. Doll came with only white shoes, no clothing. Marks: MADE IN CHINA, on back. $5.00.

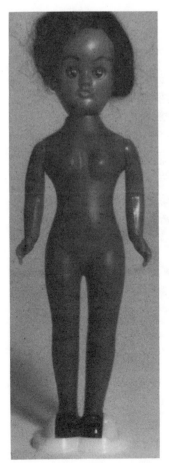

Plate 662: Fibre Craft. "Black Flat Heel Doll." No. 3002. Doll came only wearing shoes, made for dressing. Hard plastic inexpensive head, glued on black mohair like wig, sleeping amber eyes, painted blue eyebrows, closed mouth, hard vinyl ladies body jointed only at the arms. 7½" tall. Doll came with plastic stand and is unmarked. Purchased new in 1990. $2.00.

Plate 663: Fibre. "Pillow Doll." 8". Half doll kit to make a pillow doll. Vinyl with movable head and arms, rooted black hair, sleeping eyes with lashes, closed mouth. Marks: ©1988 FIBRE CRAFT/MATERIALS CORP/MADE IN CHINA, on body. $5.00.

Plate 665: Fisher Price. "Dream Doll House Family Set," #4640. 6½" to 2½". Jointed hard vinyl. All dolls have molded hair and molded on clothing. In addition, mom has a removable cotton print skirt. Marks: ©93 F–P, INC/CHINA, on left foot of each doll. 1993. $10.00.

Plate 664: Fisher Price. "Elizabeth," 1973. Vinyl head and hands, stuffed cloth body and legs; rooted black synthetic hair; painted features. 13" tall. All original in red plaid dress, skirt portion is removable. Marks: 168530/©1973/FISHER PRICE TOYS. $65.00.

Plate 668: Fisher Price. "Puffalump Kids," ©1991. Dress-up baby, style #4079. Vinyl head, painted brown eyes, open-closed mouth, black tufts of hair sewn under the sewn on bonnet, brown cloth body, sewn on pink striped booties, removable pink dress. 12" tall. Tag sewn to body: PUFFALUMP KIDS/FISHER PRICE/EAST AURORA N.Y./©1991/4076 4078 4077 4079. Doll came with pink plastic feeding bottle. $25.00.

Plate 667: Fisher Price. "Puffalump Kids," #4095. Vinyl face with several tufts of hair sewn under the cap, painted features. The remainder of the doll is cloth and is very soft and light in sewn on pink outfit with name on bib. 14" tall. Tag sewn to body: FP/FISHER-PRICE/EAST AURORA, N.Y./PUFFALUMPS/©1990/4095/4096/MADE IN CHINA. $20.00.

Plate 666: Fisher Price. "Puffalump Pretty Hair." 14". 1993. Vinyl face, black hair attached under sewn on bonnet, cloth back of head, body, and limbs, painted features, removable skirt. Tagged body. $22.00.

Plate 669: Flagg. "Africa." 7" tall. One piece bendable, possible vinyl over wire armature, black hair, painted features. All original box reads: FLAGG AND COMPANY, INC./MANUFACTURERS OF FLEXIBLE PLAY DOLLS/6 BISMARCK ST. JAMAICA PLAINS, MASS. 02130. Flagg dolls were designed by Sheila Markham Flagg and were produced from the late 1940's until 1985. $35.00.

Plate 670: Fleetwood Toys. "Children for Children." 17" tall. Vinyl head, rooted black hair, painted eyes, freckles, brown cloth body and limbs. All original in pink and blue dress with matching pink bloomers, black shoes. Dolls available in a variety of original outfits. A portion of sales from the dolls goes to the Save the Children Foundation. Marks: © 88 FLEETWOOD TOY INC./ALL RIGHTS RESERVED/MADE IN CHINA, on head. Courtesy of Emma Hayward. $40.00.

Plate 671: Fortune Toys. "Pam." 8" tall. Walker doll, hard plastic head, sleeping amber eyes, brown wig in two braids Dolls with bangs, closed mouth, jointed hard plastic body with molded on unpainted shoes. All original in print dress with matching underpants. Unmarked. $85.00.

Plate 672: Fortune Toys. "Pam," 1950's. Walker, head turns when legs move. Hard plastic head, glued on brown saran wig, amber, molded on shoes. Original clothes. Doll is unmarked. $85.00.

Plate 673: "Pam" dressed in an Indian costume. 8" tall. Hard plastic walking doll, black wig, sleeping amber eyes, closed mouth, molded on t-strap shoes. Unmarked. All original in Native American outfit. $85.00.

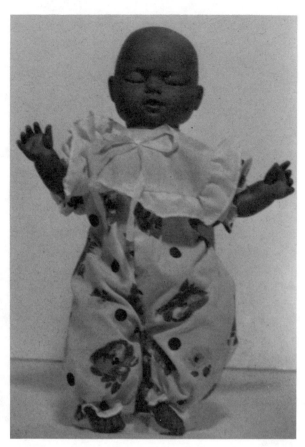

Left — Plate 674: 14R. 19" tall. 1957–1965. Rigid vinyl body, arms, and legs, soft vinyl head, brown sleep eyes, rooted black hair, high heel feet, bust. All original clothing. Halter top dress with gold brocade bodice, pink taffeta skirt with pink net overlay, gray "fur" stole, white high-heeled shoes, pearl earrings. Marks: 14R, on head. Photograph courtesy of Maureen Braeden. $85.00.

Right — Plate 675: Fung Seng. "Crying Baby." #8012. Baby starts crying when you clap hands or make any sound. The crying sound stops automatically after 10–15 seconds. Battery operated. Vinyl head, arms and legs; closed eyes, molded hair, open-closed mouth, cloth body. 14" tall. All original in cotton white print romper. Marks: F3/MADE IN CHINA, on head. $20.00.

Plate 676: Furga. "Classic." 18". Nominee for 1990 DOTY award. Vinyl head, rooted black hair, stationary black eyes, pierced ears with stud earrings, slight opening between parted lips, jointed anatomically correct baby girl's body. All original in red striped dress under red pinafore, ecru pantaloons. Marks: FURGA ITALY/474 © 1988, on head; FURGA/ITALY/459, on body. Doll comes with a birth certificate that can be filled in by the owner, giving the doll a name. $125.00.

Plate 677: Furga. "Brenda" from the Furga Boutique collection. 24". Vinyl head, arms, and legs, white cloth body, rooted black hair, brown sleeping eyes with lashes, closed mouth. Marks: FURGA ITALY/611, on head. Courtesy of Xzena Moore of the Chubbyhole. $125.00.

181

Plate 678: Furga. 17" tall. 1975–78. Vinyl head and jointed body, sleep black eyes, rooted black hair. All original in long white eyelet gown with pink lining, matching bonnet, white high-heeled boots. Marks: FURGA, ITALY/17601, on head. From the collection of and photo courtesy of Maureen Braeden. $100.00.

Plate 679: Furga. "Mamie." 13" tall. Vinyl head and jointed body, curly black rooted hair, sleeping eyes. All original in red and whited striped outfit with matching headscarf. Marks: FURGA/ITALY 20 245, on head. Collection of Reevah Turner. $65.00.

Plate 680: Furga. All original "native" type doll. 12½". Vinyl head and jointed body, rooted black hair, sleeping brown eyes with lashes, closed mouth, tribal-type painting on chin. Marks: FURGA/ITALY, on back. $65.00.

Plate 681: Gabriel Industries. "Pretty Cut & Grow." You can style her hair, cut it, and replace it whenever you like. Vinyl head with opening in the top for replacing black yarn hair, painted eyes, closed smiling mouth, jointed vinyl body with an opening in the back for replacing hair. 13" tall. All original in red and white print dress. Marks: GABRIEL/©1980 CBS INC./LANCASTER, PA 17602/MADE IN U.S.A./PAT. PENDING, on body. $40.00.

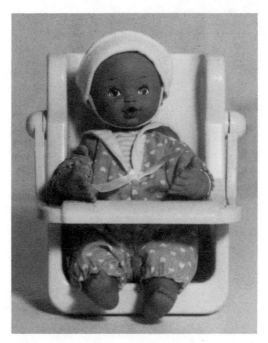

Plate 682: Galoob. "Walkin' Baby and her Walker" from the "Bouncin' Babies" series. Vinyl head, painted eyes, closed mouth, molded hair, jointed hard plastic body. Battery operated. All original in pink striped and white cotton knit romper suit, white cotton knit cap, and pink plastic shoes. Marks: ©1988 L.G.T./MADE IN CHINA, on body. $15.00.

Plate 683: Galoob. "Peek-A-Boo Baby And Her Car Seat," ©1988 #3303. When you turn her on she plays peek-a-boo or reaches for you. All vinyl with movable arms, legs, and head, painted eyes, open mouth, molded painted black hair, on switch on back of doll, no batteries required. All original in pink print romper and white hat. 6½" tall. Marks: ©1988 LGTI/CHINA, on back. Pink plastic car seat is marked the same. $15.00.

Plate 684: Galoob. "Cutie Club Kids," "Summer Fun Collection." 1" tall. All vinyl with molded painted on clothing, rooted tufts of hair. In the set of five dolls, two are black. One of the black dolls has green hair, the other has pink hair. The two black dolls are bottom left and top right in the photograph. $10.00.

Plate 685: Galoob. "Baby Talk." 20" tall. Vinyl head, arms, and legs, stationary brown eyes with lashes, rooted black hair, open-closed mouth with painted teeth, pink cloth body. Talking doll, batteries required. All original in pink teddy-bear print overalls, cotton knit pink pullover shirt, pink booties and pink bib with doll's name. Marks: ©1985/GALOOB INC., on head; ©1985 LEWIS GALOOB TOYS, INC., on battery case. Courtesy of Patricia Martin. $60.00.

Plate 686: Galoob. "Happy Baby Hannah" from the "Bathtub Baby Face" collection. Vinyl head, rooted dark brown hair, stationary brown eyes with eyelashes, open-closed mouth with molded tongue and two lower teeth, jointed vinyl baby body with red "magic" shirt with white short sleeves, white plastic diapers imprinted in pink with Baby Face, hearts, squares, and swirly lines, plastic bib with "baby" imprint. ©1991 L.G.T.I./#20 CHINA, on head; ©1991 L.G.T.I./CHINA, on body. $20.00.

Plate 687: Galoob. "Curious Baby Cara" from the "Bathtub Baby Face" collection. Vinyl head, rooted dark brown hair, stationary brown eyes with real eyelashes, open-closed mouth with molded tongue sticking out, five piece jointed vinyl bent-leg baby body, green "magic" bath shirt that disappears in water. 13" tall. Marks: ©1991 L.G.T.I./CHINA, on body. All original in white knit shirt imprinted with aqua bows and tiny circles, pink ribbon is inserted eyelet trim on top, and pale pink "Baby Face" plastic diapers. $20.00.

Plate 688: Galoob. "Bashful Baby Abby" from the "Bathtub Baby Face" collection. Vinyl head, rooted brown hair, stationary brown eyes with eyelashes, closed mouth, jointed vinyl body with red "magic" bath shirt. 13" tall. All original in white and pink cotton knit shirt trimmed with white lace and pink vinyl printed diapers. Marks: ©1991 L.G.T.I./#22 CHINA, on head; ©1991 L.G.T.I./CHINA, on body. $20.00.

Plate 689: Galoob. "Excited Baby Becca" from the "Bathtub Baby Face" collection. Vinyl head, rooted brown hair, stationary brown eyes with eyelashes, wide open-closed mouth, vinyl jointed baby body. 13" tall. All original in aqua cotton knit top with bear decal in front and pink plastic diapers. Marks: ©1991 L.G.T.I./#23 CHINA, on head; ©1991 L.G.T.I./CHINA, on body. Doll has red "magic" bath shirt. $20.00.

Plate 691: Galoob. "Ron Simmons" from "World Championship Wrestling." 5". Vinyl one piece action figure with molded blue pants, white shoes, removable gold belt imprinted "WCW." Marks: ©1990 WCW INC./MFD GALOOB CHINA, on back. $5.00.

Plate 690: Galoob. "Onyx," action figure from "Golden Girl and the Guardians of the Gemstones." 6" tall. ©1984. Vinyl head, painted eyes, closed mouth, rooted black hair, jointed hard vinyl body with molded on pink outfit, boots, armbands with removable gold cape lined in pink. Doll comes with gemstone shield, headdress, weapon, and weapon belt. Unmarked. $25.00.

Plate 693: Galoob. "Whispering Wishes." Doll whispers answers to your questions. You never know what she'll say. Batteries required. 14" tall. Vinyl head, painted eyes, brown fancy yarn hair, open-closed mouth, cloth body and limbs. All original in long pink gown and pink tiara. Marks: ©1993 GALOOB INC./ MADE IN CHINA, on head. $20.00.

Plate 692: Galoob. "Butch Reed" from "World Championship Wrestling." 5". Vinyl wrestling figure with molded on purple pants, white shoes, and removable belt imprinted "WCW." Marks: ©1990 WCW, INC. MFD GALOOB/CHINA, on body. $5.00.

Plate 694: Gama. "Les Creations Gama," #19801F. Vinyl doll, rooted black hair, sleeping hazel eyes, closed mouth, jointed vinyl body. 7" tall. All original in cotton print dress with matching gelee, white pantaloons, and white plastic slipper shoes. Doll is unmarked, shoes are marked CINDERELLA/SIZE 04. Made in France. $35.00.

Plate 695: Gambina. "Odelia," praline lady. 11" tall. Jointed vinyl brown sleeping eyes, dark rooted hair, holding a tray of pralines. All original in blue dress with print trim, matching print headwrap. Doll was available in assorted prints. Marks: GAMBINA DOLL, on head. Marked clothing and stand. Courtesy of Lin Murphy. $25.00.

Plate 696: Gambina. "Virginia." 14" tall. Vinyl head, rooted brown hair, painted eyes, closed mouth, pierced ears with gold-tone hoop earrings, jointed vinyl body. Dressed to represent a Caribbean island woman circa 1850 in a long red print dress trimmed with white lace, matching head-scarf, blue waist scarf. Unmarked. $25.00.

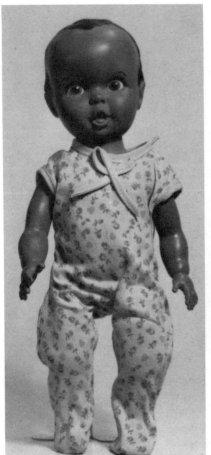

Left — Plate 697: Gerber Products. "The Gerber Baby." 1972. 11" tall. Vinyl head, molded painted black hair, painted eyes, nursing mouth, jointed vinyl body. Said to be the third issue of the Gerber baby doll. All original in tagged print footed sleeper. Marks: THE GERBER BABY/GERBER PROD. CO. 19©72, on head. Collection of the Museum of African American History (Detroit). $150.00.

Right — Plate 698: Gerber Products, Atlanta Novelty Division. "Gerber Baby Doll." 17" tall. Vinyl head, molded painted black hair, brown flirty eyes, open-closed mouth, yellow gingham dress forms the body. Removable white eyelet bib and overskirt. Marks: GERBER PRODUCTS CO./©1979, on head. Collection of the Museum of African History (Detroit). $95.00.

Left — Plate 699: Golden Ribbon Playthings. "Huggy Bean Kulture Kids," 1991. 12" tall. Vinyl head, arms, and legs; painted eyes; closed mouth; rooted brown yarn hair; cloth body. All original in two piece pant outfit in yellow and Kente cloth-like print with white socks and plastic shoes. Marks: HUGGY BEAN/©1984 GOLDEN RIBBON PLAYTHINGS INC./ORIGINAL CHOCOLATE FOREST DESIGN/MFG. FOR GOLDEN RIBBON PLAYTHINGS INC./..., on tag sewn to body. $12.00.

Right — Plate 700: Golden Ribbons. "Super Style Huggy," No. 45130 from the "Huggy Bean" collection. 17" tall. Vinyl head, arms, and legs, brown cloth body, rooted dark brown hair, painted features. Doll was available in several different outfits. All original in yellow and black print two-piece pantsuit, white socks, yellow plastic shoes. Marks: GOLDEN RIBBON PLAYTHINGS/ ©1984 * HB-1084, on head. Box is marked ©1991. Made in China. $30.00.

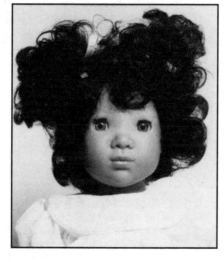

Plate 702: Gotz. "Lucille," #44002. vinyl head, rooted black synthetic hair, sleeping brown eyes with lashes, closed mouth, vinyl arms and legs, brown cloth body. 18" tall. All original in white lace trimmed taffeta dress embroidered with "Gotz" in pink toward the hemline, white plastic shoes, and socks. Marks: GOTZ/139–17/, on head. Doll was on the market in 1992. $125.00.

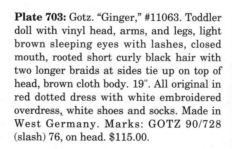

Plate 701: Golden Ribbon Playthings. "Huggy Stylette," #88170, ©1992. 12". This is the first doll in the "Huggy Bean" series with hair you can comb and style. The previous dolls had yarn hair. Vinyl head, arms, and legs, painted eyes, closed mouth, rooted brown synthetic hair, brown cloth body. All original in white and orange outfit. Doll is available in several different outfits with varying hairstyles. Head is unmarked. Tag sewn to body: ALL NEW MATERIAL/POLYESTER/REG. NO. PA-4075 (HK)/GOLDEN RIBBON PLAYTHINGS INC./MADE IN CHINA. $10.00.

Plate 703: Gotz. "Ginger," #11063. Toddler doll with vinyl head, arms, and legs, light brown sleeping eyes with lashes, closed mouth, rooted short curly black hair with two longer braids at sides tie up on top of head, brown cloth body. 19". All original in red dotted dress with white embroidered overdress, white shoes and socks. Made in West Germany. Marks: GOTZ 90/728 (slash) 76, on head. $115.00.

Plate 704: Grow Time, Div. of Cutoy Coop Assoc. "Squeak Babies," boy and girl. 5" tall. Brown rubber, molded on clothing, boy with white cap that says "Ace," girl with pink bonnet. Made in Taiwan. Photograph courtesy of Faith Wyse. $3.00.

Plate 705: HCN Enterprises, Inc. "Here Comes Niya." 22" tall. Talking doll that counts in English, Swahili, and Spanish and says positive, self-esteem building phrases. Battery required. Vinyl head, arms, and legs, black rooted hair, stationary dark brown eyes, open-closed mouth with molded teeth, white cloth body. All original in pink dress. Doll was available in several different pastel colored dresses. Marks: NIYA 1990., on head. $75.00.

Plate 706: Hamilton Toys. "Candy Girls Spring Fashions," 1990. All vinyl, brown painted eyes, brown rooted hair. All original. Marks: HAMILTON TOYS INC./1990, on head. Photograph courtesy of Stephanie Lisoski. $30.00.

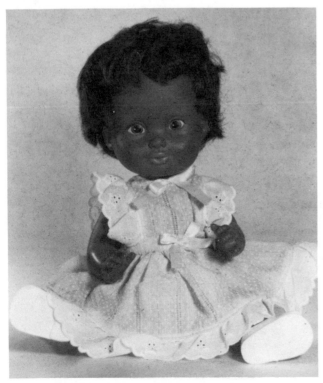

Left — Plate 707: Hasbro. 15". Jointed vinyl bent-leg baby doll. Painted eyes, rooted brown hair, nursing mouth. Redressed. Marks: 3957/18, on head; HASBRO IND INC./©1976/PAT. PEND., on body. $45.00.

Right — Plate 708: Hasbro. "Baby Peek-A-Boo." 14". Vinyl head, rooted short black curly hair, painted eyes, open-closed mouth with molded tongue, vinyl arms and legs, hard plastic body. Doll's arms move up and down when string in her back is pulled. All original in pink gingham sunsuit. Marks: ©HASBRO INC./1972, on head; HASBRO INDUSTRIES, INC./ PAWTUCKET, RHODE ISLAND 02861/MODEL NO. 4810, on body. $95.00.

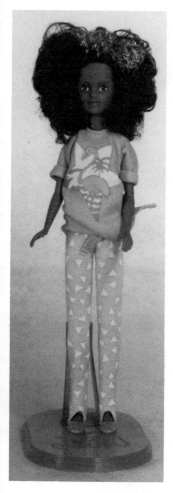

Plate 710: Hasbro. "Shana" from "Jem and the Halograms." 12½" tall. All vinyl, jointed waist, wrist, snap knees and elbows, brown painted eyes with heavy eye makeup, violet rooted hair. First issue is MIB 1985. The second issue is doll on stand. Besides the clothing being different, this doll has orange earrings. Clothes are all original. Marks are the same on both dolls: HASBRO INC., on head; 1985 HASBRO INC./CHINA, on back. Photograph courtesy of Stephanie Lisoski. $35.00.

Plate 709: Hasbro. "Krissie" of the "Starlight Girls" from the Jem collection. 11" tall. Fully posable vinyl doll, painted eyes, rooted brown hair, closed mouth, snapping knees, swivel waist. All original in orange sweatshirt with flamingo, yellow, and pink stirrup pants. Marks: ©1987 HASBRO INC./MADE IN HONG KONG/ALL RIGHTS RESERVED, on body. $35.00.

Plate 711: Hasbro. "Aimee." 18" tall. Vinyl head, black sleep eyes with lashes, rooted black hair, closed mouth, jointed vinyl body with swivel waist, pierced ears with goldtone drop earrings. Doll comes with extra hairpieces, a long fall and a braid, hairbrush, and an extra pair of earrings. All original in long print dress with gold braid trim. Marks: HASBRO IND./19©72, on head. Made for 1972 only. $250.00.

Plate 712: Hasbro. "Baby oh-no!" All vinyl jointed baby doll that comes with her own ice cream cone and drinking cup. When you dip the cone in ice water and feed her or give her a drink of cold water, a chocolate mess appears on face, hand and bib. 14" tall. Rooted dark brown curly hair, painted brown eyes, open-closed mouth. All original in print panties and bib. Marks: ©HASBRO 1989/MADE IN CHINA, on head. $35.00.

Plate 713: Hasbro. "Baby Wanna Walk" ©1990. She walks and crawls by herself. Batteries required. Vinyl head, painted eyes, rooted dark brown hair, closed mouth, vinyl arms, hard plastic body, and jointed legs, molded on white laceup shoes. 15½" tall. All original in pink and white striped romper suit with white dotted collar. Marks: HASBRO 1991, on head; ©1991 HASBRO/MADE IN CHINA, on body. $35.00.

Plate 714: Hasbro. "Debbie Dear," ©1990, from the "Tell Me Tots" series. Debbie says "mama" when the heart button on her chest is pushed. Except for straight hair in a different style and different clothing, doll is identical to the next "Tell Me Tots" doll. All original in short aqua print romper suit. $7.00.

Plate 715: Hasbro. "Cutie Cammie," ©1990, from the "Tell Me Tots" series of talking dolls. Doll says "kiss me" when you press the button on her chest and comes with three A-76 batteries. Vinyl head, rooted dark brown hair, painted brown eyes, open-closed mouth, jointed hard vinyl baby body. All original in pink and aqua print sunsuit. 5½" tall. Marks: HASBRO INC./MADE IN CHINA, on body. $7.00.

Plate 716: Hasbro. "Sleepy Susie," ©1990, from the "Tell Me Tots" series. This doll in the series says "nite-nite" and is identical to the previous "Tell Me Tots" except for hair style and clothing. All original in purple and white pajamas. $7.00.

Plate 718: Hasbro. "Starla." 15" tall. Electronic doll whose lips really move when she sings or talks. Batteries required. Doll comes with two microphones, one for the doll and a larger one for the child. Vinyl head, rooted brown hair with glitter streaks in the bangs, painted eyes, open-closed mouth, hard vinyl body and jointed limbs. All original in pink and black outfit. Marks: ©1990 HASBRO, on head; ©1992 HASBRO, INC/PAWTUCKET, R.I. 02861/ALL RIGHTS RESERVED/MADE IN CHINA, on body. $50.00.

Plate 717: Hasbro. "Darling Dena," ©1990, from the "Tell Me Tots" series. This doll says "love you" when the heart button on her chest is pushed. Except for clothing and hair style, doll is identical to previous dolls. All original in pink and lavender print dress. $9.00.

Plate 719: Hasbro. "Posable Cabbage Patch Kids," 1991. "Darcie Gisele." Vinyl head, long brown yarn hair pulled back on top with bangs, molded tongue licking corner of her mouth, cloth posable body. All original in purple gymnastics outfit with yellow tights and pink plastic slipper shoes. 15" tall. Marks: FIRST EDITION/©COPYRIGHT 1990/O.A.A. INC./MANUFACTURED BY HASBRO, INC./K25 8/MADE IN CHINA, on head. Pink signature on body. $45.00.

Plate 720: Hasbro. "Cabbage Patch Kids Kissin' Kids" girl, 1991. Vinyl head, decal eyes, rooted fancy brown yarn hair, puckered open mouth, pierced ears with gold heart earrings, dimpled chin, cloth body. 15" tall. All original in pink, orange print, and green romper outfit with pink plastic slipper shoes. Marks: ©COPYRIGHT 1991/O.A.A. INC./MANUFACTURED BY HASBRO INC., on head; green signature, on body. $35.00.

Plate 721: Hasbro. "Cabbage Patch Kids Kissin' Kids" boy, 1991. "William Bernard." Lips pucker up and doll makes a kissing sound when you squeeze the tummy. Vinyl head, painted eyes, rooted brown yarn hair, open-closed mouth, cloth body and limbs. All original green, orange, and black print shorts outfit with green and black shoes. 15" tall. Marks: ©COPYRIGHT 1991/O.A.A. INC./(2) MANUFAC-TURED BY HASBRO INC., on head. Another mark is probably under the "2" on the last line but vinyl head has a defect in that area. Body has a green signature. $35.00.

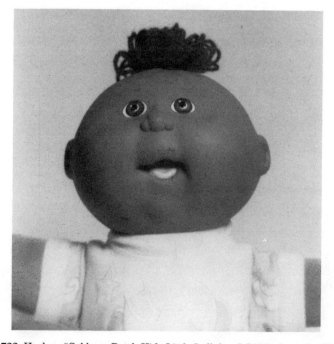

Plate 722: Hasbro. "Cabbage Patch Kids Little Lullabye," ©1991 from the "Baby-land Collection." Doll sings when it is hugged. Batteries required. Vinyl head, small tuft of rooted brown yarn hair on top of head, molded tongue, open mouth with molded tongue, cloth body. 12" tall. Machine washable. All original in sewn on blue print sleeper, blue plastic musical unit is inserted into zippered body. Marks: ©COPYRIGHT 1991/O.A.A., INC./MANUFACTURED BY HASBRO, INC., embossed on head; LL (2), incised on head. Tag sewn to body: CABBAGE PATCH KIDS/LITTLE/LULLABY, one side; Xavier Roberts, reverse side. $35.00.

Plate 723: Hasbro. "Cabbage Patch Kids My Own Baby" can cry, become quiet or make happy sounds using a special locket. Batteries required. Viny head, decal eyes, open pacifier mouth, rooted synthetic brown hair, brown cloth body. 14" tall. All original in lavender romper with purple pacifier attached with ribbon. Marks: FIRST EDITION/©1990/O.A.A., INC./MANUFACTURED BY HASBRO INC., embossed on head; B20, incised on head. Green signature on body. $85.00.

Plate 724: Hasbro. "Pretty Crimp 'n Curl" from the "Cabbage Patch Kids," 1991. Vinyl head, decal eyes, closed mouth, brown cloth body and limbs, rooted brown yarn hair. 13½" tall. All original in blue striped cotton blouse, pink cotton knit pants, and blue plastic lace-up shoes. Marks: FIRST/EDITION/©COPYRIGHT 1990/O.A.A. INC./MANUFACTURED BY HASBRO INC., embossed on head; T7 3(in a circle), incised on head. Green signature on body. $35.00.

Plate 725: Hasbro. "Cabbage Patch Kids Newborn with Magical Monitor." Magical monitor makes real sounds like a baby: cries, giggles, calls "ma ma." Batteries required. 13" tall. Vinyl bald head, decal eyes, open-closed mouth with molded tongue, dimples in both cheeks, brown cloth body and limbs. All original in diaper and shirt. Shirt is imprinted: NEWLY BORN AND BABYLAND GENERAL HOSPITAL. Marks: ©COPYRIGHT 1991/O.A.A., INC./MANUFAC-TURED BY HASBRO INC./P(8) , on head. Black signature. $35.00.

Plate 726: Hasbro. "My First Cabbage Patch" from the "Babyland Collection," #31841. 10". Doll has a chime inside the body. Vinyl head, cloth body and limbs with sewn-on clothing. Available in several different face styles with different colored outfits. $15.00.

Plate 727: Hasbro. "Cabbage Patch Kids Heart to Heart Baby," ©1992, a "Toys 'R' Us" exclusive edition. Doll has an electronically controlled heartbeat. 14" tall. Bald vinyl head, decal eyes, open-closed mouth with gold sleeves and car bib. Doll's name is "Stanford Les." Marks: ©1978 1983 O.A.A. INC./21, on head. $30.00.

Plate 728: Hasbro. "Cabbage Patch Kids Teeny Tiny Preemies," #30005. 11" tall. Vinyl head, painted hair, decal eyes, open-closed mouth, cloth body and limbs, baby powder scented. All original in print shirt, white diapers, blue cap. Birth certificate has name "Willis Heath." Marks: ©COPYRIGHT 1992/O.A.A. INC./MANU-FACTURED BY HASBRO, INC., on head; black signature, on body. Collection of Katherine Lois Clark. $20.00.

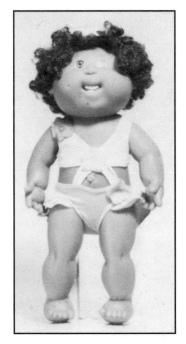

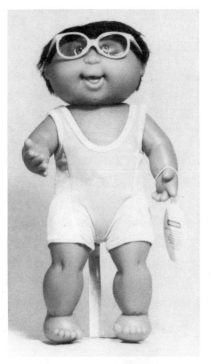

Plate 729: Hasbro. "Cabbage Patch Kids Splash 'n Tan Kids," girl. Vinyl head, decal eyes, open-closed mouth, nine teeth, rooted synthetic dark brown hair, jointed vinyl body. 14" tall. All original in one piece multicolored swimsuit. Marks: ©COPYRIGHT 1991/O.A.A., INC./MANUFACTURED BY HASBRO INC., embossed on head; BB (3), incised on head. Dark blue signature on lower body. $35.00.

Plate 730: Hasbro. "Splash 'n Tan Kids," boy. 14" tall. Vinyl head, decal eyes, rooted dark brown synthetic hair, open-closed mouth with molded tongue, jointed vinyl body. All original in yellow and orange swimsuit. Marks: MADE IN CHINA/©COPYRIGHT 1991/O.A.A., INC./MANUFACTURED BY HAS-BRO INC., embossed on head; ST (4), incised on head. Doll's name is Saul Walt. $35.00.

Plate 731: Hasbro. Cabbage Patch Kids "Peek 'n Play," #31850 from the "Babyland Collection." 12" tall. Vinyl face, painted eyes, open-closed mouth, cloth head, body, and limbs, sewn on clothing. Heart shaped rattle sewn into front of playsuit. Doll was also available with peek-a-boo mirror. 1992. Tagged body. $20.00.

Plate 733: Hasbro. "Cabbage Patch Kids Love 'n Care Baby," #31860 from the "Toddler Collection." Sewn on play features teach children to zip, snap, tie, button, and dress. 13" tall. Vinyl head, rooted tuft of brown yarn hair on top of head, painted features, open-closed mouth showing tongue, cloth body and limbs. All original in pastel print bunting with pink plastic bottle attached. Marks: © COPYRIGHT 1992/O.A.A. INC. MANUFACTURED BY HASBRO, INC./DM (2), on head. $93.00.

Plate 732: McDonald's Happy Meal toy "Jennifer Lauren 'Fun on Ice.'" 3½" tall. Vinyl doll movable at hips and neck, rooted tufts of black yarn hair, molded on green and red outfit, and white ice skates. One of a series of five dolls in 1992. Marks: ©1992. O.A.A./CHINA SV 23, on back. $5.00.

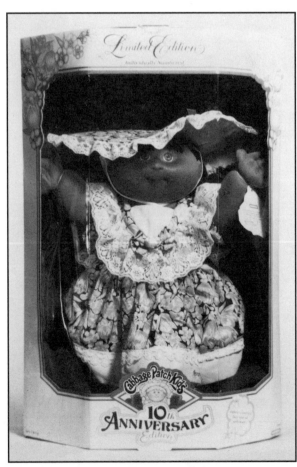

Plate 735: Hasbro. "Tom Stone" #607-404 from the "Action Team." 12". Doll is a regular "G.I. Joe" marketed by Hasbro for the European market as Tom Stone. All

Plate 734: Hasbro. "Cabbage Patch Kids 10th Anniversary." Limited edition, individually numbered. Cloth body with fabric face and nylon hair. 16" tall. Made in China. $75.00.

original. Box is marked: SCHILDKROT SPIELWAREN BMBH, MANNHEIM/© 1975 HASBRO INDUSTRIES INC. PAWTUCKET R.J. 02862 U.S.A. (Note, the "J" in the address was probably due to a translation error.) Most of the other writing on the box is in German. Photograph courtesy of Lu Lane. $300.00.

Plate 736: Hasbro. "GI Joe Stalker" from the "Hall of Fame" collection. Numbered collectors edition. This is number 0028552 (printed on doll's back). 12" tall. Vinyl head, arms and legs, plastic body, molded hair, painted features including mustache, closed mouth, fully posable. All original in battle dress uniform, black shirt, black and white camouflage pants, black hat trimmed in gold, gold back pack, black vinyl boots, dog tags with name imprinted. Set also includes electronic light and sound weapon and G.I. Joe combat manual and gear. Marks: ©1992 HASBRO INC/PAWTUCKET, RI 02862/ MADE IN CHINA, on back. $25.00.

Plate 737: Hasbro. "G.I. Joe Heavy Duty" #6114. ©1992. 12" tall. Fully posable vinyl doll from the "Hall of Fame" series. Molded painted hair, painted eyes, closed mouth, scar on right cheek. All original in authentic style U.S. Army Battle Dress Uniform, metal dog tags, "Fritz" styled helmet, automatic combat assault rifle, standard issue battle footwear. Marks: ©1992 HASBRO INC/PAWTUCKET, RI 02865/ MADE IN CHINA, on body. $18.00.

Plate 738: Hasbro. "G.I. Joe Heavy Duty." 3¾". Jointed action figure with molded on white vest, forest green pants with bright green camouflage marks, bright green cap turned backwards, black belt and boots. Marks: MADE IN CHINA/H-1, on back; ©199 (last numeral unclear)/HASBRO, on leg. Package is marked ©1990. $6.00.

Plate 739: Hasbro. "G.I. Joe Bullet-Proof," Drug Elimination Force (D.E.F.) leader. 3¾" tall. All vinyl with painted features, molded black hair in hi-top fade style, closed mouth, molded on green clothing with beige marks printed on, beige boots, gloves, belt, green helmet, and accessories. Included in package is green plastic electronic battle-flash missile launcher. Marks: ©1992/HASBRO, left leg; MADE IN CHINA, back. $7.00.

Plate 740: Hasbro. "Bullet Proof" from "Cops" TV show. 5¾". Fully articulated vinyl action figure, molded black hair, molded on black sunglasses, closed mouth, All original in molded on clothing in yellow, silver, and brown. doll came with a removable white trench coat. Marks: ©1988 HASBRO/MADE IN CHINA, on right leg. $15.00.

Plate 741: Hasbro. "Roadblock" from "GI Joe." 3¾" tall. Jointed vinyl action figure with molded on navy blue shirt, royal blue pants, brown boots, green holsters. Marks: ©1991/HASBRO, left leg. Collection of Todd Perkins. $4.00.

Plate 742: Hasbro. "Roadblock," "G.I. Joe" action figure. 3¾." Jointed vinyl with molded on chartreuse vest, gray pants. Marks: ©1986/HASBRO, left leg; MADE IN HONG KONG, on back. $5.00.

Plate 743: Hasbro. "G.I. Joe Roadblock" with a backpack. 3¾". Molded on forest green t-shirt, brown pants with gold camouflage marks, olive green backpack and holster, drab green boots and gloves. Bald head with mustache and goatee. Marks: MADE IN HONG KONG, lower back; ©1988 HASBRO, on leg. $5.00.

Plate 744: Hasbro. "G.I. Joe Roadblock." 1984. 3¾". Jointed action figure with molded on olive tank top with green camouflage, brown pants, black boots and belt, green gloves. Marks: MADE IN HONG KONG, lower back; ©HASBRO, left leg. $5.00.

Plate 745: Hasbro. "G.I. Joe." 3¾". Vinyl action figure with molded on olive vest under white jacket, olive pants with brown camouflage, brown boots, olive gloves, olive cap with brown spots. Marks: MADE IN CHINA/H-1, on lower back; ©1989/HASBRO, left leg. $5.00.

Plate 746: Hasbro. "G.I. Joe Alpine." 3¾". Jointed vinyl action figure in molded white shirt under olive and black jacket, brown pants, olive boots, black and olive cap, black eyeglasses. Marks: MADE IN HONG KONG, on lower back; ©1985/HASBRO, on leg. $5.00.

Plate 747: Hasbro. "G.I. Joe." 3¾". Jointed vinyl action figure with molded on shirt, pants, blue above the knee and olive below the knee, white breast shield over shirt, white gloves, boots, and helmet. Marks: ©1989 HASBRO/MADE IN CHINA/H-1, on lower back. $5.00.

Plate 748: Hasbro. "G.I. Joe." 3¾". Molded on tan outfit with orange red cross on sleeve and left chest, orange belt, olive sunglasses, brown shoes. Marks: MADE IN HONG KONG, on lower back; ©1983/HASBRO, on leg. $5.00.

Plate 749: Hasbro. "G.I. Joe Stretcher." 3¾". Jointed vinyl action figure with molded on light gray shirt with bright blue shirt showing around the neckline, dark gray pants, gray boots and cap. Stretcher is a medical specialist and comes with accessories. Marks: MADE IN CHINA/H-1, on back; ©1990/HASBRO, on leg. $8.00.

Plate 750: Hasbro. "G.I. Joe Hardball." 3¾". Molded on baseball outfit: white shirt imprinted with "G.I. Joe," blue baseball cap, brown pants, olive belt and leg holster, black boots. Marks: MADE IN HONG KONG, lower back; ©1988/HASBRO, left leg. $12.00.

Plate 751: Hasbro. "Stalker" from "Battle Talking Commanders" collection. 3¾". Jointed vinyl action figure with "talking" backpack that says: "Let's Party," "Attack," "Blitz 'Em" and makes a combat sound. Batteries required. Molded on black shirt and beret with gold accessories and beige pants with black camouflage marks, black boots. Yellow attached backpack. $12.00.

Plate 752: Hasbro. "G.I. Joe Colonel Courage." 3¾". Molded on mustache and full beard. Molded on white shirt, drab green pants, brown boots, mint green belt and holster below the belt, black holster and assorted arms strapped on chest Marks: MADE IN/CHINA/H-1, on back; ©1992/HASBRO, on leg. $5.00.

Left — Plate 753: Hasbro. "G.I. Joe." 3¾". Jointed vinyl action figure with molded on white outfit, mint green vest, white boots, black gloves, white arctic looking cap with olive sun glasses. Marks: MADE IN HONG KONG, lower back; ©1986/HASBRO, left leg. $5.00.

Right — Plate 754: Hasbro. "Koko B. Ware" of the "World Wrestling Federation." 4½". Vinyl action figure with bird man bounce. Molded on white sunglasses and headband, yellow pants, blue boots with yellow soles, pink wristbands. Comes with blue and yellow plastic bird. Marks: ©1991 TITAN SPORTS INC./ALL RIGHTS RESERVED/MADE IN CHINA/FOR HASBRO, INC. C-012, on body. $8.00.

Plate 755: Hasbro. "Spring Song" from "Perfume Secret Beauties" series. 5" tall. Doll sprays "real" perfume when you squeeze her wings. Vinyl head, rooted pink hair with white flower attached to her head, painted eyes, closed mouth, jointed vinyl body, white painted on bodysuit with pink stone at neckline, purple plastic wings attached to back, removable yellow skirt. Marks: HASBRO 1992, on head. $10.00.

Plate 756: Hasbro. "Lusciously Lilac" from the "Perfume Secret Beauties." 5" tall. Vinyl head, rooted lilac hair with red flower in the crown, painted eyes, painted open mouth with teeth, jointed body with molded on fuchsia bodysuit, "topaz" stone in chest, removable orange skirt, plastic fuchsia wings attached to back. Marks: ©HASBRO 1992, on head. $10.00.

Left — Plate 757: "Violet Bouquet" from the "Lipstick Secret Beauties" series. 6" tall. Tiara hides "real" lipstick. Vinyl head, rooted violet hair with plastic silver colored tiara, painted eyes, closed mouth, vinyl body movable only at waist, molded on pink bodysuit, painted violet legs, painted on white ballet shoes, removable pink petal skirt. Doll comes with a pink plastic stand. Marks: HASBRO 1992, on head. $10.00.

Right — Plate 758: Hasbro. "Ruby Red" from the "Lipstick Secret Beauties" series. 6". Vinyl head, pink rooted hair with gold-tone tiara and lipstick holder, painted eyes, painted smiling mouth with teeth, vinyl body movable only at the waist, molded on yellow body suit, lilac painted legs for tights, painted on pink shoes, removable yellow flower petal skirt. Marks: ©HASBRO 1992, on head. $10.00.

Left — Plate 759: Hasbro. "Chocolate Delight" from "Lip Gloss Secret Beauties" series. 6½" tall, including hat. Jointed vinyl with attached orange and white hat that holds lip gloss, rooted lavender hair, painted eyes, open mouth, molded on coral bodysuit with ruby colored "gem" in chest, removable net skirt, pink plastic wings attached to doll's back. When you squeeze wings, she blows a scented kiss. Comb serves as a doll stand. Marks: HASBRO 1992, on head. $10.00.

Right — Plate 760: Hasbro. "Purple Blossom" from "Nail Polish Secret Beauties." 5". Vinyl head, rooted pink hair, painted eyes, closed mouth, one piece vinyl body with molded on long lilac gown, red heart-shaped "gem" in bodice. Removable silver and pink net skirt. Bottle of nail polish is held in plastic base. Marks: ©HASBRO 1992, on head. $10.00.

Plate 763: Hasbro. "Hyacinthia," jewelry doll from the "Charmkins" jewelry playmates collection. 1¼" tall. One piece molded vinyl charm doll. Marks: © 1983/1/HASBRO, on feet. $6.00.

Plate 761: Hasbro. "Rosedust" from the "Nail Polish Secret Beauties." 6" tall, including the base. Vinyl head, rooted purple hair with aqua streaks, painted eyes, painted smiling mouth with teeth, one piece vinyl body in molded on pink gown with purple "gem" in bodice, removable white and pink net skirt. Nail polish is stored in base of doll. Marks: ©HASBRO 1992, on head. $10.00.

Plate 762: Hasbro. "Strawberry Shine" from "Lip Gloss Secret Beauties." 6½" to the top of her hat. Vinyl head, painted eyes, open mouth, rooted lilac hair with blue and pink plastic hat attached, jointed vinyl body with molded pink bodysuit, blue "jewel" on doll's chest, removable pink dotted net skirt, blue plastic wings attached to body. When wings are squeezed, doll blows a scented kiss. Hat on doll's head holds the scented lip gloss. $10.00.

Plate 764: Horsman. "My Gal." Approximately 21". Vinyl head, rooted dark brown hair, painted eyes, closed mouth, dimpled chin, vinyl hands, brown cloth body, printed sneakers form feet. All original in blue, red, and yellow outfit. Marks: HORSMAN DOLLS INC./1973 (1973 is stamped twice). Collection of Shirley Jackson. $75.00.

Plate 765: Horsman. "Thirstee Walker," 1988, walks, drinks, and wets. Vinyl head, brown sleep eyes, rooted dark brown hair in two ponytails and bangs, jointed hard vinyl body. All original in white sweat shirt trimmed in red and striped pants. 26" tall. Marks: 6–1/HORSMAN DOLLS INC./19©64/TB26, on head; MADE IN CHINA, on body. $31.00.

Plate 766: Horsman. Drink and wet baby doll. Vinyl head, rooted short brown hair, sleeping amber eyes, nursing mouth, one piece vinyl body. 15" tall. Redressed. Marks: 3/HORSMAN DOLLS INC./ 19©71, on head; 20/ HORSMAN DOLLS INC, on body. $40.00.

Plate 767: Horsman. "Baby Sofskin Tears." 16". Drinks from a baby bottle and cries real tears. Vinyl head, rooted brown hair, sleeping brown eyes with lashes, nursing mouth, one piece vinyl body with urethane foam filling. All original in two piece white knit outfit trimmed with pink and blue, with booties. Marks: 10-81/HORSMAN DOLLS INC./ 19©71, on head. Collection of the Museum of African American History (Detroit). $70.00.

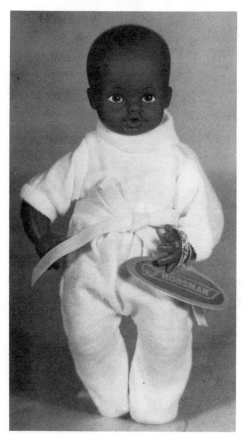

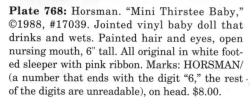

Plate 768: Horsman. "Mini Thirstee Baby," ©1988, #17039. Jointed vinyl baby doll that drinks and wets. Painted hair and eyes, open nursing mouth, 6" tall. All original in white footed sleeper with pink ribbon. Marks: HORSMAN/ (a number that ends with the digit "6," the rest of the digits are unreadable), on head. $8.00.

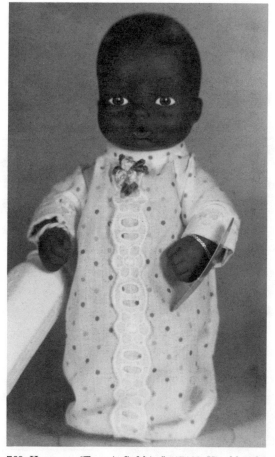

Plate 769: Horsman. "Teensie Sofskin," #17129. Vinyl head, painted features, nursing mouth, wets and drinks, jointed vinyl baby body. 7" tall. All original in white dotted cotton baby bunting. Marks: ©HORSMAN DOLLS INC./197? (the last numeral is not clear), on head; MADE IN/CHINA, on body. Box is marked ©1988. $10.00.

Plate 770: Horsman. "Dr. Denton," ©1989. Vinyl head, large painted eyes, rooted brown hair, closed mouth, vinyl arms and legs, brown cloth body. All original in pink printed Dr. Denton long johns. 15½" tall. Marks: HORSMAN (inside logo)/KK — 16 1988, on head. Long johns are marked Dr. Denton on the left foot. $30.00.

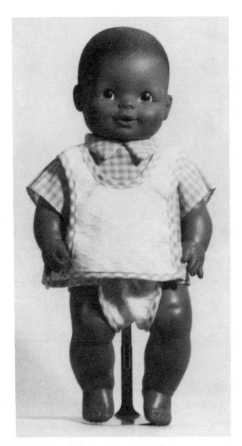

Plate 771: Horsman. 1975. 14". Anatomically correct baby boy. Vinyl head, painted eyes, nursing mouth, sculptured hair, one piece vinyl body. All original in blue and white checked two piece outfit. Marks: HORSMAN DOLLS INC./ 19©75, on head; HORSMAN DOLLS/©1976, on body. Collection of the Museum of African American History (Detroit). $75.00.

Plate 772: Horsman. 1975. Anatomically correct baby girl. The doll does not have a name but comes with a birth certificate on the bottom of the box so you can name your own baby girl. This identical doll was later issued a "Li'l Ruthie." The following message is printed on the box: This doll has true-to-life features which differentiate little girls from little boys. For those who feel they do not want their children to be aware of this difference, we do not recommend this doll. Vinyl head, painted eyes, nursing mouth, dimpled cheeks, painted hair, one piece vinyl body. 14" tall. All original in pink gingham outfit. Marks: 7/HORSMAN DOLLS INC./ 19©75, on head; HORSMAN DOLLS INC./1976, on body. Collection of the Museum of African American History (Detroit). $75.00.

Plate 774: Horsman. 12". Baby doll. Vinyl head, molded hair, painted side glancing eyes, nursing mouth, jointed vinyl bent-leg baby body. Redressed. Marks: HORSMAN (remainder of line unclear)/©19 (remainder of line unclear), on head; HORSMAN DOLLS INC./PAT PEND, on body. Similar doll is shown in author's earlier book, *Black Dolls, 1820-1991,* plate 615, page 161. In this doll, eyes are not side glancing and eyelashes are painted differently. $45.00.

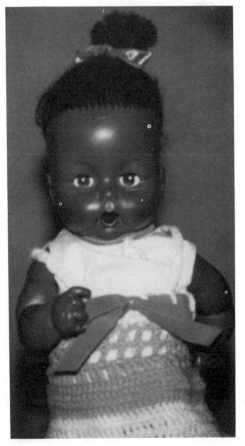

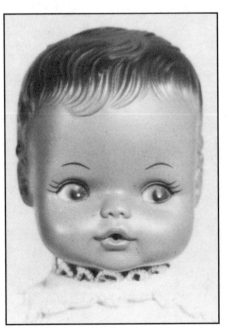

Plate 773: Horsman. Approximately 18". Jointed vinyl head and body, rooted brown hair, sleeping amber eyes with lashes, wide-open nursing mouth. Redressed. Marks: 3437/15 EYE/HORSMAN DOLLS INC., on head; HORSMAN DOLLS INC., on body. Collection of Tanya Mitchell Charles. $45.00.

Plate 775: Horsman. Walt Disney's official "Mouseketeer" girl. Vinyl head, rooted dark brown hair, painted eyes, open-closed mouth, jointed vinyl toddler body. All original in one piece dress with white bodice and blue skirt, red mouseketeer hat. 8½" tall. Marks: 6/HORSMAN DOLLS INC./19©69, on head. $70.00.

Plate 776: Horsman. "Mouseketeer" boy. Except for hairstyle and clothing, this doll is identical to previous Mouseketeer girl. All original in white shirt and blue pants. Mouseketeer decal is missing from his hat. $70.00.

Plate 777: Horsman. Walt Disney's official "Mouseketeer," girl. 8" tall. 1972. Vinyl head, rooted brown hair, sleeping brown eyes with lashes, closed mouth, jointed toddler body. All original in dress with blue skirt and white bodice with Mickey Mouse emblem, black plastic hat with mouse ears. Marks: 11 70/HORSMAN DOLLS INC./ 19©71, on head; 14, on body. Collection of the Museum of African American History (Detroit). $70.00.

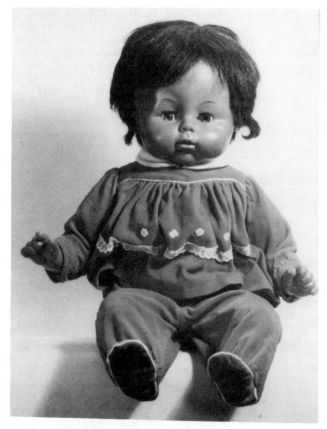

Plate 778: Horsman. 21" tall. Baby doll with vinyl head, arms, and legs, sleeping brown eyes with lashes, rooted brown hair, open-closed mouth, brown cloth body. It is not known whether clothing is original. Marks: © HORSMAN DOLL INC./256/13, on head. Collection of the Museum of African American History (Detroit). $85.00.

Plate 779: Horsman. "Especially Yours," manufactured exclusively for Toys 'R' Us, Inc. Box is marked: ©1989 GEOFFREY, INC. Vinyl head, sleeping brown eyes, rooted dark brown hair, slightly open-closed mouth, vinyl hands, brown cloth body and legs with sewn on white cloth feet. 14" tall. All original in white and pink print blouse and blue print pants. Marks: HORSMAN DOLLS, INC./19©76, on head. $18.00.

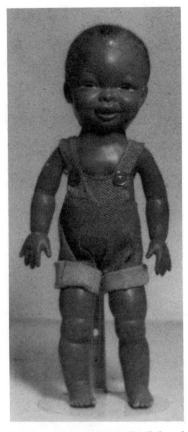

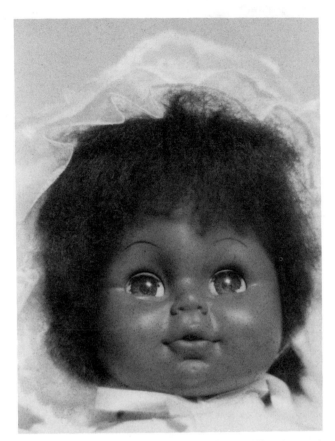

Plate 780: Horsman. "Pete." 1950's. Stuffed early vinyl head, painted eyes, open-closed smiling mouth with four painted upper teeth, movable head, molded wavy hair, one piece stuffed vinyl body. 13" tall. He was marketed along with a girl doll "Polly." Redressed. Marks: 14-VS/103, on back. $200.00.

Plate 781: Horsman. "Sleepy" vinyl head baby doll with rooted dark brown hair, sleeping amber eyes, slightly open-closed mouth, brown cloth body, vinyl arms and legs. 22" tall. Redressed in white baby dress and bonnet. Marks: HORSMAN DOLLS INC./19©74, on head. $75.00.

Plate 782: Horsman. "Baby Sofskin" #14639. ©1988. 16" tall. Vinyl head, rooted dark brown hair, brown sleep eyes with lashes, nursing mouth, movable head, one piece soft vinyl stuffed body. All original in white cotton dress trimmed with white lace, matching bonnet and white booties. Marks: 5-82/HORSMAN DOLLS INC./19©71, on head. Made in China. $30.00.

Plate 783: Horsman. "Lively Sofskin" #14556. 13" tall. Vinyl head, rooted brown hair, sleeping brown eyes with lashes, nursing mouth, one piece vinyl body. All original in blue and white dotted dress, white booties. Marks: HORSMAN DOLLS INC./19©72, on head; 1-1 HORSMAN DOLLS INC., on body. Box is marked ©1990 HORSMAN — DIVISION OF GATA BOX LTD. $20.00.

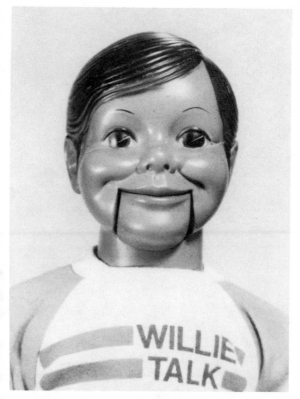

Plate 785: Horsman. 11" tall. Vinyl head, rooted brown hair, painted eyes, closed mouth, jointed vinyl toddler body. Redressed in Effanbee Bobbsey Twins' clothing. Marks: 8/HORSMAN DOLLS INC./19©69, on head. $35.00.

Plate 784: Horsman. "Willie Talk." 23". Ventriloquist doll. Vinyl head and hands, brown cloth body, arms and legs, molded painted black hair, painted eyes. Pull string in back of neck controls movement of mouth. All original in shirt imprinted "Willie Talk," blue and white striped pants. Marks: HORSMAN DOLLS INC./10, on head. $75.00.

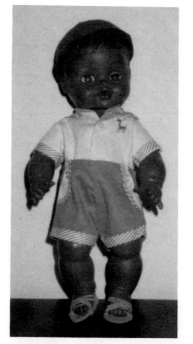

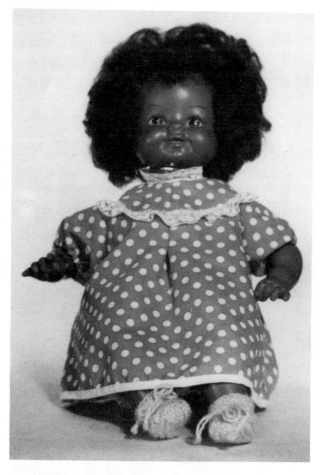

Plate 787: Horsman. "Baby Laugh and Cry." 16". Laughs when you hold her and cries when you put her down. Vinyl head, rooted dark brown hair, painted eyes, open-closed mouth, vinyl arms and legs, brown cloth body with zipper compartment. Redressed. Original clothes were 2-piece pink pajamas. Marks: HORSMAN DOLLS INC./19©60, on head. $85.00.

Plate 786: Horsman. 13". Vinyl head and jointed body, molded hair. sleeping eyes. Redressed. Marks: HORSMAN, on head; 513, on back. Collection of and photograph courtesy of Mary June Hill. $60.00.

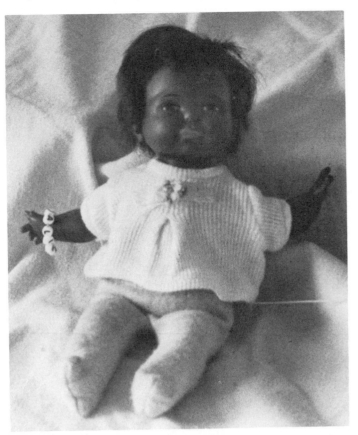

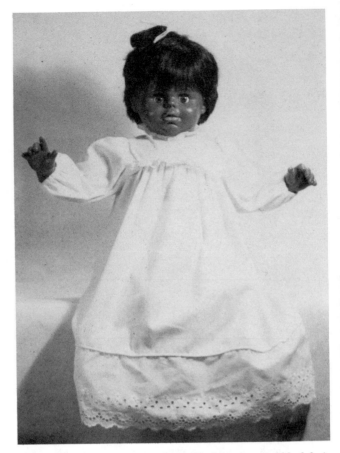

Plate 788: Ideal. "Newborn Thumbelina," 12" tall. Vinyl doll, short straight black hair, brown painted eyes. Baby bracelet with Thumbelina spelled out in beads. All original. 1968. Marks: ©1967 IDEAL (in oval)/7T-9-J108/JAPAN. Collection of and photograph courtesy of Jerel Black. $95.00.

Plate 789: Ideal. "Thumbelina." 25". Vinyl head, rooted black hair over molded hair, sleeping brown eyes with lashes, open-closed mouth, vinyl arms and legs, brown cloth body with "ma-ma" voice inside. All original in white gown trimmed in pink, pink hairbow. Marks: ©1982/IDEAL TOY CORP. H386, on head. Collection of the Museum of African American History (Detroit). $125.00.

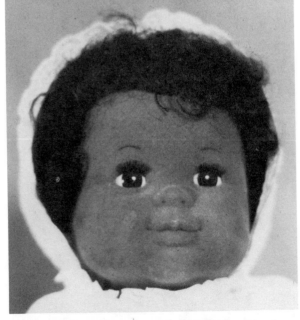

Plate 791: Ideal. "Diana Ross of the Supremes." All original. Soft vinyl head and arms, black sleep eyes with lashes, painted smiling lips, black rooted synthetic hair. Jointed hard plastic body

Plate 790: Ideal. "Baby Dreams," 1975. Soft vinyl head covered with special soft velvet; large black eyes with eyelids that close when she is put on her side; full head of black rooted hair; stuffed cloth body with floppy arms and legs. Arms are velvet like the head, vinyl legs. 17" tall. Marks: BABY DREAMS/©1975, IDEAL< HOLLIS, NEW YORK, 11423/HEAD MADE IN U.S.A./DOLL BODY MADE IN HONG KONG, tag sewn to body. $60.00.

and legs. 18" tall. Marks: ©1969/IDEAL TOY CORPDR-18-H148, head; ©1969/IDEAL TOY CORP/GH-18/U.S. Pat. #3,162, 976, body. Box is marked jointly: ©1969 IDEAL TOY CORP and ©1969 MOTOWN INC. $200.00.

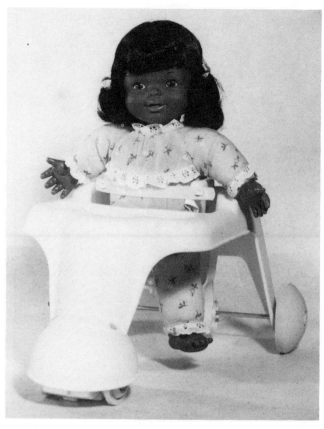

Plate 792: Ideal. "Happy Returns," #12773. 14". 1983–1984. Vinyl head, rooted black hair, painted eyes, open-closed mouth, vinyl hands and feet, cloth body, arms, and legs. Sewn on pink print clothing forms body. Doll laughs and moves with her yellow plastic "action" walker. Batteries required. Marks: IDEAL/©1982 CBS INC./H392, on head. Doll head was made in Santiago, Dominican Republic. $45.00.

Plate 793: Ideal. "Tippy Tumbles." She sits up, stands on her head, does a front and back flip, does a handstand, pulls herself up, and many more tricks. Batteries required. Vinyl head, painted eyes, rooted black hair, open-closed mouth, hard plastic body and limbs. 16" tall. All original in red jumpsuit trimmed in blue print and white eyelet ruffle. Marks: ©1976/IDEAL TOY CORP, T-16 G-H - 276, on head; U.S. PAT. NO. 3500577/IDEAL TOY CORP/HOLLIS NY 11423/©1977, on body. $55.00.

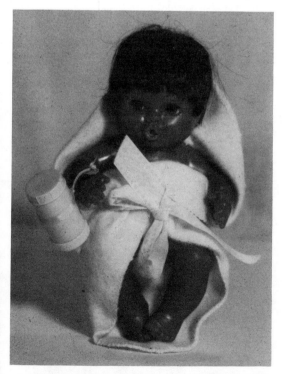

Plate 795: Ideal. "Pattie Playful." 15". She can move her head to yawn, clap her hands, wave, suck her thumb or pacifier, or open and close her mouth by moving a pink plastic control in her back. Vinyl head, original rooted brown hair has been covered with a wig, sleeping eyes, open mouth with two teeth, vinyl arms and legs, cloth body with sewn on pink outfit, removable white smock with name imprinted. This particular doll no longer works, part of the mechanism in back is missing. Marks: ©1970/LL-16-H-162, on head. $35.00.

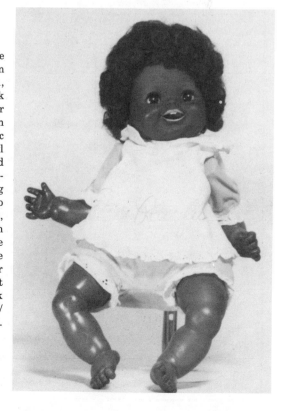

Plate 794: Ideal. "Baby, Baby," 1976. When you give her a bottle and press gently, dimples appear in her cheeks; she closes her eyes when you turn the bottle to the left. Vinyl head, rooted black hair, brown eyes with one piece lashes, nursing mouth, one piece vinyl body. 6½" tall. All original in diapers and pink flannel blanket tied with a ribbon, blue and pink baby bottle. Marks: IDEAL (in logo) 1974/8-6-8-52/HONG KONG/17, on back. $35.00.

MODELS for the doll were children of Belle Glade, Fla. of all ages up to 8, whom Miss Creech photographed full face, in profile and from the back. Miss Creech also took detailed head measurements of each of the children and sent a composite of these along with the photographs of them to the sculptress, Mrs. Burlingame.

Doll for Negro Children

NEW TOY WHICH IS ANTHROPOLOGICALLY CORRECT FILLS AN OLD NEED

At an early age U.S. Negro children have had their many disadvantages illustrated for them by one fact: there has never been a doll they could call their own. They have always had to play with unsatisfactory "pickaninny" dolls or white dolls painted brown. But recently Sara Lee Creech of Belle Glade, Fla., reflecting on that fact, decided to have a doll made that would be anthropologically correct and something a Negro child could be proud of. The result is the first truly Negro doll ever made (below).

To make sure that the doll would be just right, Miss Creech photographed and carefully measured scores of Negro children in her home town and got Sculptress Sheila Burlingame interested in the project. Mrs. Burlingame, who has done many statues of Negroes, used Miss Creech's material for reference in creating four head models (next page) which are a fair sample of anthropological characteristics of U.S. Negroes. The Ideal Toy Corporation agreed to manufacture them. Then a jury, including Dr. Ralph Bunche, Walter White and Eleanor Roosevelt, met to determine the exact shade of the doll's skin.

The baby doll model, introduced last month as the "Saralee Negro Doll," is made of Vinylite plastic, has eyes which move, and sells for $6.95. Stores reported it was selling unusually well and noted that the doll is so cute that it is enjoying a brisk trade not only among Negro children but among white children as well.

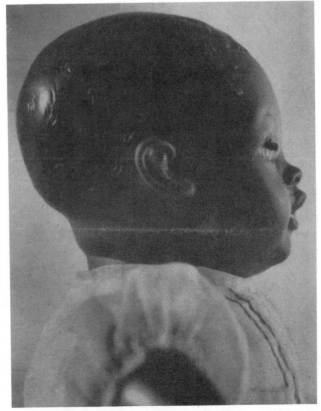

PROFILE shows large upper lip, a characteristic Negroid feature. The doll also has a fold at the back of the neck, true of all babies but usually left out in dolls.

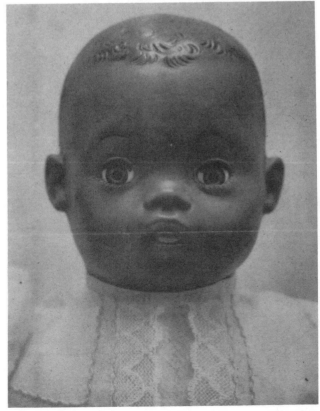

FULL FACE shows broad nose, eyes wide apart. Unlike even best white dolls, this one is so true that two sides of face, as in human beings, are not quite alike.

CREATOR, Miss Creech, sells insurance, works in interracial group.

SCULPTRESS Sheila Burlingame holds one of finished head models.

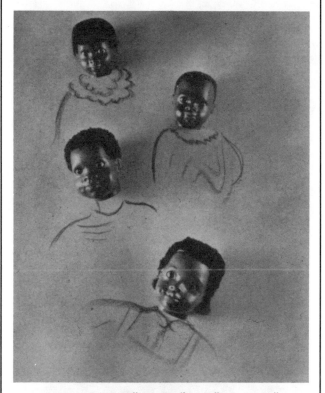

FULL FAMILY will include "Little Miss" (*top*), "Little Brother" (*center, left*), "Little Sister" (*bottom*). To date only the baby (*center, right*) is on sale.

IN USE baby doll delights 5-year-old Judy Lyons, who immediately began feeding it Pablum and cuddling it, then named it Diane after a white playmate.

Page 208 and Left — Plate 796: Reprint of an article on the "Saralee Negro Doll" by Ideal Toy Corporation. Article appeared in *Life* magazine, 1951.

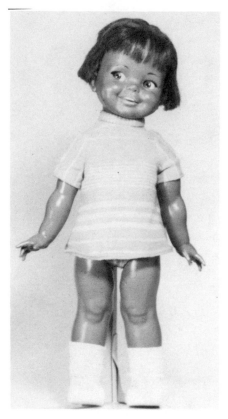

Plate 797: Ideal. "Giggles." 18" tall. Vinyl head, rooted brown hair, brown "flirty" eyes, open-closed mouth with molded teeth, hard plastic body and limbs. When arms are raised, doll giggles and moves her head from side to side. No batteries required. All original in hot pink and yellow striped cotton knit dress with matching panties, white shoes and socks, Marks: ©1966/IDEAL TOY CORP./GG-18-H-77, on head; ©1967/IDEAL TOY CORP./GG-18, on body. $350.00.

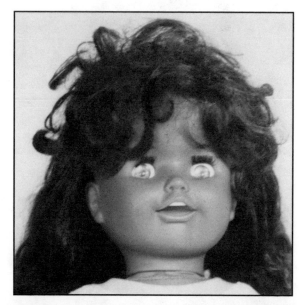

Plate 798: Ideal, Inc. "Patty Play Pal." 27" tall. Animated talking doll. Vinyl head, brown eyes with upper lashes, open-closed mouth with upper teeth, vinyl arms and legs, brown cloth body, rooted long dark brown hair. Doll comes with specially programmed "Synchromation" cassette that makes Patty move her eyes, cheeks, and mouth while she sings songs and tell exciting stories. Extra cassettes were sold separately as well as extra outfits. Pink plastic remote cassette recorder also comes with the doll. Marks: ©1987 IDEAL INC, on head. $375.00.

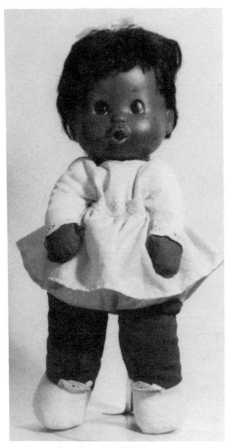

Plate 799: Ideal. "My Bottle Baby." 1978. 14" tall. Vinyl head, rooted black hair, painted eyes, open-closed mouth with a piece of pink plastic that can be pushed backwards about ¼ of an inch when bottle is placed in her mouth, brown cloth body and limbs. Sewn on clothing, a print top, pink dotted skirt and shoes. Pull string in back lets doll move her head up and down while making a "clicking or sucking" sound. Doll comes with a white plastic baby bottle. Marks: ©1978/IDEAL TOY CORP./H-320, on head. Collection of the Museum of African American History (Detroit). $85.00.

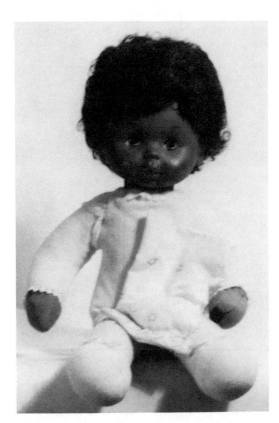

Plate 800: Ideal. "Snuggles." 1978. 14" tall. Vinyl head, rooted black hair, painted eyes, open-closed mouth, cloth body with sewn on pink outfit, Velcro® sewn to top of left hand. Pull string in back lets doll move her head in a circular motion. Doll is holding a pillow imprinted "Baby." Marks: ©1977/IDEAL TOY CORP./H-287 1, on head. Collection of the Museum of African American History (Detroit). $65.00.

Plate 801: Ideal. "Karen and her Magic Carriage." Doll is 14" tall. Carriage is 26" x 22" x 9½". Doll is attached to carriage with white plastic tubing. Vinyl head, painted eyes, rooted black hair, open-closed mouth, cloth body and limbs with sewn on clothing. Marks on doll: ©1979/IDEAL TOY CORP./H-333, on head. Carriage is white and blue plastic with pink checked lining and comes with a pink blanket. Collection of the Museum of African American History (Detroit). $125.00.

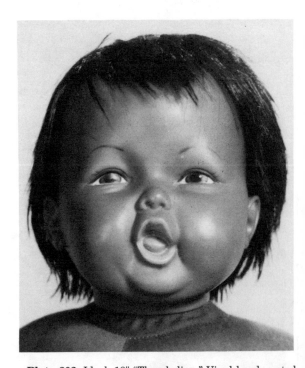

Plate 802: Ideal. 18" "Thumbelina." Vinyl head, rooted black hair, painted eyes, open-closed mouth with molded tongue, vinyl arms and legs, brown cloth body with cry box. Marks: IDEAL TOY CORP./YTT-19-L-3, on head. Body is tagged ©1984. Made in Haiti. $75.00.

Plate 804: Ideal. "Betsy Wetsy #1123. #11½" tall. Baby doll drinks from a bottle and when squeezed, will cry out loud, shed tears, and wet the diaper. Vinyl head and jointed vinyl body, rooted short curly black hair, black sleep eyes with upper lashes, nursing mouth, hold for wetting on right side of body. All original in pink print sundress with yellow felt giraffe and green grass on front, green bloomers. Doll is shown in Ideal's 1971 catalog. Marks: ©1967/IDEAL TOY CORP./BW-12-H88/ HONG KONG, on head; © IDEAL TOY CORP./1964/BW/12 HONG KONG, on back $75.00.

Plate 803: Ideal. "Movin' Groovin' Crissy." 18" tall. All vinyl. Black sleep eyes, rooted black "grow" hair, swivel waist. All original in orange jersey midi dress, orange boots, purple and orange tie belt. Marks: IDEAL TOY CORP; GH-17-121, on head; 1972 IDEAL TOY CORP/MG-18-2M-5318-02, on body. Collection of and photograph courtesy of Maureen Braeden. $125.00.

Plate 805: Ideal. "Hair Doodler Cinnamon." 13½" tall. All original in two piece dotted shorts outfit. Vinyl head, jointed vinyl body, rooted "growing" black hair, painted eyes, open-closed mouth with two teeth. Marks: © 1971/IDEAL TOY CORP./GH-12-J-138/ HONG KONG P, on head; ©1972/IDEAL TOY CORP./HONG KONG P, on body. Collection of and photograph courtesy of Jerel Black. $135.00.

Far Right — Plate 806: Ideal. "Look Around Velvet." 15" tall, vinyl head and jointed body, rooted "growing" black hair, black sleep eyes, closed mouth. All original in plaid dress. Marks: 1969/IDEAL TOY CORP./GM-15-H-157, on head; 1972 IDEAL TOY CORP./HONG KONG P/U.S. PATENT NO. 3 162 976/OTHER PAT. PEND., on back. Collection of and photograph courtesy of Frank Sposato. $125.00.

Left — Plate 807: Ideal. "Betsy Wetsy." 1956. 13" tall. All vinyl, brown sleep eyes, copper, rooted hair. Open nurser mouth. Re-dressed. Marks: IDEAL DOLL/VW-2, on head. Photograph courtesy of Stephanie Lisoski. $95.00.

Right — Plate 808: Ideal Toy Corp. "Bubble Gum" from the "Jelly Belly" collection. 12". Vinyl head, rooted tuft of bangs for hair, painted eyes, dimpled cheeks, closed mouth. Pink terrycloth and cotton print sleeper with hood forms the body. Marks on head (hood must be pulled back to read): ©1977/IDEAL TOY CORP. H-288 2. Tag sewn to body has been cut off. Doll is bubble gum scented. $35.00.

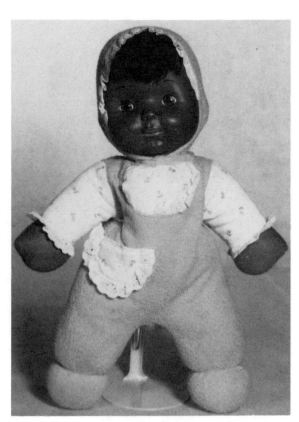

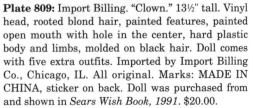

Plate 809: Import Billing. "Clown." 13½" tall. Vinyl head, rooted blond hair, painted features, painted open mouth with hole in the center, hard plastic body and limbs, molded on black hair. Doll comes with five extra outfits. Imported by Import Billing Co., Chicago, IL. All original. Marks: MADE IN CHINA, sticker on back. Doll was purchased from and shown in *Sears Wish Book, 1991*. $20.00.

Plate 810: In Time Products. "General Colin Powell." 6½". Limited edition vinyl figure from "America's Heroes" series. Item #91-1993. General Powell served as Chairman of the Joint Chiefs of Staff during Bush and Clinton administration. Unmarked. $15.00.

Plate 811: In Time Products Co. "Rapid Deployment Force." 12". Bald vinyl head, jointed vinyl body, painted features. All original in olive tank-top and camouflage shorts, black shoes, metal dog tags around neck. Marks: IN TIME PRODUCTS/MADE IN CHINA, on body. $10.00.

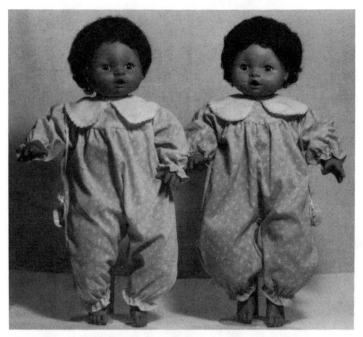

Plate 813: Irwin. "Rosie Hip" from the "Tea Pot Tots" collection. 7" tall. Vinyl head, painted brown eyes, rooted black hair, closed mouth, jointed vinyl body with right hand molded to hold a tea cup. White plastic tea cup is included with doll. All original in red print blouse, yellow skirt trimmed in green, red plastic shoes. Marks: CHINA, on head; TEA POT TOT ©1987 M.G.C.E./IRVIN TOY LTD. R.U./MADE IN CHINA, on body. Doll is made under license from Mel Goldberg Creative Enterprises Inc. $15.00.

Plate 812: Irwin. "The Twins," ©1990, #50030. The twins giggle when they are together and cry when they are apart. They will cry when one has a pacifier and the other does not. When they both have a pacifier, they are quiet and content. Vinyl head, sleeping amber eyes, rooted dark brown hair, open mouth for pacifier, vinyl arms and legs, brown cloth body. One 9V Alkaline battery required for each doll. One doll is all original in blue print cotton romper and pacifier, the other in pink with a pink pacifier. 18" tall. Marks: IRWIN TOY LTD ©1990, on head. $125.00.

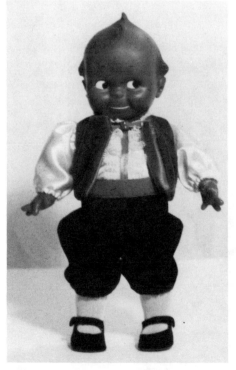

Plate 814: Jesco. "Black/White Klown" from the "Kewpie Aktivities" collection, 1991, #02135B. Vinyl jointed doll with painted features. All original in clown outfit. 12" tall. Marks: JLK/21/Cameo, on head; JESCO/©CAMEO, on body. $35.00.

Plate 815: Jesco. "Karoler Boy" from the "Kewpie Karolers" collection, 1991, #02161. 12" tall. All original in green velvet knickers, red velvet vest, white satiny shirt, white stockings and black shoes. Marks: JLK/4/CAMEO©, on head; JESCO/©CAMEO/16, on back. $35.00.

Plate 816: Jesco. "Flapper" from "Kewpie Thru the Ages" collection, 1991, #01969B. Vinyl jointed doll with painted features. 12" tall. All original in red flapper costume, white tights, black strap shoes. Marks: JLK/13/CAMEO ©, on head; JESCO/© CAMEO/9, on body. $35.00.

Plate 817: Jesco. "Pastel Klown" #B886 and "Primary Klown" #B887 from the "Kewpie Kouples" collection. 8" tall. Jointed vinyl with painted features, molded hair. All original. Marks: JESCO ©1985/T.M./MADE IN CHINA, on back. $20.00.

Plate 818: Jesco. "Kewpie Flower Girl" #02184B. 12" tall. Jointed vinyl with painted eyes. All original in pale lavender dress, white tights and shoes. Marks: 21/CAMEO/JLK, on head; JESCO/CAMEO/15, on body. $30.00.

Plate 819: Jesco. Girl and boy, #2105B and #2104B, 1983. 12" tall. Girl is wearing a pink dress, boy has blue romper with "ABC" buttons. Collection of Reevah Turner. $35.00 each.

Plate 820: Jesco. "Karoler Girl" from the "Kewpie Karolers" collection, 1991, #00860B. All vinyl with painted features, jointed body. 8" tall. All original in red and green velvet dress, white tights and shoes. Marks: JESCO ©1986/T.M./MADE IN CHINA, on back. $25.00.

Left — Plate 821: Judith Corporation. "The Mommy-To-Be Doll." 11½". Pregnant doll that has a removable baby inside of her body. Vinyl head, painted eyes, rooted black hair, closed mouth, jointed body with bendable knees. All original in denim maternity dress. Marks: JUDITH, on back. Baby is fully jointed vinyl, molded hair, 2" long, unmarked. $30.00.

Right — Plate 822: Judith. "The Father-To-Be Doll" #62105. ©1992. 11½". Vinyl head, painted hair, painted eyes, and smiling mouth with teeth showing, jointed vinyl body. All original in red jacket, white shirt, blue pants, red print tie. Unmarked. Made in China. $30.00.

Plate 823: Justin. "Renee," #1105. Vinyl fashion doll with twisting body, bendable arms and legs, rooted long black hair, stationary glassine eyes, closed mouth, pierced ears with gold tone drop earrings. 11½" tall. All original in red velvet, satin, and net gown. Doll was also available in other outfits. Marks: ©1991/J P I, on head. Made in China. $18.00.

Plate 824: Justin. "My Slumber Party." 7½". Set of six jointed hard vinyl dolls, two black, two Hispanic, and two white. One of the black dolls has black hair, the other has dark brown hair. Both have painted eyes, closed mouths, and bendable knees. Dolls come with extra outfits and accessories. Available 1993. Marks: JPI — INC, on head; JPI/MADE IN CHINA, on back. $40.00.

Plate 825: Justin Products. "Bridal Party Renee" from "Here Comes The Bride" collection. All dolls are jointed vinyl. Set includes two 12" male dolls, two 11½" female dolls, and two 7" dolls. All have rooted black hair except the two 12" males which have painted black hair. The four larger dolls have stationary glassine eyes, the two smaller ones have painted eyes. All four of the larger dolls have different faces, they were not made from the same molds. Marks on the flower girl: JPI. INC, on head; JPI/MADE IN CHINA, on body. Marks on bridesmaid: ©1991/JPI, on head; MADE IN CHINA, on body. Marks on bride: JPI, on head; MADE IN CHINA, on body. Marks on groom: ©1992/JPI, on head; MADE IN CHINA, on body. Marks on best man: JPI, on head; MADE IN CHINA, on body. Marks on ringbearer: JPI, INC., on head; JPI/MADE IN CHINA, on body. $45.00 set.

Plate 827: Karsuji, "Benny & Brandi" from "Mi Bebes" collection. 28" tall. Vinyl head, arms, and legs, cloth body, brown sleep eyes, black rooted hair. Boy has open-closed mouth, two bottom teeth; girl had open-closed mouth, sucks thumb. Made in Spain. Photograph courtesy of Phyllis Schlatter. $75.00.

Plate 826: Karsuji Inc. "Dream Babies." 18½" tall. Vinyl head, arms, and legs, light brown cloth body, sleeping black eyes with lashes with a tiny white star in each eye, freckles on cheeks, rooted black looped yarn hair, closed mouth. The vinyl on the arms and legs is made to look like the "stockinette" material in the Cabbage Patch dolls. All original in pink dotted dress with matching romper, white socks, and black shoes. Marks: B.B./MADE IN SPAIN, on head. Courtesy of Xzena Moore of the Cubbyhole. $175.00.

Plate 828: Kenner, "Stacy Two Wheeler," 1991, rides her bike all by herself. No batteries needed. Vinyl head and hands, painted eyes, closed mouth, rooted dark brown hair, cloth body made in sitting position and cloth legs. Sewn on clothing is a white with black dotted bodysuit and a bright pink skirt. 14" tall. Tag sewn to body: © STACY TWO-WHEELER DOLL/1991/KENNER/CE/CINCINNATI, OH 45202/MADE IN CHINA NV. Plastic bicycle is 14" long with Velcro® on seat and petals to hold the doll in place. $40.00.

Plate 829: Kenner. "Dawn" #08550 from "Tropical Treat Cupcakes" series with tropical citrus scent. Vinyl head, rooted brown hair with pink streak, painted blue eyes, painted smiling open mouth, vinyl movable arms, hard vinyl body to the waist with painted on tank top in pink with blue dots. Lower part of doll is a pink plastic cupcake. All original in pink and orange dress with orange hat that doubles as frosting on the cupcake. 6" tall. Marks: TONKA/©TONKA CORP./ PAT. PEND./MADE IN CHINA/CE, under the cupcake. $15.00.

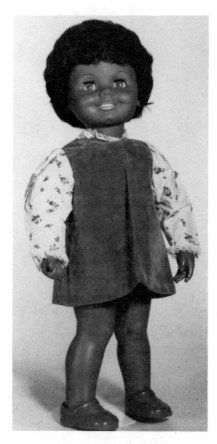

Left — Plate 830: Kenner. "Crumpet," #3502. 1971. 18". Doll that serves "tea," comes with party table, tea pot and lid, four cups and saucers and special cookie plate. One "D" battery required. Vinyl head, sleeping amber/brown eyes with lashes, rooted black hair, open-closed mouth with painted teeth, dimpled chin, hard plastic jointed body and limbs with swivel waist and wrists. Right hand is molded to hold a tea pot. Original green dress, shoes, and socks are missing. Marks: © 1970/KENNER PRODUCTS CO./223-225, on head; ©1970 KENNER/PRODUCTS CO./CINCINNATI, OHIO/PATENT PENDING/MADE IN HONG KONG, on back. $100.00.

Right — Plate 831: Kenner. "Sleep Over Dolly." 16½" tall. Vinyl head and jointed body, rooted black hair, amber sleep eyes with lashes, open-closed mouth with painted teeth. All original in print granny gown and bonnet. Doll originally came with a miniature Kenner "Skye" doll which is missing. Marks: G.M.F.G.I./19©75, on head. $75.00.

Plate 832: Kenner. "Bonnie Bride," #8532, from the "Cupcakes Princess Parfaits" series. Starts as a parfait dessert, changes into a scented vinyl doll with rooted brown streaked hair, painted eyes, painted open smiling mouth, plastic parfait dish from the waist down. All original in white lace dress and veil with pink plastic flowers. 6" tall. Marks: ©TONKA 1991/CE, on stem of parfait dish. $18.00.

Plate 833: Kenner. "Baby Won't Let Go," 1977. She holds your hand, her rattle, or her squeaker. Vinyl head, painted eyes, open/closed mouth, rooted brown hair, hard plastic body and legs, hard plastic hands covered with vinyl. All original in yellow and white sunsuit. 17" tall. Marks: HONG KONG/©G.M.F.G.I. 1977/G.M.F.G.I. 1977/KENNER PROD. DIV./CIN'TI OHIO 45202/26100 26150, on body. $50.00.

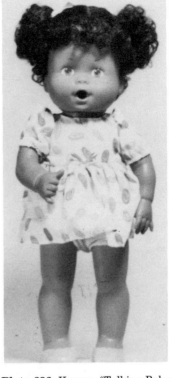

Plate 834: Kenner. "Play-Doh Hairdo Dolly," ©1991. One piece plastic doll with molded on clothing, painted features, molded dark brown hair except for the crown. Doll comes with play-doh and four interchangeable hair caps to "grow" the play-doh hair into four different styles. 10" tall. Marks: ©KENNER 1991/CE/MADE IN MEXICO, on back. $20.00.

Plate 835: Kenner, a division of Tonka Corp. "Baby All Gone." She can be fed again and again with her "magical" spoon and bottle. Comes with "magic" bottle and spoon, formula container, and cherry-scented jar. Vinyl head, rooted dark brown hair, painted eyes, open-closed mouth, vinyl arms and legs, white cloth body. 13" tall. All original in pink romper outfit with name on front. Marks: BABY ALL GONE DOLL/MADE IN CHINA/©KENNER 1991/CE/ CINCINNATI, OH 45202, tag sewn to body. $25.00.

Plate 836: Kenner, "Talking Baby Alive," 1992. She talks, eats, and goes to potty. Vinyl head, rooted dark brown hair in scalp painted black, painted eyes, open mouth, vinyl arms and legs, hard plastic body. 16" tall. All original in print cotton dress, pink terry cloth underpants, and pink plastic shoes. Doll says seven different phrases: "I'm still hungry, mommy!"; "Yum, that's good!"; "I have to go potty"; "Aren't I a big girl?"; "All done now!"; "I love you mommy!"; and "Let's play!" Batteries required. Doll comes with potty, dish, spoon, training cup, and doll food packets. Additional packets sold separately. $55.00.

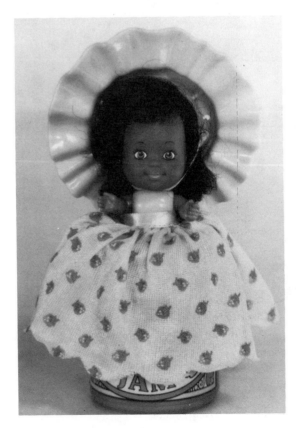

Plate 837: Kenner. "Beri Ann" from "Cupcakes Jam Pops" collection. Changes from a jam jar into a doll. Fruity scented. 5" tall, including base. Vinyl head, rooted dark brown hair, painted eyes, closed mouth, vinyl arms, hard plastic upper body. Lower body is the jam jar. All original in pink "fruit" print skirt with pink plastic hat. $10.00.

Plate 838: Kenner. "Orange Blossom with Marmalade," left and "Orange Blossom with Paintbrush," right, from the "Strawberryland Miniatures" collection. 2" tall. One piece vinyl figures with molded on clothing and painted features. $5.00.

Left — Plate 839: Kenner. "Newborn Baby Alive," #18770. Doll drinks and cries "real" tears. Vinyl head, molded painted hair, tuft of rooted brown hair, colorful stationary eyes, nursing mouth, jointed vinyl body with push button in back. 11" tall. Marks: ©1992 KENNER, A DIVISION/OF TONKA CORPORATION/CINCINNATI, OHIO 45202/ALL RIGHTS RESERVED/MADE IN CHINA/CE, on body. All original in print shirt and diaper. $25.00.

Right — Plate 840: Kenner. 16" tall. Vinyl head, arms and legs, hard plastic body, rooted brown hair, sleeping brown eyes with lashes, nursing mouth, ball-jointed limbs. Marks: ©C.P.G. PRODUCTS 27350. 27360 PATENT PENDING, on body. Collection of Valerie Burbank-Pugh. $45.00.

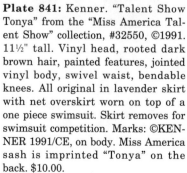

Plate 841: Kenner. "Talent Show Tonya" from the "Miss America Talent Show" collection, #32550, ©1991. 11½" tall. Vinyl head, rooted dark brown hair, painted features, jointed vinyl body, swivel waist, bendable knees. All original in lavender skirt with net overskirt worn on top of a one piece swimsuit. Skirt removes for swimsuit competition. Marks: ©KENNER 1991/CE, on body. Miss America sash is imprinted "Tonya" on the back. $10.00.

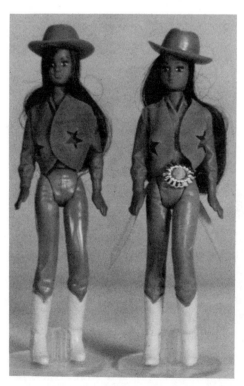

Plate 842: Kenner. "Jana" in "Rodeo Rose." 4¼." Doll on the left is #50270 from the "Glamour Gals" collection. Doll on the right is #51710 from the "Glamour Gals with Jewelry" collection. The only difference is that the one on the right is wearing a fancy belt. Dolls are jointed vinyl with long brown rooted hair, painted features, molded on clothing except for removable vest. Marks: © CPG 1981/HONG KONG, on back. $20.00 ea.

Plate 843: Kenner. "Jana" from "Glamour Gals" collection in "Sunshiner" outfit, ©1991. 4¼". Jointed vinyl, rooted long brown hair, painted eyes. All original in molded on fuchsia swimsuit and platform shoes. $25.00.

Plate 844: Kenner. "Larvelle Jones" from "Police Academy." 4½" tall. Jointed action figure with molded on clothing, white shirt, blue pants, red headband. Marks: ©1989 WARNER BROS. INC./MADE IN CHINA, on leg. His mouth drops open when arm is lifted. $15.00.

Plate 845: Kenner. 4¾". Jointed vinyl action figure with molded on gray long sleeved shirt, shorts, and boots, orange belt. Marks: TM:MCP & WBI 91, on left leg; KENNER CE/CHINA, on right leg. $10.00.

Plate 846: Kenner. "Sgt. Apone" from "Aliens." 4½". Jointed vinyl action figure with molded on clothing, a yellow shirt imprinted "No Bugs," olive pants, and red cap. $8.00.

Plate 847: Kenner. "Bayou Jack" with swamp water blaster from "Swamp Thing" series. Jointed vinyl action figure with olive shirt, brown pants, tan belt. 4½". Collection of Todd Perkins. $8.00.

Left — Plate 848: Kenner. "Winston Zeddmore" from "The Real Ghostbusters with Super Fright Features." 5½". Head disappears into the chest. Molded on green outfit with red and blue accessories and trim. Figure comes with red plastic Meanie Weanie Ghost and red plastic Ghostbuster. Marks: ©1989/COLUMBIA/PICTURES, on lower back. Collection of Todd Perkins. $10.00.

Right — Plate 849: Kenner "Winston Zeddmore" from "The Real Ghostbusters." 5". Jointed vinyl action figure. Molded on mint green outfit with drab green belt, boots, and shoulder straps. Marks: ©1984/COLUMBIA/PICTURES, on back. $10.00.

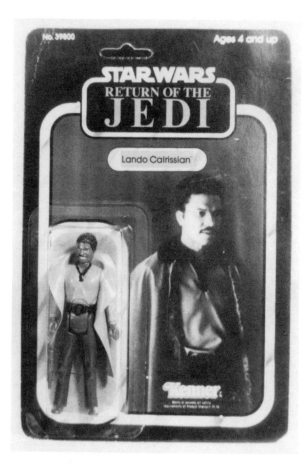

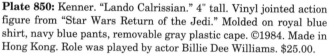

Plate 850: Kenner. "Lando Calrissian." 4" tall. Vinyl jointed action figure from "Star Wars Return of the Jedi." Molded on royal blue shirt, navy blue pants, removable gray plastic cape. ©1984. Made in Hong Kong. Role was played by actor Billie Dee Williams. $25.00.

Plate 851: Kenner. "Lando Calrissian" from "Star Wars Return of the Jedi" in "Skiff Guard Disguise." Molded on brown and tan outfit. $25.00.

Left — Plate 852: Kenner. "Baby Check-Up." 13". Vinyl head, arms, and legs, sewn on purple print outfit makes the body, painted eyes, open-closed mouth, rooted brown hair. Doll comes with "magical" stethoscope, toy medicine dropper, bottle, and thermometer. Name tag sewn to body. $28.00.

Right — Plate 853: Kenner. "Baby Needs Me." 13". Vinyl head, arms, and legs, brown cloth body, rooted brown hair, painted eyes, open-closed mouth. Doll comes with a "magical mommy" watch for the child to wear that lets you know what baby needs. Batteries required. All original in cotton flannel print sleeper. Head is unmarked. Tag sewn to body: BABY NEEDS ME DOLL/ MADE IN CHINA ©-015A/KENNER 1993/CINCINNATI, OH 45202/DIVISION OF TONKA CORPORATION,/A SUBSIDIARY OF HASBRO, INC./CE. $25.00.

Plate 854: Kid Kore. "Satin n' Lace," ©1990. 11½" fashion doll. Vinyl head, painted brown eyes, rooted black curly hair, painted open mouth, jointed body with swivel waist, bendable knees. All original in blue lingerie outfit trimmed with white lace. Marks: ©KID KORE/1990, on head; CHINA/©KID KORE/1990, on body. $10.00.

Plate 855: Kid Kore. "LA Blading Club," #1206, 1991. 11½" fashion doll available in three different outfits. Vinyl head, painted eyes, rooted black hair, painted open mouth with painted teeth, jointed vinyl body with swivel waist. Wheels really turn on roller blades. Marks: © KID KORE/1990, on head; CHINA/©KID KORE/1990, on body. $10.00.

Plate 856: Kid Kore. "My Big Sister...," #91043 from the "LA Blading Club." Set included two vinyl dolls 11½" and 6½". Both dolls have black rooted hair, painted eyes. All original. Marks on big sister: ©KID KORE/1991, on head; CHINA/KID KORE/1990, on body. Marks on little doll: ©KID KORE/1990; CHINA/©KID KORE/1990, on body. $11.00.

Plate 857: Kid Kore. "Katie," #91125. 7½" tall. Vinyl head, rooted long black hair with bangs, painted eyes, closed mouth, jointed vinyl body with bendable knees and swivel waist. Doll is shown in two all original outfits. Marks: ©KID KORE/1990, on head; ©1992 KID KORE/CHINA, on body. Each doll came with an extra outfit and tube of hair styling gel. $10.00.

Plate 858: Kid Kore. "Makin' Music Birthday Celebration," 1991. 11½" tall. Raise left arm to play "Happy Birthday." Brown painted eyes, black rooted hair, all vinyl. Photograph courtesy of Stephanie Lisoski. $20.00.

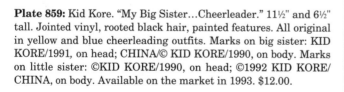

Plate 859: Kid Kore. "My Big Sister...Cheerleader." 11½" and 6½" tall. Jointed vinyl, rooted black hair, painted features. All original in yellow and blue cheerleading outfits. Marks on big sister: KID KORE/1991, on head; CHINA/© KID KORE/1990, on body. Marks on little sister: ©KID KORE/1990, on head; ©1992 KID KORE/CHINA, on body. Available on the market in 1993. $12.00.

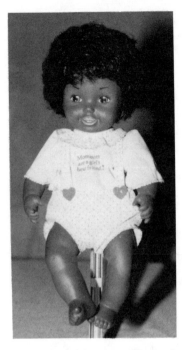

Plate 860: Kidco, Inc. "Mommy's Little Girl." 12" tall. Vinyl with rooted hair, painted eyes, two top and two bottom teeth, nursing mouth. Original outfit, white top, red and white shorts. Top is printed "Mommies are a girl's best friend." Marks: KIDCO INC. 1981, on neck. Photograph courtesy of Etta Houston. $50.00.

Plate 861: Kid's Goods. "Vanessa." 11½". Vinyl fashion doll, swivel waist, jointed arms and legs, rooted black hair, painted eyes, painted mouth with lips slightly parted showing teeth. Doll was available in a variety of outfits. Very inexpensive doll. Light weight vinyl. Marks: MADE IN CHINA, on head and on body. $3.00.

Plate 862: Kid's Goods. "Summer Dream." 11½". Jointed vinyl doll with molded painted black hair, painted eyes, painted mouth with teeth showing, swivel waist. Doll was available in a variety of outfits. Doll is made of very thin vinyl. Unmarked. $3.00.

Plate 863: Konigseer Puppen. "Family." 1987. Vinyl dollhouse dolls. Mother and father are 4¼" tall, children are 3¼" and baby is 1¼". Painted features, molded painted black hair, jointed arms and legs Made in East Germany. $20.00.

Plate 864: Kow Toy's. "Lovely Baby," #K651-4. Vinyl head, painted blue eyes, rooted black hair over molded hair, open-closed mouth with molded tongue, jointed bent-leg vinyl body. 6" tall. All original in pink and white striped dress with white collar. Unmarked. Made in China. $7.00.

Plate 865: L.J.N. "Junk Yard Dog," wrestling action figure. One piece solid vinyl figure, molded hair and beard, painted eyes, painted on red pants and white lace-up boots. 7½" tall. Marks: TITAN SPORTS INC./1984 LJN LTD./2, on body. $20.00.

Plate 866: L.J.N. "Slick," #5624 from "Wrestling Superstars." 7½" One piece vinyl figure with molded on clothing, a gray suit, white shirt, and yellow tie. Removable black hat with yellow band came with the figure. $8.00.

Plate 867: L.J.N. Toys. Original outfit, #2511, from "Florence Griffith Joyner Glamour Collection." Outfit is yellow with pink, purple, and turquoise accessories. ©1989. $25.00. Doll is shown in *Black Dolls, 1820–1991*, page 188, plate 751.

Plate 868: L.J.N. Toys. "Flo Jo" outfit, #2508 from the "Florence Griffith Joyner Glamour Collection." Outfit is white with hot pink knee wraps. $25.00.

Plate 869: L.J.N. Toys. Original "Flo Jo" outfit, #2510, from "Florence Griffith Joyner Glamour Collection" of six outfits. Two piece dress is navy blue. ©1989. $25.00.

Plate 870: L.J.N. "Flo Jo" outfit, #2509. $25.00.

Plate 871: L.J.N. "Flo Jo" outfit, #2505. Red and black print dress, black tights. 1989. $25.00.

Left — Plate 872: L.J.N. Michael Jackson's "Billie Jean" stage outfit with glittering "magic" glove. ©1984. One of six Michael Jackson outfits that were sold separately. Other outfits were: "Human Nature," "Thriller," "Grammy Awards," "Motown," and "Beat it." $20.00. Doll is shown in *Black Dolls, 1820–1991*, pages 187–188, plates 747 to 750.

Right — Plate 873: This Michael Jackson "Billie Jean" outfit is identical to previous one but has slightly different packaging. Full shot of Michael Jackson is shown in previous picture in bottom left hand corner of package. $20.00.

Plate 874: Michael Jackson's "Human Nature" stage outfit. $20.00.

Plate 875: L.J.N. Michael Jackson's "Motown" stage outfit. 1984. Silver jacket, black pants, multicolored top with gold collar, gold belt, glittering silver socks and glove, black shoes. $20.00.

Left — Plate 876: L.J.N. Michael Jackson's "Thriller" outfit. Red faux leather jacket and pants, silver socks and glove, black shirt and shoes. 1984. $20.00.

Right — Plate 877: L.J.N. Michael Jackson's "Grammy Awards" outfit. Blue jacket, gold pants, white knit top, silver socks and glove, black shoes. 1984. $20.00.

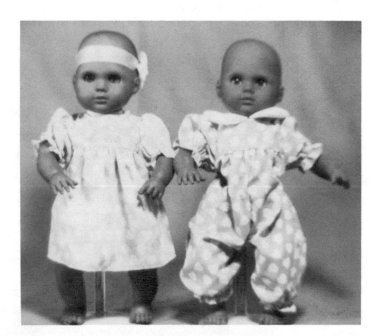

Plate 878: Lanard. "Flashfire" from "The Corps." 1986. 3¾". Jointed vinyl action figure with molded on clothing and accessories. Gray shirt, khaki pants, black boots. Marks: ©1986/LANARD, inside right leg. $6.00.

Plate 879: Lanard Toys. "Scorpion" from "Roller Warriors." 1991. Jointed action figure with molded on yellow and blue outfit with rollerblades. Marks: ©1991 LANARD TOYS INC./PAT PEND MADE IN CHINA, on body. $8.00.

Plate 880: LIN Toys, Inc. "Stephanoodle," on left, and "Michaeloodle" from the "Cootchy Coodles." 2" tall. Solid vinyl. Purchased from Sears, 1989. Photograph courtesy of Faith Wyse. $2.00.

Plate 881: Laiko. "Shontay." 11½" vinyl fashion doll. Rooted reddish brown hair, painted features, closed mouth. All original in pastel print jumpsuit with matching jacket. Doll was available in an assortment of outfits. Marks: ©1991 LAIKO/INT'L CO. INC., on head. Made in China. $5.00.

Plate 882: Lissi Dolls and Toys Hong Kong Lts. "Two Hearts Collection." Vinyl twin dolls sold on TV Home Shopping Club. Box is marked ©Copyright from the old German Doll Factory, dress designed by Anneliese S. Batz. Importer Lissi Batz, 8632 Neustadt. Vinyl head, arms, and legs, sleeping amber eyes, closed mouth, faintly sculpted painted black hair, brown cloth body. 15" tall. All original. Girl has on pink heart printed dress with pink hair ribbon, boy has matching blue print romper with matching cap. Marks: LB (in diamond)/LISSI DOLL ©1986/12/EST GERMANY, on head. Tag sewn to body: LISSI PUPPE/9632 NEUSTADT/CE/100% NEW MATERIAL/MADE IN CHINA. Both dolls have the same marks. Boy is missing his cap in the photo. $50.00.

Plate 883: Lissi Batz. "Rhea." Limited edition vinyl doll for Home Shopping Club. Edition of 1000. 19¾" tall. Vinyl head, sleeping amber eyes with lashes, rooted black hair in two ponytails with bangs, closed mouth, vinyl arms and legs, brown cloth body. All original in pink dotted dress with lavender dotted overdress, white socks, and black plastic mary jane shoes. Certificate that comes with doll says that it was made in the Lissi-Doll-Factory in April, 1992, Neustadt/Coburg, West Germany. Marks: 113, on head; LISSI BATZ, on front of cloth body. $120.00.

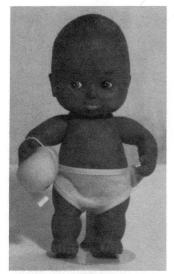

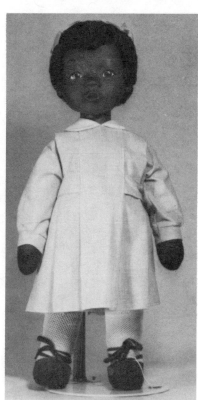

Plate 884: Lovee. "Li'l Dee Dee Diapers," ©1991, style #88710. Jointed vinyl character doll, sculptured hair, painted eyes, closed mouth. 8½" tall. Doll came wearing diapers and holding a baby's sponge. Also included was a play diaper box, play diaper powder, and wash cloth. Marks: MADE IN HONG KONG, on back. $12.00.

Plate 885: Lovee Doll Co. 31". Vinyl head, rooted black hair, sleeping amber eyes with lashes, closed mouth, jointed hard vinyl body. Redressed. Marks: ©1974 LOVEE DOLL, on head. $35.00.

Plate 886: German vinyl doll. 20" tall. Vinyl head, rooted black hair, painted eyes, molded on un-painted earrings, closed mouth, cloth body and limbs. All original in pin-striped blue dress, white stockings, brown felt shoes. Doll is the same as following doll except for unpainted ear-ring and clothing. Marks: CREATION/MARIE-LUIC, on head. Some of these dolls were sold wear-ing a "ZAPF" pin. (Zapf is a manufac-turer of vinyl dolls.) Courtesy of Patricia Martin. $250.00.

Plate 887: Marie-Luic. 20" tall. Vinyl head, painted eyes, closed mouth, rooted black curly hair, pierced ears with goldtone stud earrings, brown cloth body and limbs. All original in two-piece blue and white sailor outfit, black stockings. Marks: CRE-ATION/MARIE-LUIC, on head. Courtesy of Xzena Moore of the Cubbyhole. $250.00.

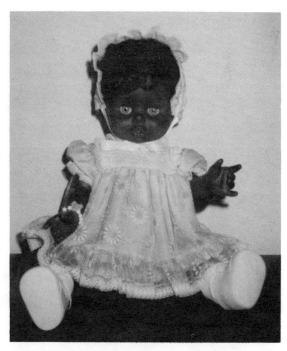

Plate 888: Marcellino. 20". Jointed vinyl baby doll, sleep eyes, black rooted hair. Doll cries like a real baby, says "Ma Ma." Batteries required. Dressed in peach and white dress, peach panties, white bonnet, shoes, and socks. Made in Italy. Marks: MARCELLINO, on head; MINIFON, on body. Collection of and photograph cour-tesy of Mary June Hill. $100.00.

Plate 889: Mark International. "Amy." 13" tall. Vinyl head, jointed vinyl bent-leg body, rooted black hair, sleeping brown eyes with lashes, nursing mouth. All original in knitted red three piece outfit. Unmarked. $7.00.

Plate 890: Marx. "Jed Gibson" from the "Johnny West Adventure" series. Vinyl action figure. 11½" tall. Negroid features, molded black curly hair, painted features, closed mouth, molded on green western clothing. Replaced hands. Marks: MARX TOY/©/MCMLXXIII/ MADE IN/U.S.A., in circle logo on back at waistline. $200.00.

Plate 891: Matchbox. "King of Cartoons," #35690. ©1988. 6" vinyl posable action figure from "Pee-Wee's Playhouse." Molded on suit. Doll came with a removable goldtone crown which is missing in the photo. $15.00.

Plate 892: Matchbox. "Cowboy Curtis" from "Pee Wee Herman's "Playhouse." Role was played by actor Larry Fishburne. 5¾" tall. Molded on cowboy outfit, pink shirt, gold vest, purple pants. Marks: COPYRIGHT ©1987/ HERMAN TOYS, INC./ALL RIGHTS RE-SERVED/MATCH-BOX INT'L LTD./MADE IN CHINA, on back. $20.00.

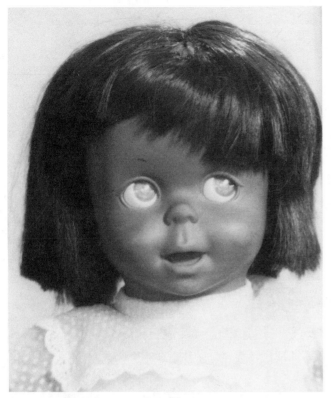

Plate 894: Mattel. "Lois Locket," #3723. 2". From "Lucky Locket Kiddle" series. Jointed vinyl, long brown hair, painted features. All original in green dress with original green locket. Marks: © M.I., on head. Locket is marked: 1966 MATTEL INC./LUCKY LOCKET/KIDDLE/HONG KONG/U.S. PAT. PEND. $45.00.

Plate 893: Mattel. "Baby Say 'N See." 18". Talking doll moves her mouth and eyes while talking. Vinyl head, arms, and legs, brown cloth body, rooted brown hair, brown eyes, open-closed mouth, pull string in body. Doll says the following phrases: "If I look way up high, I can see the man in the moon"; "I can see in the dark. Can You?"; "If I look down like this, I can see my nose"; "My eyes are magic. I can see through anything"; "You're my best friend in the whole world"; "Can you make your eyes go round and round like this?"; "Wouldn't it be fun if you were a doll like me?"; "I wish you and I were twin sisters"; "I have beautiful eyes cause I eat carrots." Clothing is appropriate but does not appear to be original to this doll. Marks: ©1966 MATTEL, INC. U.S.A./U.S. PATENT PENDING, on head. Tag sewn to body: QUALITY ORIGINALS BY/MATTEL/BABY SAY N' SEE/©1965 MATTEL, INC./HAWTHORNE, CALIF./SEWN BODY/MADE IN JAPAN/PAT'D IN U.S.A./OTHER PATS. PEND. $150.00.

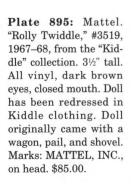

Plate 895: Mattel. "Rolly Twiddle," #3519, 1967–68, from the "Kiddle" collection. 3½" tall. All vinyl, dark brown eyes, closed mouth. Doll has been redressed in Kiddle clothing. Doll originally came with a wagon, pail, and shovel. Marks: MATTEL, INC., on head. $85.00.

Plate 896: Mattel. "Valerie." 1967. 10" tall. Vinyl head, rooted black hair, painted eyes, open-closed mouth with two upper and lower teeth, jointed vinyl body. All original in ecru cotton dress with yellow lace overlay, brown socks, white shoes. Marks: ©1967 MATTEL, INC./U.S. & FOR./PATS. PEND./HONG KONG, on body. Collection of the Museum of African American History (Detroit). $125.00.

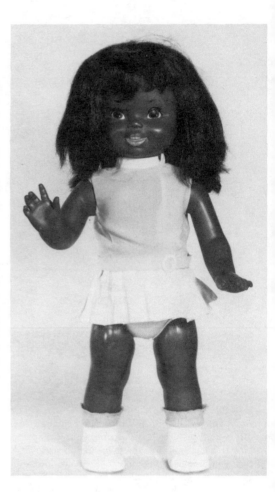

Left — Plate 897: Mattel. "Baby Go Bye-Bye." 1970. 11". Vinyl head, arms, and legs, hard plastic body, painted eyes, black rooted hair, open-closed mouth with two upper teeth. Doll came with a pink buggy. Marks: © 1968 MATTEL, INC./HONG KONG, on head; © 1968 MATTEL, INC./U.S.A./U.S. PATENT PEND-ING, on body. Collection of Valerie Burbank-Pugh. $95.00.

Right — Plate 898: Mattel. "Swingy." 1969–70. 20". dancing and walking doll. Vinyl head and arms, hard plastic body and legs, attached white plastic shoes, tan socks, rooted black hair, painted eyes, open-closed mouth with four upper teeth. Original dress. Marks: ©1967 MATTEL INC. US & FOR. PATS. PEND, on head. Batteries required. $95.00.

Left — Plate 899: Mattel. "Newborn Baby Ten-derlove." 13" tall. Vinyl head, rooted black hair, nursing mouth, painted eyes, one piece vinyl body. Earrings were added by a previous owner and doll has been redressed. Marks: ©1972 MATTEL INC. MEXICO, on head; ©1972 MAT-TEL INC./MEXICO/U.S. AND FOREIGN PATENTED, on body. Courtesy of Linda Boul-ware of Dolls of Color, Inc. $60.00.

Right — Plate 900: Mattel. "Bless You Baby Tenderlove." 1974. 13" tall. Vinyl head, rooted black hair, painted eyes, pierced nostrils, nurs-ing mouth, one piece vinyl bent-leg baby body. Dressed in two piece print sunsuit. Doll squeaks "mama" when tummy is pressed. Marks: ©1974 MATTEL INC., on head; ©1972 MATTEL INC./ U.S.A., on body. Collection of the Museum of African American History (Detroit). $55.00.

Plate 901: Mattel. "Hug-N-Talk." 14" tall. Vinyl head, rooted brown hair for bangs, painted eyes, open-closed mouth with molded tip of tongue, cloth body with sewn on yellow print outfit, sewn on cap. Doll talks when "hug me" button on stomach is pushed. No batteries required. Marks: © 1977 MATTEL, INC., on head. Collection of the Museum of African American History (Detroit). $65.00.

Plate 902: Mattel. "Baby Grows Up," 1978. Doll can grow 1½". Vinyl head and arms, hard plastic jointed body, rooted dark brown hair, painted eyes, open-closed mouth with two painted upper teeth. All original in blue print dress, pink dotted panties, and bonnet. 18" tall. Marks: ©MATTEL INC. 1978, on head; ©MATTEL, INC. 1978. 1978/USA, on body. $100.00.

Plate 903: Mattel. "Luv-a-Bubble Tenderlove." 1978. 14" tall. Vinyl head, rooted brown hair, painted eyes, closed mouth, one piece vinyl toddler body. Dressed in blue print flannel dress with attached hood. Marks: ©1978 MATTEL INC. U.S.A., on head; ©1975 MATTEL INC/USA, on neck. Collection of the Museum of African American History (Detroit). $60.00.

Plate 904: Mattel. "Love 'n Touch Real Sister" ©1980. 15" tall. Vinyl head and arms, rooted brown curly hair, painted eyes, open-closed mouth with molded tongue, white cloth body, brown cloth legs. All original in pink print dress, pink tights, and white plastic shoes. Marks: ©MATTEL INC./1980/TAIWAN, on head. Cloth body is also tagged. $85.00.

Plate 905: Mattel. "Baby Cries for You." 1979. 14" tall. Vinyl head, rooted brown hair, painted eyes, nursing mouth, vinyl arms, cloth legs and body, sewn on pink flannel outfit with white plastic bib. Pull string in back allows doll to move her right hand. Marks: ©1979 MATTEL INC., on head. Collection of the Museum of African American History (Detroit). $60.00.

Plate 906: Mattel. "Pretty Bonnet Beans" from "Baby Bonnet Beans" series, ©1980. Vinyl head, tufts of brown hair for bangs sewn under bonnet, painted brown eyes, closed mouth, brown velour body in sitting position. All original in yellow gingham with sewn on bonnet and removable shorts, removable yellow bib, sewn on yellow shoes. 8" tall. Tag sewn to body: A QUALITY ORIGINAL BY/MATTEL/MATTEL, INC./HAW-THORNE, CA 90250/MADE IN TAIWAN... $25.00.

Plate 907: Mattel. "The Long Legs — Entertainer," #G2525. 40" tall. 1983. Vinyl head and hands, cloth body, rooted brown hair, painted eyes, attached moustache. All original in black tuxedo. Hand tag reads: "Emotions/Division of Mattel." Collection of Emma Ranson Hayward. $125.00.

Plate 908: Mattel. "Bottle Time Baby," 1984. When you put her bottle in her mouth and twist it, she moves her arms and legs. No batteries required. Vinyl head, painted eyes, rooted brown hair, nursing mouth, jointed vinyl body. All original in lavender two piece outfit with matching hat. 10" tall. Marks: © MATTEL, INC. 1984/TAIWAN, on head; © MATTEL, INC. 1984/TAIWAN, on body. $35.00.

Left — Plate 909: Mattel "Soft P.J. Sparkles." Vinyl head, painted eyes, closed mouth, painted on stud earrings, rooted brown hair with pastel colored bangs on forehead, pink cloth body and feet, brown cloth arms, legs, and hands. Pink plastic heart in chest lights up. Batteries required. 11". Marks: ©1988 MATTEL INC./CHINA, on head; P.J./SPARKLES, decal on left foot. $20.00.

Right — Plate 910: Mattel. Action figure from the "She-Ra" series, jointed vinyl, painted eyes, rooted long blue hair, molded on white outfit with blue trim, including boots and arm bands. 5½" tall. Marks: ©M.I. 1985, on head; ©MATTEL, INC. 1985/TAIWAN, on body. $25.00.

Plate 911: Mattel. "Totally Hair Barbie Styling Head," ©1992. Rooted very dark brown hair, painted eyes, painted smiling mouth with teeth, pierced ears, pink plastic stand with drawer, vinyl arms and hands, swivel head. 11" tall, including stand. Marks: © MATTEL INC 1988, on head. $25.00.

Plate 912: Mattel. "Cherry Merry Muffin," #9570. Vinyl head, painted eyes, painted open smiling mouth, rooted pink hair, jointed vinyl body. Doll is cherry scented and comes with real ice cream topping and dish. All original in pink net outfit. 6½" tall. Marks: ©MATTEL INC./1989, on head; ©MATTEL INC. 1988/CHINA, on body. $15.00.

Plate 913: Mattel. "Li'l Miss Magic Jewels." 13" tall. With the touch of a "magic" wand, "jewels" on clothing light up. Batteries required. Jointed vinyl doll, rooted long dark brown hair, painted eyes, red heart on left cheek, painted earrings. All original in long pink gown. Marks: © MATTEL, INC. 1988, 1977/CHINA, on head: © MATTEL, INC. 1988/CHINA, on body. $35.00.

Plate 914: Mattel. "Wee Li'l Miss Makeup Lipstick Doll." 7" tall. Vinyl jointed doll, rooted black hair, painted features, open-closed mouth. All original in pink leotard and pink bubble skirt with pink plastic shoes. Marks: ©1990 MATTEL INC., on head; © MATTEL INC 1988/CHINA, on body. $20.00.

Plate 915: Mattel. "Wee Li'l Miss Bedtime," #1052, ©1990. Her eyes magically open or close when you wet them. Vinyl head, painted eyes, lips slightly open, long rooted black hair, jointed vinyl body. 7" tall. All original in pink and green outfit. Marks: ©1990 MATTEL INC., on head; ©MATTEL, INC. 1988/CHINA, on body. $15.00.

Plate 916: Mattel. "Wee Li'l Miss Makeup Nail Polish Doll," #4057. ©1991. 7" tall. Vinyl head, painted eyes, open-closed mouth, rooted long dark brown hair, jointed vinyl body. Nail polish and makeup appears on the doll when you apply icy water and disappears with warm water. All original in yellow two piece sunsuit and bubble skirt. Marks: ©MATTEL INC. 1988/CHINA, on back. $15.00.

Left — Plate 917: Mattel. "Li'l Miss Singing Mermaid." 14½". Doll sings and changes colors. Vinyl head, rooted long brown hair, painted eyes, closed mouth, vinyl "mermaid" body with movable arms, removable boa. Marks: ©1988–77 MATTEL INC., on head; ©MATTEL, INC. 1991, on body. Collection of Mackenzie Scott. $40.00.

Right — Plate 918: Mattel "Magic Nursery First Surprise," girl. 15". Surprise is baby's first teeth. Vinyl head, painted eyes, brown eyeshadow and brown under the pupils, small opening in mouth for teeth to grow, black rooted hair, cloth body. All original in red and white romper suit. Marks: ©1989 MATTEL INC./CHINA, on head. $30.00.

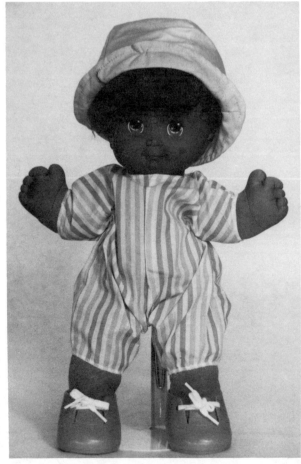

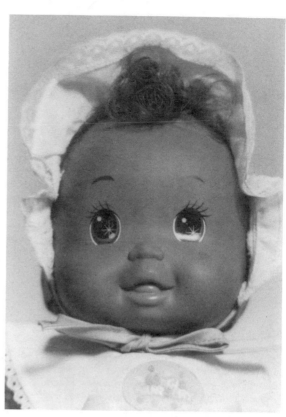

Left — Plate 919: Mattel. "Magic Nursery First Surprise," girl. 15". Surprise is baby's first haircut. Vinyl head, painted eyes, green eyeshadow and green under the pupils, closed mouth, black rooted growing hair, cloth body. All original in purple and pink romper suit. Marks: ©1989 MATTEL INC./CHINA, on head. $30.00.

Right — Plate 920: Mattel. "Magic Nursery Real Sounds Newborn," girl. Baby makes little baby sounds when you lay it down, pat its back, or bounce baby on your knee. When heart on cheek is kissed, it becomes a star. Vinyl head, decal green eyes, rooted tuft of brown hair, open mouth with molded tongue slightly sticking out, brown cloth body. 13" tall. All original in printed romper suit and bonnet. Marks: ©1991 MATTEL INC./CHINA, on head. $25.00.

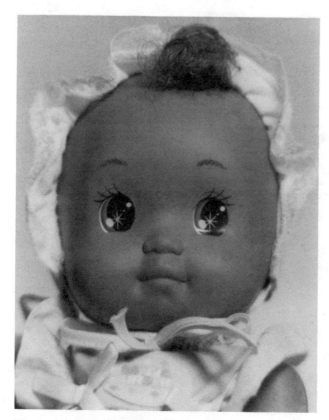

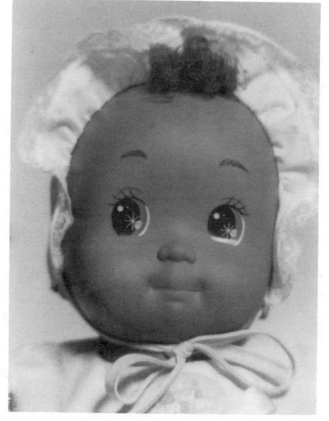

Plate 921: Mattel. "Magic Nursery Real Sounds Newborn," girl with slightly different facial expression. Vinyl head, rooted tuft of brown hair, green decal eyes, closed mouth. 13" tall. All original in purple and pink print dress and orange bonnet. Marks: ©MATTEL, INC. 1989/CHINA, on head. $25.00.

Plate 922: Mattel. "Magic Nursery Real Sounds Newborn," girl with another different facial expression and brown decal eyes. All of the dolls in this series have a cry box inside the cloth body. Marks: ©1991 MATTEL INC./CHINA, on head. $25.00.

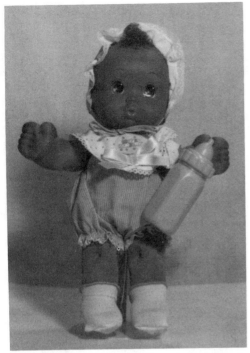

Plate 923: Mattel. "Magic Nursery Real Sounds Newborn," girl with another different facial expression. This one has lips slightly parted with brown decal eyes. Marks: © 1991/MATTEL INC. CHINA, on head. $25.00.

Plate 924: Mattel. "Magic Nursery Fuss 'n Giggle Triplets." Vinyl head, cloth body and limbs, painted eyes. Each doll has a different mouth expression. Batteries required. Dolls are available in four different colored outfits. This one has a yellow cotton printed carrier, clothing is aqua, pink, and lilac. $32.00.

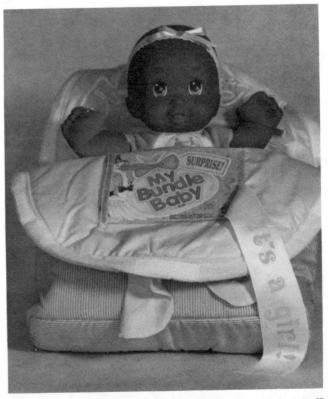

Plate 925: Mattel. "Magic Nursery Tiny Wonders Preemie," 1991. 11½" long. Vinyl head, brown painted eyes, molded brown hair, closed mouth, painted red heart on left cheek, cloth body and limbs. When pillow was dipped in water, it revealed the magic surprise, the baby is a 4 lb. girl. All original in aqua bunting with pink trim. Extra outfit is a pink flannel diaper and pink gingham tee shirt. Marks: ©1991 MATTEL INC., on head. $20.00.

Plate 926: Mattel. "My Bundle Baby." 10". Comes with "magical" bundle that makes sounds and motions like a real baby. Batteries required. Vinyl bald head, painted features, open-closed mouth, cloth body and limbs. All original in lavender romper. Dolls available in assorted outfits. When you open the box, you find out if its a girl, boy, or twins. This one is a girl. Marks: ©1991 MATTEL INC. CHINA, on head. $30.00.

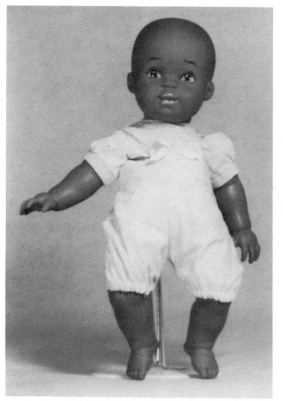

Plate 928: Mattel. "Style Me Pretty," #4347A from "Lovable Babies." 13" tall. Vinyl head, rooted brown hair, painted eyes, open-closed mouth with upper teeth, jointed vinyl body. All original in lavender outfit. Marks: © MATTEL INC. 1992/CHINA 1283, on head. $20.00.

Plate 927: Mattel. "Lovable Babies Nursery Baby," #4124. 12". Vinyl head, arms, and legs, bald head, painted eyes, closed mouth, pink cloth body, smells like baby powder. All original in pink print romper, blouse imprinted "Little Wishes" (the name of another Mattel doll). Marks: ©1991 MATTEL INC./CHINA 1203B, on head. $14.00.

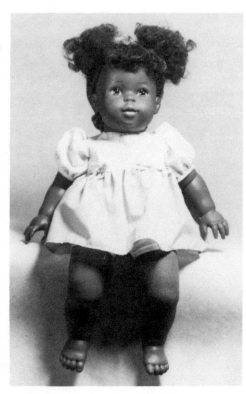

Plate 929: Mattel "Lovable Babies Nursery Baby." 18" tall. Vinyl head, rooted brown hair, painted eyes, closed mouth, vinyl arms and legs, pink cloth body. All original in dress with yellow print bodice that is printed "Little Wishes" which is the name of another Mattel doll. The skirt of the dress is lavender. Marks: ©MATTEL, INC./ CHINA 1803B, on head. $25.00.

Plate 930: Mattel. "Lovable babies Drinks 'N Wets," #4336. 12". Wet and drink doll, vinyl bald head, painted eyes, nursing mouth, jointed vinyl baby body. All original in blue striped sunsuit. Marks: ©MATTEL, INC./CHINA, on head. ©1992, on box. $12.00.

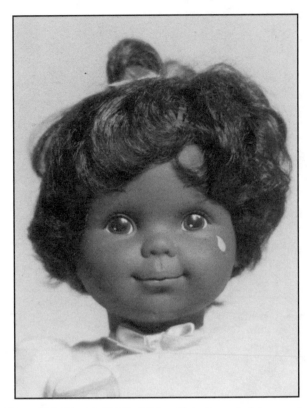

Plate 931: Mattel. "Lovable Babies Birthday Babies," #4342. 13". Vinyl head, rooted curly brown hair, painted eyes, closed mouth, vinyl arms and legs, pink cloth body. All original in dress with a pink print front, solid pink back and sleeves, pink plastic shoes, pink hair ornament. A pink plastic birthday cake comes with the doll. Marks: MATTEL, INC. 1992/CHINA, on head. Collection of Haille Nichole Perkins. $18.00.

Plate 932: Mattel. "Little Wishes Baby," magical tear on her face disappears with a kiss. Vinyl head, rooted brown hair, painted brown eyes, closed smiling mouth, blue teardrop on her left cheek, vinyl arms and legs, pink cloth body. 14" tall. All original in yellow dress with "Little Wishes" printed on skirt part, matching booties. Additional sparkling outfit is included inside her cloth rattle. Some dolls have a cloth teddy bear instead of the rattle. Marks: ©1991 MATTEL INC, on head. $25.00.

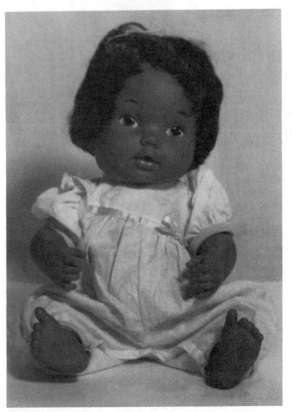

Left — Plate 933: Mattel. "Little Wishes Wet 'n Cry." She cries like a real baby when her diaper is wet. Batteries required. Vinyl head, painted eyes, rooted short brown hair, nursing mouth, green tear on her left cheek, jointed vinyl baby body. 14" tall. All original in pink print long leg romper. Marks: ©1991 MATTEL INC, on head. $30.00.

Right — Plate 934: Mattel. "Baby Rollerblade." 15" tall. ©1991. Vinyl head and arms, rooted brown hair, painted eyes, molded tongue, hard plastic pink body and legs, attached rollerblades. All original in pink print outfit. Marks: ©MATTEL INC. 1980/ CHINA, on head. Doll is very similar to "Baby Skates" from 1982. $27.00.

Left — Plate 935: Mattel. "Baby Walk 'n Roll," #4576. 11" tall. You make the baby go with a wireless radio controller. Vinyl head, rooted brown hair, painted eyes, open-closed mouth with two lower teeth, vinyl arms and legs, hard plastic body. Doll comes in a pink plastic walker with blue trim. Dressed in an aqua print romper outfit. Marks: ©1992 MATTEL INC., on head; ©1992 MATTEL, INC./CHINA, on body. $50.00.

Right — Plate 936: Mattel "Sally Secrets," #10204. 13" tall. Vinyl head, rooted dark brown hair, painted eyes, pierced ears with pink plastic earrings, hard plastic body, vinyl arms and legs. All original in two piece pink and green dress, black shorts, pink socks, white plastic shoes. Marks: ©1992 MATTEL, INC., on head. $22.00.

Left — Plate 937: Mattel. "Merry Mint Violet," #0794 from the "Peppermint Rose" series. 10" tall. Vinyl head, rooted long black hair, painted eyes, closed mouth, pierced ears with aqua earrings, jointed vinyl body with swivel waist and bendable knees. All original. Doll comes with two bottles of "perfume" you can make. Marks: ©1986 TCFC, on head; MATTEL INC. 1987/ MALAYSIA, on body. Box is marked: ©1992 THOSE CHARACTERS FROM CLEVELAND, INC. $18.00.

Right — Plate 938: Mattel. "Morocco" from Disney's "It's a Small World!" collection. 1993. 6½" tall. Jointed vinyl doll, rooted black hair, painted eyes, closed mouth. all original. Marks: ©MATTEL, INC. 1988, on head; ©MATTEL, INC. 1988/ CHINA, on body. Doll has molded on deep pink shoes and is made from the same mold as "Apple Amy" and "Greta Grape" from the Cherry Merry Muffin series, plates 837 and 838 in my earlier book *Black Dolls, 1820-1991*. $10.00.

Plate 939: Mattel. "Nigeria" from Disney's "It's a Small World!" collection. 6½". 1993. Jointed vinyl with rooted black hair, painted eyes, closed mouth. All original. Marks: ©MATTEL, INC. 1988, on head; ©MATTEL INC. 1988/CHINA, on body. Doll has molded on yellow shoes. $10.00.

Plate 940: Mattel. "My First Barbie," 1988. Open smiling mouth with teeth showing, long black hair. All original in white ballet bodysuit and white tutu with gold threads. Marks: MATTEL INC./1987, on head; ©MATTEL, INC. 1966/MALAYSIA, on body. $20.00.

Plate 941: Mattel. "Ice Capades Barbie," #7348. ©1989. Long black hair, dressed in pink and blue ice skating outfit. Made in Malaysia. $35.00.

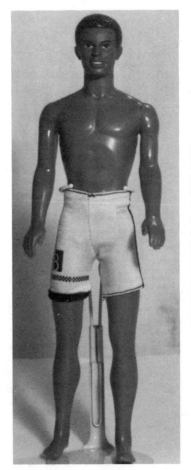

Plate 942: Mattel. "Beach Blast Steven," 1988. Jointed vinyl doll with bendable knees, molded hair, painted open mouth, painted eyes, 12" tall. Product #3251. All original in pink and yellow swim trunks. Marks: ©MATTEL, INC. 1987, on head; ©1968/MATTEL, INC./US & FOR PATD/OTHER PATS/PENDING/MALAYSIA, on body. $20.00.

Left — Plate 943: Mattel. "Dance Club Devon," #3513. 1989. Long black rooted hair, painted open mouth with teeth showing, aqua eyeshadow. Doll and costume made in China. $45.00.

Right — Plate 944: Mattel. "Dance Magic Barbie," 1989. Long dark brown wavy hair, open mouth with painted teeth. All original in long pink gown with white net overlay. Doll wears pink ring on right hand. Marks: ©MATTEL INC./1987, on head; ©MATTEL INC. 1966/MALAYSIA, on body. $25.00.

Left — Plate 945: Mattel. "Happy Birthday Barbie," 1990. Very dark brown rooted hair, open smiling mouth, blue eyeshadow and eyeliner. All original in long two-piece pink gown with "Happy Birthday" sash. Marks: ©MATTEL INC./1987, on head; ©MATTEL 1966/MALAYSIA, on body. $30.00.

Right — Plate 946: Mattel. "My First Barbie," 1989. Marks: MATTEL INC./1987, on head; MATTEL INC. 1966/MALAYSIA, on body. All original in long white gown with purple bodice, white crown, and shoes. Long black hair and blue eyeshadow. $20.00.

Plate 947: Mattel. "Summit Barbie," 1990. A special edition to celebrate the first annual Barbie Summit. Fifty cents from the proceeds of this doll is distributed to nonprofit organizations established for the purpose of promoting education or literacy for children around the world. Long dark brown hair, smiling mouth. Marks: ©MATTEL INC/1987, on head. ©MATTEL INC 1966/CHINA. $30.00.

Plate 948: Mattel. "Fashion Play Barbie," 1990. Open mouth long black hair. All original in white with lavender swimsuit. Marks: MATTEL INC./1987, on head. $10.00.

Plate 949: Mattel. "Lights & Lace Barbie" #9728. ©1990. Long black wavy hair with bangs, olive eyeshadow, pierced ears with large green earrings. All original in yellow lace dress and hair ribbon. Green plastic "jewel" belt flashes to its own bet. Batteries required. Made in Malaysia. $20.00.

Left — Plate 950: Mattel. "Starlight Splendor Barbie" by Bob Mackie, second in series and the first black doll in the series. Barbie is dressed in long black, white, and silver fitted gown that is covered with over 5,000 hand-sewn sequins and beads from her headdress to the train on her gown. Barbie has on two shades of green eyeshadow. $350.00.

Right — Plate 951: Mattel. "Happy Holidays Barbie," 1991 special edition. Painted open smiling mouth, green eyes with green eyeshadow, pierced ears with red and silver bead earrings, long dark brown hair. All original in green velvet gown with sequins and beads. Package can be used as a display case. $50.00.

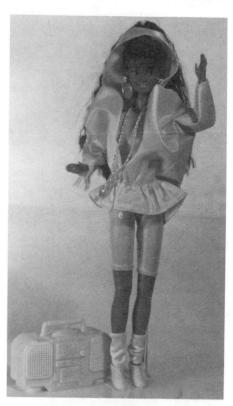

Left — Plate 952: Mattel. "Spring Parade Barbie," ©1991, Toys 'R' Us limited edition. All vinyl, rooted long black hair, brown painted eyes, olive green eyeshadow, painted smiling mouth, pierced ears with pearl-like earrings and matching ring, swivel waist, bendable knees. All original in orchid and white gown, white hat, and matching basket of flowers, pearl necklace. Mark: ©MATTEL INC./1987, on head; ©MATTEL, INC. 1966/CHINA, on body. $20.00.

Right — Plate 953: Mattel. "Rappin' Rockin' Christie," 1991. Doll comes with real rap beat boom box. Vinyl head, painted brown eyes, lime green eyeliner, painted smiling mouth with teeth showing, pierced ears with gold and lime earrings, jointed vinyl body with swivel waist. All original in lime bodysuit and orange jacket. Boom box is orange plastic. Marks: ©MATTEL INC./1987, on head; ©MATTEL INC. 1966/CHINA, on body. $18.00.

Plate 954: Mattel. "Special Expressions Barbie," 1991, Woolworth's special edition. Painted open smiling mouth, brown eyes, green eyeshadow, long black hair. All original is short aqua party dress and matching hair bow. Marks: ©MATTEL INC./1987, on head; ©MATTEL INC. 1966/MALAYSIA, on body. $15.00.

Plate 955: Mattel. "Pet Pals Skipper," 1991. Vinyl head, long dark brown wavy hair, painted eyes with deep pink eyeshadow, closed mouth, jointed hard vinyl body. All original in pink print shirt and matching jumper, bright yellow bicycle pants, pink shoes. White puppy comes with the doll. 10" tall. Marks: ©MATTEL INC./1987, on head; ©MATTEL INC. 1987/MALAYSIA, on body. $12.00.

Plate 956: Mattel. "My First Barbie," 1991. Vinyl head, long rooted black hair, painted open smiling mouth, painted eyes with blue eyeshadow, jointed hard vinyl body and limbs. All original in blue ballet outfit with blue ballet slippers. Marks: ©MATTEL INC./1987, on head; ©MATTEL INC. 1966/MALAYSIA, on body. $12.00.

Left — Plate 957: Mattel. "Sun Sensation Christie," 1991. Vinyl head, long rooted black hair with brown highlights, painted eyes with blue and gold eyeshadow, painted open mouth, pierced ears with gold star earrings and matching necklace, jointed vinyl body with swivel waist, two piece blue swimsuit. 11½" tall. Marks: ©MATTEL INC./1987, on head; ©MATTEL INC. 1966/MALAYSIA, on body. $15.00.

Right — Plate 958: Mattel. "Sun Sensation Steven," ©1991. Vinyl head, painted black hair, smiling mouth, jointed vinyl body. All original in orange shorts, silver net tank top. Marks: ©MATTEL, INC. 1987, on head; ©1968/MATTEL, INC./ MALAYSIA, on body. $12.00.

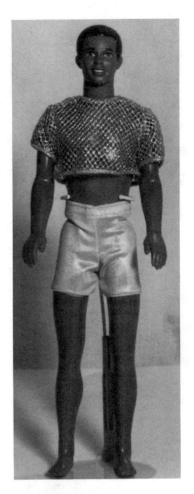

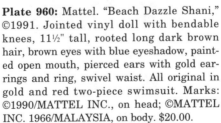

Plate 960: Mattel. "Beach Dazzle Shani," ©1991. Jointed vinyl doll with bendable knees, 11½" tall, rooted long dark brown hair, brown eyes with blue eyeshadow, painted open mouth, pierced ears with gold earrings and ring, swivel waist. All original in gold and red two-piece swimsuit. Marks: ©1990/MATTEL INC., on head; ©MATTEL INC. 1966/MALAYSIA, on body. $20.00.

Plate 959: Mattel. "Beach Dazzle Asha" from the "Shani" collection. The lightest in complexion of the Shani dolls, long reddish brown hair, brown eyes, mauve eyeshadow, painted open mouth, pierced ears with gold drop earrings, swivel waist, bendable knees. All original in two piece pink with blue swimsuit. Marks: ©1990/MATTEL INC, on head; ©MATTEL INC 1966/MALAYSIA, on body. $20.00.

Plate 961: Mattel. "Beach Dazzle Nichelle," #5775. ©1991. 11½". Jointed vinyl doll, rooted black hair, painted eyes, pink eyeshadow, closed mouth, swivel waist, bendable knees. All original in gold two-piece swimsuit, goldtone dangle earrings, gold ring. Marks: ©1990/MATTEL INC, on head; ©MATTEL INC. 1966/MALAYSIA, on body. $20.00.

Left — Plate 962: Mattel. "Jamaican Barbie," ©1991. Special edition Barbie from the "Dolls of the World" collection, dressed in traditional costume of blue print dress, orange print apron and head scarf, black rooted curly hair, brown eyes, blue eyeshadow, painted open mouth, pierced ears with blue hoop earrings, bendable knees; swivel waist. Marks: ©MATTEL INC./1987, on head; ©MATTEL INC. 1966/CHINA, on body. $25.00.

Right — Plate 963: Mattel. "Fashion Play Barbie," 1991. Jointed vinyl doll, painted brown eyes, rooted dark brown hair, painted open mouth, aqua eyeshadow. All original in pink, aqua, blue, and purple body suit with pink scarf tied around the waist. Marks: ©MATTEL INC./1987, on head; ©MATTEL INC. 1966/MALAYSIA, on body. $10.00.

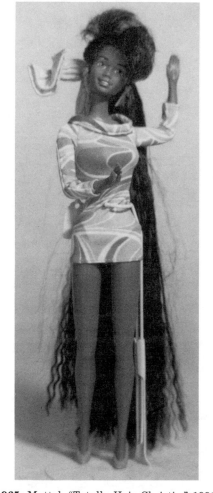

Plate 965: Mattel. "Totally Hair Christie," 1991. Vinyl head, painted eyes with green, pink, and gold eyeshadow, painted open mouth with painted teeth, brown rooted hair that goes down to her feet, pierced ears with blue geometric earrings and matching ring, hard vinyl jointed body with swivel waist. All original in short print dress in cool colors with green hair bow. Marks: ©MATTEL INC./1987, on head; ©MATTEL INC 1966/MALAYSIA, on body. $25.00.

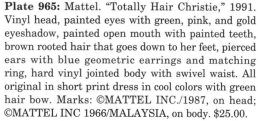

Plate 964: Mattel. "Rollerblade Christie," ©1991. Vinyl jointed doll, rooted long dark brown hair, painted brown eyes with lime green accents, blue eyeshadow, painted open mouth, pierced ears with hot pink triangular earrings, matching ring. All original in purple and lime green outfit with matching roller blades. Marks: ©MATTEL INC./1987, on head; ©MATTEL INC. 1966/CHINA, on body. $25.00.

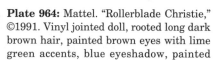

Plate 966: Mattel. "My First Ken," 1991, ballet partner of black Barbie, made from Barbie's "Steven" mold. All original in glittering aqua ballet outfit. Marks: ©MATTEL INC. 1987, on head; ©MATTEL INC./1968/MALAYSIA, on body. $15.00.

Plate 967: Mattel. "Bath Magic Barbie," 1991. Doll comes with three bath beads that "magically" change into fashion decorations. Vinyl head, rooted dark brown hair, painted eyes with red eyeshadow, pierced ears with pink stud earrings, jointed vinyl body with swivel waist and bendable knees. 11½". All original in yellow and pink swimsuit with pink and yellow overskirt. Marks: ©MATTEL INC/1987, on head; © MATTEL INC 1966/MALAYSIA, on body. $12.00.

Plate 968: Mattel. "Snap 'n Play Barbie," ©1991, on the market in 1992. Vinyl head, painted eyes with olive green eyeshadow, painted open mouth with teeth. Long rooted dark brown hair, jointed vinyl body. All original in snap on yellow-green top and blue skirt with print trim. An extra set of snap on clothes with pink plastic top and multicolored skirt came with the doll. Marks: ©MATTEL INC/1987, on head; ©MATTEL, INC. 1966/CHINA, on body. $12.00.

Plate 969: Mattel. "Sparkle Eyes Barbie," 1991. Vinyl head, rooted dark brown hair, green rhinestone eyes, green eyeshadow, painted smiling mouth with teeth showing, pierced ears with pink drop earrings, matching ring, jointed vinyl body with swivel waist. All original in silver mini dress, pink net overskirt, and ruffled boa, pink plastic necklace that can be a child's ring. Marks: ©MATTEL INC./1987, on head; ©MATTEL, INC. 1966/MALAYSIA, on body. $20.00.

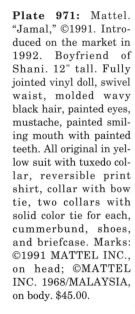

Plate 970: Mattel. "Birthday Surprise Barbie," ©1991. Doll comes with a surprise gift, either a bracelet, necklace, or earrings. A child size necklace came with this doll. Also included was a collector doll stand. All vinyl doll has rooted long dark brown hair, royal blue eyeshadow, painted open smiling mouth and eyes, pierced ears with peach drop earrings, and matching ring. All original in long peach gown trimmed with pearls. Marks: MATTEL INC, on head; ©MATTEL INC 1966/MALAYSIA, on body. $30.00.

Plate 971: Mattel. "Jamal," ©1991. Introduced on the market in 1992. Boyfriend of Shani. 12" tall. Fully jointed vinyl doll, swivel waist, molded wavy black hair, painted eyes, mustache, painted smiling mouth with painted teeth. All original in yellow suit with tuxedo collar, reversible print shirt, collar with bow tie, two collars with solid color tie for each, cummerbund, shoes, and briefcase. Marks: ©1991 MATTEL INC., on head; ©MATTEL INC. 1968/MALAYSIA, on body. $45.00.

Plate 972: Mattel. "Marine Corps Barbie," ©1991. Special edition from the "Stars 'n Stripes" series. All vinyl with swivel waist, bendable knees, rooted short brown hair, painted eyes with dark gray eyeshadow, painted open mouth with teeth, gold stud earrings. All original in the authentic Marine Corps "Dress Blues" uniform for enlisted women, worn during parades, on family visits, and to all official formal Marine Corps events. Her rank is sergeant. Marks: ©MATTEL INC./1987, on head; ©MATTEL, INC 1966/MALAYSIA, on head. $22.00.

Plate 973: Mattel. "Christie, United Colors of Benetton Shopping," ©1991, special limited edition for the European market. All original in blue skirt and poncho, red and gold sweater, gold leg warmers, blue and red hat. $45.00.

Plate 974: Mattel. "Marine Corps Ken," #5352, special edition from the "Stars 'n Stripes" series, ©1991. All original in the authentic Marine Corps "Dress Blues" uniform for enlisted men. His rank is sergeant. $25.00.

Plate 975: Mattel. "Barbie For President," ©1991, Toys 'R' Us limited edition. All vinyl, long black hair, painted eyes with blue eyeliner and olive eyeshadow, painted smiling mouth with teeth, jointed body with swivel waist and bendable knees, white stud earrings and matching ring. All original in long gown with silver bodice trimmed in red and blue skirt with overlay imprinted with stars. Included with the doll is a knee length red outfit with matching jacket and white plastic suitcase. Marks: ©MATTEL INC./1987, MATTEL, INC 1966/CHINA, on body. $35.00.

Plate 976: Mattel. "Teen Talk Barbie," #1612, ©1991. Jointed vinyl talking dol with bendable knees and swivel waist. 11½". Rooted black hair, green eyes with green and gold eyeshadow, painted smiling mouth with teeth, pierced ears with pink earrings, and matching ring. Doll was available in a variety of hairstyles, costume colors, and eye colors. Each doll says four phrases but not all dolls say the same phrases. This doll says the following: "Our friends are having a party"; "Let's drive to the ski lodge"; "Don't you love art class?"; and "Let's try a new dance move." Batteries required. Marks: ©MATTEL, INC./1987, on head; ©MATTEL, INC. 1966/CHINA, on body. Other phrases said by Teen Talk Barbies are as follows: "Want to go to the Concert?"; "Help me throw a surprise party"; "I love dressing up"; "Ken's a great dancer"; "You're my best friend"; "I can't wait for summer"; "Let's celebrate after the game"; "Let's sing songs around the campfire"; "Meet me at the swimming pool"; "It's fun to shop with friends"; "Tonight's the school dance." $75.00.

Plate 977: Mattel "School Fun Barbie," #4111, 1991. Toys 'R' Us Limited Edition. Jointed vinyl, rooted black hair with bangs, white hoop earrings, and ring. All original in white print skirt, top and matching backpack with pink jacket. ©MATTEL INC/1987, on head; ©MATTEL INC. 1966/CHINA, on back. $125.00.

Left — Plate 978: Mattel. "Radiant in Red Barbie," #4113, ©1992. Toys 'R' Us special edition. Vinyl head, rooted long wavy brown hair, painted green eyes, painted smiling mouth with teeth, earrings and ring, jointed vinyl body with swivel waist and bendable knees. All original in long red gown with gold net overlay on top. Marks: ©MATTEL INC/1987, on head; ©MATTEL INC 1966/MALAYSIA, on body. $30.00.

Right — Plate 979: Mattel "Sweet Lavender," #2523. ©1992. Woolworth special limited edition. Dressed in white glitter evening gown with lavender overskirt, matching long gloves. $15.00.

Plate 982: Mattel "Barbie Fashion Brights Collection," ©1992, Toys 'R' Us limited edition. Long rooted brown hair, painted open smiling mouth, faux pearl dot earrings. All original in pink lace trimmed teddy with over 14 pieces of clothing. Made in China. $18.00.

Plate 980: Mattel. "Special Expressions Barbie," #3198, 1992. Woolworth special edition Barbie. Long dark brown hair, pink stud earrings, painted open smiling mouth. All original in pink sateen off-the-shoulder short party dress. Made in Malaysia. $12.00.

Plate 981: Mattel. "Pretty in Purple," #3121. K-Mart special edition Barbie. ©1992. Dressed in short purple dress with white net over-skirt, white net trim on bodice. $15.00.

Plate 983: Mattel. "Cool 'n Sassy Barbie," ©1992, Toys 'R' Us limited edition. All original in yellow tank top and leggings, blue print jacket and short skirt, fuchsia net overskirt. $15.00.

Plate 984: Mattel. "Happy Holidays Barbie," 1992, special edition. Doll is all original in "crystal" and "silver" gown, drop earrings and matching ring. $45.00.

Plate 986: Mattel. "Secret Hearts Barbie," #3836, ©1992. Long wavy black hair, painted open mouth, drop heart earrings, and matching necklace. All original in long two-piece white gown with red hearts. Doll comes with heart-shaped ice cube tray. When ice cubes are placed along ruffles, hearts "magically" appear. Hearts disappear when touched with warm hands. Marks: ©MATTEL, INC./1987, on head; ©MATTEL INC 1966/CHINA, on body. $15.00.

Plate 985: Mattel. "Earring Magic Barbie," #2374. ©1992. Long black crimped hair with bangs. All original in pink vinyl dress. Made in Malaysia. $15.00.

Plate 987: Mattel. "Beach Streak Shani." #3428, ©1992. Long dark brown hair highlighted with reddish streaks. All original in gold and black swimsuit. $20.00.

Plate 988: Mattel. "Beach Streak Nichelle," #3456, ©1992, from the "Beach Streak Shani" series. 11½". Jointed vinyl, rooted black hair with copper colored streak, painted eyes with silver eyeshadow, closed mouth, swivel waist, bendable knees. All original in one-piece aqua and black swimsuit, goldtone earrings. Marks: ©1990/MATTEL INC., on head; ©1991 MATTEL, INC./MALAYSIA, on body. $20.00.

Plate 989: Mattel. "Beach Streak Asha," #3457. 1992. Long brown hair with highlight streak in three braids, painted eyes, painted open mouth with painted teeth. All original in pink and black one-piece swimsuit, goldtone drop earrings. Marks: ©1990/MATTEL INC., on head; ©1991 MATTEL INC./MALAYSIA, on body. $20.00.

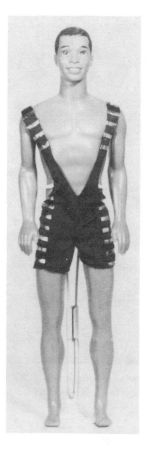

Plate 990: Mattel. "Jamal," #3802 from "Beach Streak Shani" series. ©1992. All original in black body tank suit, black sandals. Marks: ©1991 MATTEL, INC., on head; ©1968/MATTEL, INC./ MALAYSIA, on body. $25.00.

Plate 991: Mattel. "Shani Sizzling Style Fashions," #5967. Gold raincoat and print scarf. ©1991, on package. $10.00.

Plate 992: Mattel. "Shani Sizzling Style Fashions," #5968. Black long dress and gold jacket. ©1991, on package. $10.00.

Plate 993: Mattel. "Shani Sizzling Style Fashions," #5969. Three piece outfit in red, black, and a print. $10.00.

Plate 994: "Shani Fashions," #1896. Gold spaghetti strap dress, long print jacket with fringe at bottom, and blue shoes. $25.00.

Plate 995: Mattel. "Shani Fashions," #1872. Gold top, leather-look jacket and shirt, white shoes. $25.00.

Plate 996: Mattel. "Shani Fashions," #1884. Yellow dress/jacket, long print skirt, briefcase/purse, and yellow shoes. $25.00.

Plate 997: Mattel. "Shani Fashions," #1969. Outfit is shown on "Asha" from the "Shani" collection of dolls by Mattel. Outfit consists of a fuchsia swimsuit and print skirt. $15.00.

Plate 998: Mattel. "Special Expressions Barbie," #10049, ©1992. Woolworth limited edition. All original with long black hair, blue stud earrings, blue print dress, blue shoes. Marks: ©MATTEL, INC./1987, on head; © MATTEL, INC. 1966/CHINA, on body. $10.00.

Plate 999: Mattel. "Birthday Party Barbie," #7948, ©1992. Black rooted hair, painted eyes with pink and blue eyeshadow, pink earrings, swivel waist, bendable knees. All original in long white gown trimmed in blue and pink, holding a birthday cake. Marks: ©MATTEL INC./1987, on head; ©MATTEL INC 1966/MALAYSIA, on body. $25.00.

Plate 1000: Mattel. "Glitter Beach Steven," #4918, ©1992. 12" tall. Molded hair, painted features with painted open mouth, jointed vinyl. All original in green tank top and print glitter shorts, wearing a surfer charm on a string. Marks: ©MATTEL, INC. 1987, on head; ©MATTEL INC/1968/MALAYSIA, on body. $10.00.

Plate 1001: Mattel. "Glitter Beach Christie," #4907, ©1992. Long dark brown hair with lower half in crinkle curl, painted eyes with tan eyeshadow, painted open mouth, bendable knees, swivel waist, necklace with faceted beads, stud earrings, two piece glitter swimsuit. Marks: ©MATTEL INC./1987, on head; ©MATTEL INC. 1966/MALAYSIA, on body. $15.00.

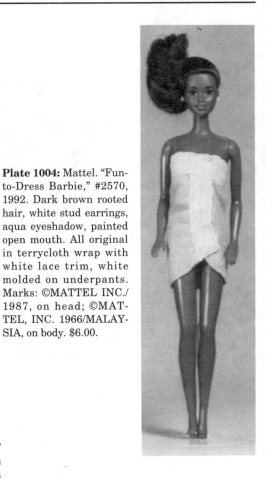

Plate 1004: Mattel. "Fun-to-Dress Barbie," #2570, 1992. Dark brown rooted hair, white stud earrings, aqua eyeshadow, painted open mouth. All original in terrycloth wrap with white lace trim, white molded on underpants. Marks: ©MATTEL INC./ 1987, on head; ©MATTEL, INC. 1966/MALAYSIA, on body. $6.00.

Plate 1002: Mattel. "My First Ken," #3876, ©1992. 12" tall. Easy to dress ballet partner of "My First Barbie." Jointed vinyl, molded hair, painted features with teeth showing. All original in white split back, one-piece jacket with pink and blue trim, and white pants with blue waistband. Marks: ©MATTEL. INC. 1987, on head; ©MATTEL INC./1968/MALAYSIA, on body. $15.00.

Plate 1003: Mattel. "My First Barbie," #2767, ©1992. Long black rooted hair with bangs, straight arms and legs, molded on pink ballet slippers, and white tights. All original in pink ballet outfit. Marks: ©MATTEL, INC./ 1987, on head; ©MATTEL INC. 1966/CHINA, on body. $10.00.

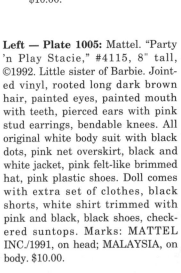

Left — Plate 1005: Mattel. "Party 'n Play Stacie," #4115, 8" tall, ©1992. Little sister of Barbie. Jointed vinyl, rooted long dark brown hair, painted eyes, painted mouth with teeth, pierced ears with pink stud earrings, bendable knees. All original white body suit with black dots, pink net overskirt, black and white jacket, pink felt-like brimmed hat, pink plastic shoes. Doll comes with extra set of clothes, black shorts, white shirt trimmed with pink and black, black shoes, checkered suntops. Marks: MATTEL INC./1991, on head; MALAYSIA, on body. $10.00.

Right — Plate 1006: Mattel. "Romantic Bride Barbie," #11054, ©1992. Jointed vinyl, long dark brown hair, pale lavender eyeshadow, pearlike button earrings, and matching ring. All original. Marks: ©MATTEL INC/1987, on head; MATTEL INC. 1966/CHINA, on body. $22.00.

Plate 1009: Mattel. "Bath Blast Barbie," #3830, ©1992. Dressed in print swimsuit, pierced ears with pink stud earrings. $12.00.

Plate 1007: Mattel. "Army Barbie," #5618 from the "Stars 'n Stripes" series. Special edition doll. ©1992. All original in authentic desert battle dress uniforms of camouflage material. Clothing designed by fashion-product designer Drucilla Lindsey. Made in Malaysia. $22.00.

Plate 1008: Mattel. "Army Ken" from "Stars 'n Stripes" series. $22.00.

Left — Plate 1010: Mattel. "Baton Twirling Skipper," #7498, ©1992. 10". Vinyl head, painted eyes, closed mouth, rooted long dark brown hair, jointed vinyl body with swivel waist and bendable knees. All original with baton in pink and orange cheerleading outfit, pink hat, and boots. Marks: MATTEL INC./1987, on head; ©MATTEL INC. 1987/MALAYSIA, on body. $12.00.

Right — Plate 1011: Mattel. "Fountain Mermaid Barbie," #10522. 11½" tall, 1993. All vinyl, rooted long pink hair, pearl-like stud earring, jointed body with swivel waist. "Magical" crown sprays water. Marks: ©MATTEL INC./1987, on head; MATTEL INC. 1966/CHINA, on body. $16.00.

Plate 1012: Mattel. "Soul Train Jamal," #10288 from the "Shani" collection. 1993. 12" tall. Vinyl head, molded painted black hair, painted eyes, open-closed mouth with painted teeth, pierced left ear with gold-tone earring, jointed vinyl body. All original in blue leather-like shorts and sleeveless jacket with cotton print sleeves, yellow tank top, black boots, matching print hat. Marks: ©1991 MATTEL, INC, on head; ©MATTEL, INC. 1968/MALAYSIA, on body. $25.00.

Plate 1013: Mattel. "Soul Train Asha," #10291 from the "Shani" collection, 1993. 11½". Vinyl head, rooted long brown hair, open-closed mouth with painted teeth, goldtone drop earrings and ring, jointed vinyl body. All original in one piece red short outfit, painted hat with gold braid trim, black boots, red and gold socks, jeweled belt. Marks: ©1990/MATTEL, INC., on head; ©1991 MATTEL INC./MALAYSIA, on body. $25.00.

Plate 1014: Mattel. "Soul Train Shani," #10289, 1993. 11½" tall. All vinyl, long black rooted hair, coral and lavender eyeshadow, goldtone drop earrings and ring, painted open smiling mouth, jointed body with swivel waist. All original in metallic gold short skirt, fuchsia top, African type print hat, jeweled belt. Marks: ©1990/MATTEL INC., on head; ©1991 MATTEL, INC./MALAYSIA, on body. $25.00.

Plate 1015: Mattel. "Soul Train Nichelle," #10290, 1993. 11½". Vinyl doll is from the "Shani" series. Long rooted black hair, painted eyes, closed mouth, goldtone drop earrings, and ring. All original in gold shorts, print crop top with matching hat, black boots. Marks: ©1990/MATTEL INC., on head; ©1991 MATTEL INC./MALAYSIA, on body. $25.00.

Plate 1017: Mattel. "Moonlight Magic Barbie," #10609. Special limited edition, 1993. Jointed vinyl, long black rooted hair, pink and gold eyeshadow, goldtone drop earrings and matching ring. All original. Marks: ©MATTEL INC./1987, on head; MATTEL INC. 1966/MALAYSIA, on body. $30.00.

Plate 1016: Mattel. "Police Officer Barbie," #10689, 1993. Special limited edition from "The Career Collection." This Barbie has the same skin tone as "Asha" from the "Shani" series of fashion dolls by Mattel. Long dark brown rooted hair, painted eyes, and smiling mouth with painted teeth, brown eyeshadow, pierced ears with goldtone stud earrings. Doll comes with extra party dress. $30.00.

Plate 1018: Mattel. "Western Stampin' Barbie," #100539, 1993. Jointed vinyl, rooted dark brown wavy hair, aqua eyeshadow, silvertone boots, earrings, and ring. Special boots can stamp a trail of "B's" with glitter and trail sparkles. All original. Marks: ©MATTEL INC./1987, on head; © MATTEL INC. 1966/CHINA, on body. $13.00.

Plate 1019: Mattel. "Paint 'n Dazzle Barbie," #10058, ©1993. Jointed vinyl, long black straight rooted hair, brown eyeshadow, blue drop earrings and matching ring. All original. Doll comes with Tulip paints for decorating clothing. Marks: © MATTEL INC./1987, on head; © MATTEL INC. 1966/CHINA, on body. $16.00.

Plate 1020: Simplicity Pattern Co. "Hammertime." ©1991. Simplicity pattern #7603, wardrobe design exclusively for the M.C. Hammer doll. Doll is shown in *Black Dolls, 1820–1991*, page 222. $10.00.

Plate 1021: Mattel. "M.C. Hammer Original Fashions," #1094. Red pants with red, purple, and pink striped top, black shoes. Tagged. $15.00.

Plate 1022: Mattel. "M.C. Hammer Original Fashions," #1091. Black pants with multicolored top, black shoes. Tagged. $15.00.

Plate 1023: Mattel. "M.C. Hammer Original Fashions," #1093. Blue and silver pants and jacket, fuchsia cummerbund, black shoes. Tagged. $15.00.

Plate 1024: Mattel. "Make Me Pretty Barbie." 8" tall. Vinyl head, rooted black hair, painted eyes with blue eyeshadow, pierced ears, painted open smiling mouth. Base is lavender with lavender necklace and earrings. Original box shows the same doll with pink jewelry. Marks: ©MATTEL, INC. 1988, on head. $15.00.

Plate 1025: Mattel. "Barbie Color Change Makeup Head," #7369. Made by Arco, a division of Mattel. 9½" tall. When you add water, her makeup appears. Included is a pink plastic vanity to store accessories. Vinyl head, rooted black hair, lavender base, pink jewelry, yellow and pink plastic hair bow. Marks: ©MATTEL, INC. 1988, on head; ARCO/CHINA, inside base. $30.00.

Plate 1026: Mattel "Birthday Surprise Barbie" miniature doll made for McDonald's Happy Meal. 4" tall. Molded dark brown hair, orange gown, holding a blue gift tied with a green ribbon. Mark: MADE FOR MCDONALD'S/©1992 MATTEL, INC. 04/MADE IN CHINA SV 04, on bottom. $5.00.

Plate 1027: Mattel. "Happy Birthday Barbie" miniature made for McDonald's Happy Meal. 4" tall. Molded on long pink gown. Marks: MADE FOR MCDONALD'S/©1991 MATTEL, INC. 05/MADE IN CHINA QX 05, on bottom. $10.00.

Plate 1029: Mattel. "Heart Family Kiss & Cuddle Dad & Baby Girl," 1986. Dad is wearing a red jacket with blue lapel and blue pants. Baby Girl is wearing a red dress. Also available were Mom & Baby Boy. They are shown in author's earlier book, *Black Dolls, 1820–1991* on page 223. $25.00.

Plate 1028: Mattel. "Heart Family New Arrival," 1985, #2499. Mom, Dad, and Baby. All jointed vinyl doll, mom has rooted reddish brown hair, painted brown eyes with charcoal gray eyeshadow, slightly parted lips, all original in pink dress with white lace overskirt and sleeves. Dad is jointed vinyl with molded black hair, brown painted eyes, smiling mouth with painted teeth, all original in white pants, ink shirt and blue vest and tie. Vinyl baby has molded black hair, painted features, and is all original in yellow bunting. $55.00.

Plate 1030: Mattel. "Gladiator Gemini," #4015, from the "American Gladiators." 3¾". Vinyl action figure with movable head, waist, and arms. Molded on red, white, and blue outfit. Comes with official joust equipment. Marks: ©1991/S. GOLD-WYN CO./CHINA, on lower back. Back of shirt is imprinted "American Gladiators." Collection of Todd Perkins. $10.00.

Plate 1031: Mattel. "Blue Challenger" from "American Gladiators" series "Blue Challenger VS Gladiator Laser," a white figure. #3970. 3½". Vinyl figure jointed at neck, waist, and shoulders in molded on blue tanktop imprinted with "American Gladiators" on front and back, blue pants and white boots. Marks: ©1991/S. GOLDWYN CO./CHINA, on lower back. Collection of Todd Perkins. $10.00.

Plate 1032: Mego. "Diana Ross" fashions from the "TV Stars Fashion Collection," 1977. "Rhymes" fashion, #78000, mint green long slim dress with glittery stole. $25.00.

Plate 1033: Mego. "Baby Sez So," 1976, 18" tall. Battery operated talking doll. When you press the heart on front of dress she says, "I love you, mommy." Press the flower and she says, "Baby pretty now." Insert spoon into her mouth and she says, "Yummy yummy yummy." Insert bottle in the mouth and she says, "I like my bottle." Press the diaper pin and she says, "Mommy change me." Vinyl head, arms, and legs, hard plastic body, rooted brown hair, painted eyes, open mouth. All original in pink cotton dress. Marks: MEGO CORP./19©76, on head; PAT. PEND./©1976 MEGO CORP., on body. $95.00.

Plate 1034: Mego. "Planet of the Apes." Molded "ape" face with molded hair, painted eyes, jointed vinyl body. Marks: ©MEGO CORP. 1974/REG. U.S. PAT. OFF./PAT. PENDING/HONG KONG, on body; ©APJAC PROD. INC./20TH CENTURY FOX FILM CORP. 1974, on head. 7¾" tall. $30.00.

Plate 1035: Mego. "Isaac" from "The Love Boat," ©1981. Jointed vinyl action figure with molded on clothing, red jacket, white shirt with bow tie, black pants. Isaac has molded black hair and mustache, painted eyes, closed mouth. 3½" tall. Role was played by Ted Lange. Marks: ©1981 AARON SPELLING/PRODUCTIONS,/MADE IN HONG KONG, on body. $30.00.

Plate 1036: Mego. "Falcon," 1974. 8" tall. This is the only black doll in the "Superheros" series from the 1970's by Mego. All vinyl, jointed at waist, wrist, elbow, knee, ankle. Black painted eyes, molded painted hair. All original in red and white outfit. Marks: MARVEL C. G. 1974, on head; MEGO CORP. 1974/ REG. U.S. PAT. OFF./PAT. PENDING/HONG KONG, on back. $150.00.

Plate 1037: Meritus. "Baby Beans." ©1991. Vinyl head, painted eyes, rooted black hair, closed mouth, pink flannel body and limbs with brown flannel hands, removable pink flannel bonnet. 11" tall. Marks: MERITUS INC., INC./LIVINGSTON, N.M. 07039/..., tag sewn to body. Doll's name is printed on the bib of doll's sewn on outfit. $12.00.

Plate 1038: Edward Mobley Company. "Sunbabe" or "Candy." 8" tall. Molded vinyl squeaker doll. Movable head, molded hair, painted eyes, closed mouth, squeaker in back of head, body and limbs are one piece with molded on white dress, socks, and shoes. Doll is holding a teddy bear. Marks: 6/THE EDWARD MOBLEY CO., on head; THE EDWARD MOBLEY CO./1962/ MFD. BY/ARROW RUBBER & PLASTICS CORP., on body. (Some of the marks were blurred and had to be assumed based on the parts that were completely readable.) Collection of the Museum of African American History (Detroit). $93.00.

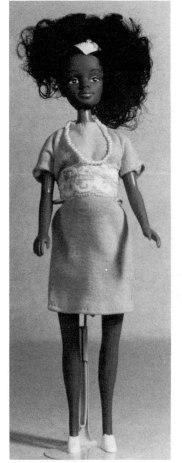

Plate 1039: Mommy to Be Inc. "Mommy-To-Be." ©1992. 11½". Vinyl doll with baby inside the tummy. Rooted black hair, painted eyes, closed mouth. All original in pink knit dressed. Doll is identical, except for clothing, to the mommy-to-be doll issued by the Judith Corporation. Marks: JUDITH/2 (backwards), on back. This doll has an unmarked baby girl inside. $20.00.

Left — Plate 1040: Multi Toys. "Wedding Bells" from the "Modern Bride" collection. 11½" fashion doll. Vinyl head, rooted long brown hair, painted features, jointed vinyl body with bendable knees. All original in tiered white wedding gown and veil. Marks: ©MULTI TOYS/CORP 1985, on head; 1985 MULTI TOYS CORP./MADE IN CHINA, on body. Style No. 6016. Box is marked ©1990, 1991. "Modern Bride" is a trademark of Cahners Publishing Company. $10.00.

Right — Plate 1041: Multi Toys. "Mermaids," ©1991. 11½". Vinyl fashion doll, rooted brown hair, painted brown eyes with pink eyeshadow, painted open mouth with teeth, swivel waist, jointed body. All original in two-piece mermaid outfit with blue nylon boa. Marks: ©MULTI TOYS/CORP 1985, on head; ©1985 MULTI TOYS CORP./MADE IN CHINA, on body. $10.00.

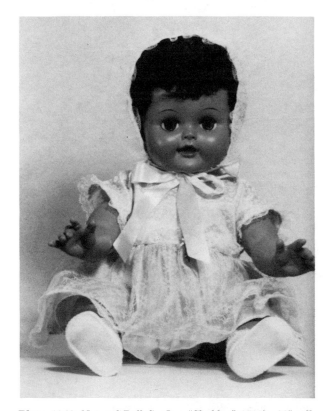

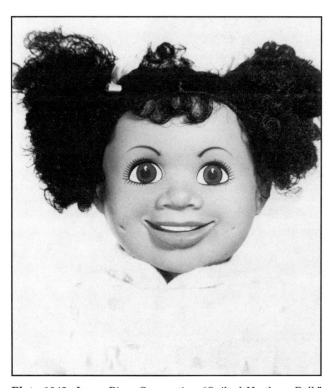

Plate 1042: Natural Doll Co. Inc. "Chubby," 1960's. 20" tall. Drinks and wets, vinyl head, rooted black hair, sleeping brown eyes with lashes, nursing mouth, vinyl body. All original in nylon dress with pink bodice and blue skirt, blue lace overskirt, matching pink bonnet, white shoes and socks. Marks: 67P, on head. $70.00.

Plate 1043: James River Corporation. "Quilted Northern Doll." 16". Vinyl head and hands, brown cloth body, limbs, and feet, painted eyes, rooted black hair. Dressed in pink flannel pajamas and comes with a cloth "quilted tissue" square. Doll available through the mail for $11.95 and two UPC symbols from Quilted Northern tissue. Marks: NORTHERN™ DOLL/©JAMES RIVER CORP. 1933, on head. $12.00.

Plate 1044: NASB. Nancy Ann Storybook "Mammy" with white baby. 5¼" tall. Painted bisque, jointed legs, molded socks, three white buttons on side of shoes. Circa 1940. Photograph courtesy of Lu Lane. $550.00.

Plate 1045: Nancy Ann Storybook Doll. "Topsy," 5¼" tall. Painted bisque, molded black boots, pudgy tummy. All original. Marks: JUDY/ANN/USA, on torso. Courtesy of Susan Girardot. $200.00+.

Plate 1046: Nancy Ann Storybook. 5½". "Topsy." Hard plastic with sleeping black eyes, black mohair wig, jointed hard plastic body. All original in cotton pastel dress in yellow, blue, green, and red stripes with lace trim, molded on black shoes. Marks: STORY BOOK/DOLLS/U.S.A./TRADEMARK/REG., on back. $120.00.

Plate 1047: Storybook. 5½". "Topsy." Hard plastic with painted eyes, black mohair wig, jointed body on black shoes. All original in red plaid taffeta dress trimmed with white lace on skirt, two red hair ribbons. Marks: STORY BOOK/DOLLS/U.S.A./TRADE MARK/REG., on body. $120.00.

Plate 1048: Nancy Ann Storybook. "Nigeria." 5½" tall. Jointed hard plastic, sleeping brown eyes with painted eyelashes and eyebrows, black mohair wig, painted mouth, painted on black slipper shoes. All original in long white dress trimmed with gold rickrack, matching long headpiece. This doll was made by Albert M. Bourla who bought the rights to NASB after the company declared bankruptcy in 1965. The Bourla dolls were made in Hong Kong. This doll is a lighter shade of brown than the original NASB dolls. Marks: STORY BOOK/DOLLS/U.S.A./ TRADE MARK/REG., on back. $85.00.

HISTORY OF OLMEC TOYS, INC.
(from information supplied by the company.)

- Olmec Toys, Inc., was founded in 1985 when Yla Eason, an African-American businesswoman and mother, realized the toy industry provided no black superhero toys for her three-year-old son to play with. Realizing this void for African-American and Hispanic children, Eason, a Harvard M.B.A. graduate, felt impelled to act. Thus, she created what has become a $2.9 million business in just eight years.

- Sun-Man, a superhero action figure, and the Bronze Bombers, a troop of 3¾" figures fashioned after an ethnic army unit from World Wars I and II, were the first products introduced by Olmec.

- In 1993, Olmec's inventory has expanded to include 26 products, including heroic action figures, fashion dolls, cuddly baby dolls, and accessories.

- Since 1990, Olmec has received financial, marketing, and technical assistance from Hasbro, Inc., the world's largest toy manufacturer.

- How did Olmec Toys get its name? Yla Eason named the company after an ancient Mexican civilization that sculpted 6-foot-high stone heads of Africans who came as traders to South America. These stone heads date back to 1600 B.C.

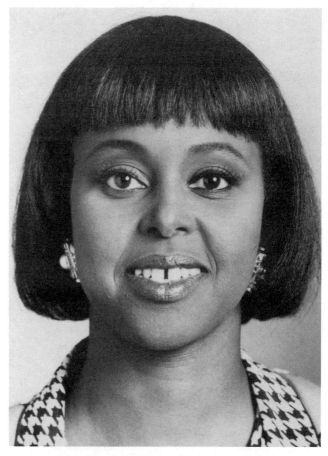

Plate 1049: Yla Eason, president of Olmec Toys, Inc. Photograph courtesy of Olmec Toys, Inc.

Plate 1050: Olmec. "Imani Royal Princess," #30035. ©1992. 11½". Vinyl head and jointed body with swivel waist and bendable knees. Head mold is new. Long black crimped hair, lavender and pink eyeshadow, lips slightly parted with thin line of teeth showing. All original in body suit under African robe. Marks: ©1992/OLMEC TOYS/INC., on head. Photograph courtesy of Olmec Toys. Inc. $18.00.

Left Above — Plate 1051: Olmec. "Dr. Martin Luther King, Jr." 6". Action figure with movable head and arms. Posed as if giving his famous "I have a Dream" speech at the Washington Monument. Figure comes with an 18 minute tape which includes a recording of the speech and brief biography. The figure is licensed with permission from Mrs. Coretta Scott King and the estate of Dr. Martin Luther King, Jr. Photograph courtesy of Olmec Toys, Inc. $18.00.

Plate 1052: Olmec. "Desk Set." ©1989. Set includes a pink and white plastic, chair, school supplies, and color changing "magic" stickers. $20.00.

Plate 1053: Olmec. "Naomi Hair Dryer Set." ©1988. Includes nine piece hair dryer set with canopy. Battery operated. $25.00.

Plate 1054: Olmec. "Naomi Fashions." ©1988. Green plaid pants and cap, pale blue sweater trimmed in yellow, green tank top, yellow shoes. $15.00.

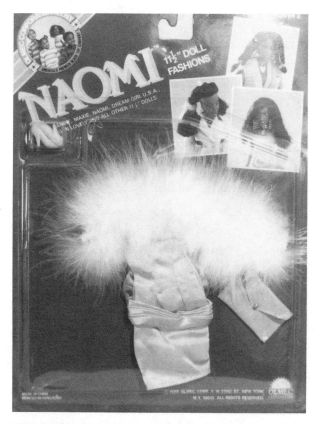

Plate 1055: Olmec. "Naomi Fashions." ©1988. Gold knee length strapless dress with pink bow in back, white feather wrap, pink plastic purse, yellow shoes. $15.00.

Plate 1056: Olmec. "Naomi Fashions." ©1988. $15.00.

Plate 1057: Olmec. "Naomi Fashions." ©1988. $15.00.

Plate 1058: Olmec. "Naomi Fashions." ©1988. $15.00.

Plate 1059: Olmec. " Naomi Fashions." ©1988. $15.00.

Plate 1060: Olmec. "Naomi Fashions." ©1988. $15.00.

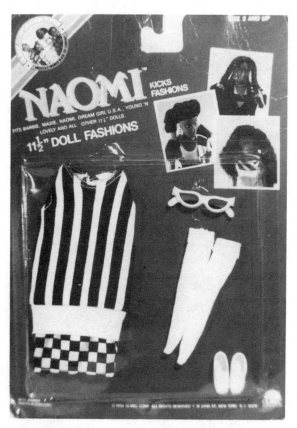

Plate 1061: Olmec. "Naomi Fashions." ©1988. $15.00.

Plate 1062: Olmec. "Naomi Fashions." ©1988. $15.00.

Plate 1063: Olmec. "Imani Wedding Magic," ©1991. Vinyl head, rooted black hair, painted brown eyes with blue eyeshadow, painted open mouth, jointed vinyl body. All original in white satiny gown with lacy overskirt and bodice, veil with lacy cap, earrings and ring. Marks: 1987/OLMEC/CORP., on head; MADE IN CHINA, on body. 11½" tall. $20.00.

Plate 1064: Olmec. "Imani Prom Time," ©1991. Vinyl head, painted brown eyes, rooted long black hair styled with bangs, painted open mouth, jointed vinyl body, pierced ears with earrings. All original in pink and white strapless gown. 11½" tall. Marks: 1987/OLMEC/CORP., on head; MADE IN CHINA, on body. $20.00.

Left — Plate 1065: Olmec. "Imani African Fantasy," ©1991. Vinyl head, long rooted black hair in braids, painted eyes, painted open mouth, pierced ears with gold earrings, jointed vinyl body. 11½" tall. All original in long skirt with gold fan bottom, two layer short skirt, sleeveless pullover tank top, gold collar style necklace, matching hat. Extra set of clothing came with the doll: puff sleeve jacket and full Kente style pants. Marks: 1987/OLMEC/CORP., on head; MADE IN CHINA, on body. Available in a variety of different outfits. $20.00.

Right — Plate 1066: Olmec. "Imani Holiday Fun," ©1991. Vinyl head, painted eyes with blue eyeshadow, painted open mouth, rooted long black hair with bangs, pierced ears with gold earrings, jointed vinyl body. All original in long red double layered skirt with shiny red strapless top and ruffled boa sleeves. 11½" tall. Marks: 1987/OLMEC/CORP., on head; MADE IN CHINA, on body. $20.00.

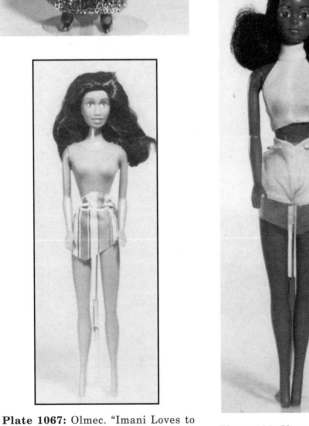

Plate 1067: Olmec. "Imani Loves to Swim," ©1991. Vinyl head, painted eyes with blue eyeshadow, rooted black hair, open smiling mouth, jointed vinyl body. 11½" tall. All original in green swimsuit and Kente cloth scarf tied around waist. Marks: 1987/OLMEC/CORP., on head; MADE IN CHINA, on body. Doll is also available in a red swimsuit. $10.00.

Plate 1068: Olmec. "Imani Loves to Swim," ©1992. 11½". Jointed vinyl doll has a new face. All original in orange and yellow outfit. Marks: ©1992/OLMEC TOYS/INC., on head; MADE IN CHINA, on body. $5.00.

Plate 1069: Olmec. "Imani and Menelik Wedding," #30023, ©1991. 11½" and 12" tall. All original in white bridal gown and black tuxedo with Kente cloth accessories. $25.00.

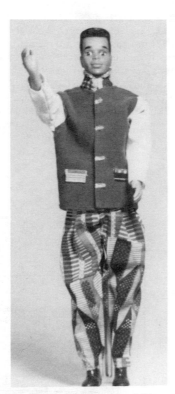

Plate 1070: Olmec. "Menelik Kente Fun," #30024. 12". Jointed vinyl, painted eyes, sculpted hair. All original in Kente-type clothing. Marks: ©OLMEC, on head. $10.00.

Plate 1071: Olmec. "Menelik," an African American Prince. Vinyl head, jointed vinyl body with swivel waist, molded black hair in hi-top fade style, painted features, closed mouth. All original in Kente cloth outfit. 12". Doll was named after the president of Olmec's son, Menelik. Marks: ©OLMEC, on head. $10.00.

Plate 1072: Olmec. "Imani Kente Fun," ©1991. 11½". Jointed vinyl fashion doll, rooted black hair, painted eyes with blue eyeliner, pierced ears with goldtone stud earrings and matching ring. All original in Kente cloth with gold scarf. Marks: 1987/OLMEC/CORP, on head, MADE IN CHINA, on body. $10.00.

Plate 1073: Olmec. "Ellisse Gift Set," ©1989. Set includes Ellisse doll and 75 piece set. Ellisse doll was previously named "Naomi." The name was later changed to "Imani." All of the clothing in this set is black and white, either solids, stripes, or checks. $30.00.

Plate 1074: Olmec. "Imani Goes Shopping," ©1992. 11½"
doll with the "new" face. Set includes 50 piece gift set in
African type print cloth. $15.00.

Plate 1075: Olmec. "Imani Gift Set," ©1990. Includes 75 piece
gift set and Imani doll. Imani was *Doll Reader* magazine's
"Dolls of the Year" nominee for 1988. On the back of this box, a
set of "Imani" paper dolls are printed as a free gift. $25.00.

Plate 1076: Olmec. "Imani Goes Shopping," #30017,
©1991. 11½". Vinyl doll with 50 piece gift set, includes
four complete outfits to mix and match. $20.00.

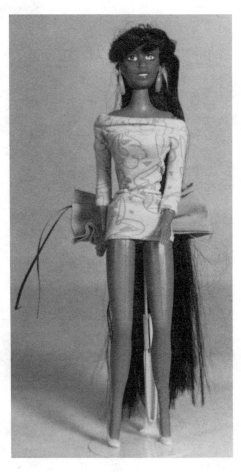

Plate 1077: Olmec. "Crimp 'n Go Imani," ©1992. 11½". Long crimped black hair that goes to her feet, blue eyeshadow, painted open mouth, swivel waist, bendable knees. All original in short, yellow print knit dress, yellow heels. Marks: 1987/OLMEC/CORP, on head; MADE IN CHINA, on back. $15.00.

Plate 1078: Olmec. "Rock & Roll Soul Imani," 1992. 11½" tall. Vinyl jointed doll, rooted long black hair in eight braids, painted features, pierced ears with silver hoop earrings. Dressed in two-toned green outfit with roller blades. Marks: ©1992/OLMEC TOYS/INC., on head; MADE IN CHINA, on back. $15.00.

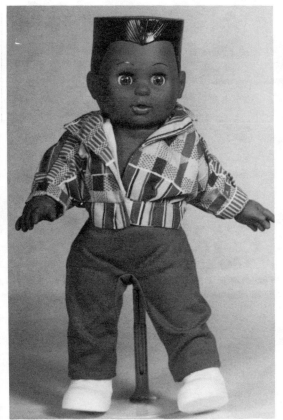

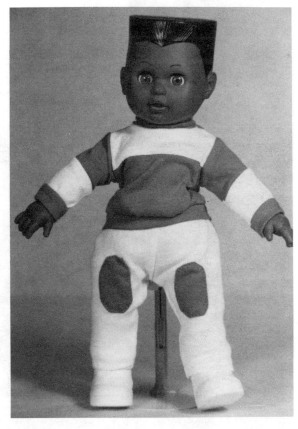

Left — Plate 1079: Olmec. "M.C. Cool," #70006C with "hi-top fade" molded hair. Vinyl head, sleeping amber eyes with real lashes, open-closed mouth, vinyl arms and legs, brown cloth body. 12" tall. All original in Kente cloth jacket, yellow cotton vest sewn to green cotton knit jumpsuit, white plastic shoes and socks. Marks: OLMEC/CHINA, on back. $15.00.

Right — Plate 1080: Olmec. "L.L. Fresh," #700061 from the "Hip Hop Kids." Vinyl head with molded black hi-top fade hairstyle, sleeping brown eyes, vinyl arms and legs, cloth body. All original in red and white sweatsuit. Marks: OLMEC/CHINA, on head. $20.00.

Left — Plate 1081: Olmec. "Lo-Lo," #7006E from the "Hip Hop Kids" series. Vinyl head, arms, and legs, brown cloth body, sleeping brown eyes, rooted black hair, open-closed mouth. All original in Kente cloth outfit. 12" tall. Marks: OLMEC/ CHINA, on head. $20.00.

Right — Plate 1082: Olmec. "Jamal," #7006 from the "Hip Hop Kids." 13" tall. Vinyl head, arms, and legs, brown cloth body, molded black hair, sleeping brown eyes, open-closed mouth. All original in three piece Kente cloth outfit. Marks: OLMEC/ CHINA, on head. $15.00.

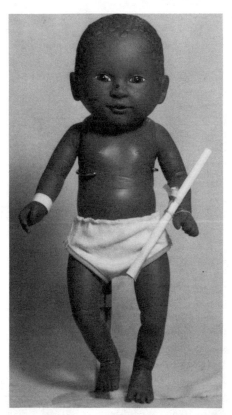

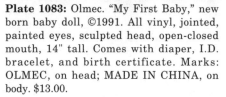

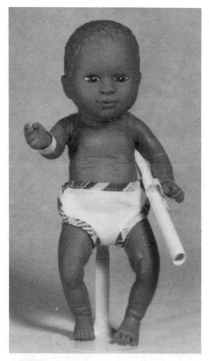

Plate 1083: Olmec. "My First Baby," new born baby doll, ©1991. All vinyl, jointed, painted eyes, sculpted head, open-closed mouth, 14" tall. Comes with diaper, I.D. bracelet, and birth certificate. Marks: OLMEC, on head; MADE IN CHINA, on body. $13.00.

Plate 1084: Olmec. "My First Baby," ©1991. 9" tall. Vinyl head, painted eyes, sculpted hair, open-closed mouth, jointed viny body. All original in white diapers with Kente cloth trim. Marks: OLMEC, on head. $5.00.

Plate 1085: Olmec. "Linda," ©1991, #9002. Vinyl head, sleeping brown eyes with lashes, rooted black hair in two braids, vinyl arms and legs, brown cloth body. 14" toddler doll. All original in Kente cloth dress. Doll was available in two other similar outfits. Marks: OLMEC©/1989, on head. $17.00.

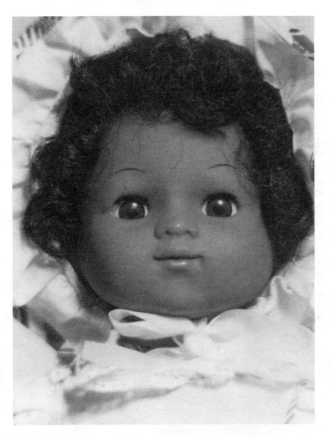

Plate 1087: Olmec. "Jean Gift Set," #9027. 14" baby doll with three outfits. Vinyl head, arms, and legs, cloth body, rooted black hair, sleeping brown eyes, closed mouth, ©1991. $30.00.

Plate 1086: Olmec. "Amandla," 1991. Vinyl head, sleeping brown eyes with lashes, rooted black hair, vinyl arms and legs, brown cloth body, closed mouth. All original in special Kente cloth outfit that came in three different styles. 16" baby doll. Marks: OLMEC/1989, on head. $18.00.

Plate 1088: Olmec. "Sunday Babies," #9009, ©1991. 7". Vinyl head, arms, and legs, rooted short black hair, sleeping brown eyes, closed mouth, brown cloth body. All original in Kente cloth outfit. Outfit is available in three different styles, tagged: GIGO TOYS. Cloth body is also tagged GIGO TOYS, MADE IN CHINA. $6.00.

Plate 1089: Olmec. "Sandy," 1991. Toddler doll 9½" tall. Vinyl head, rooted black hair styled in two braids with bangs, sleeping brown eyes, vinyl arms and legs, cloth body. All original in Kente cloth dress with white panties, socks, and shoes. Marks: OLMEC/1989, on head. $10.00.

Plate 1090: Olmec. "Jennifer," ©1991, #9001, toddler doll. Vinyl head, sleeping amber eyes with lashes, rooted black hair, closed mouth, vinyl arms and legs, brown cloth body. 12" tall. All original in Kente cloth outfit with blue striped trim. Doll was available in several different outfits. Marks: OLMEC©/1989, on head. $16.00.

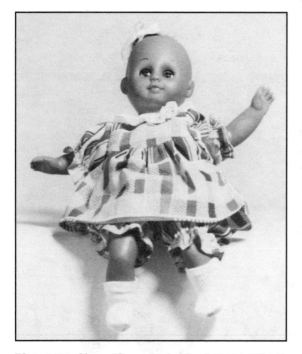

Plate 1092: Olmec "Kareema." 12". Hair fashion doll you can style and braid with beads. Vinyl head, arms, and legs, brown cloth body, rooted black hair, sleeping amber/brown eyes, closed mouth. All original in print jumpsuit. Marks: OLMEC©/1989, on head. Box is marked: ©1992. $20.00.

Plate 1091: Olmec. "Sweet Little Miss," #9017. 8½" tall. Vinyl head, tuft of rooted black hair tied with yellow ribbon, sleeping brown eyes, closed mouth, vinyl arms and legs, brown cloth body. All original in Kente dress with matching bloomers. Marks: GI-GO TOYS FTY LTD./.../ MADE IN CHINA, sewn to body. Doll was available in several outfits. $7.00.

Left — Plate 1093: Olmec. "Jamaica." 18". Vinyl head, arms, and legs, brown cloth body, rooted brown hair, painted eyes, open-closed mouth with painted teeth. Original clothes. Marks: © OLMEC CORP. 1992, on head. $25.00.

Right — Plate 1094: Olmec. "Lois," #9003. 16" tall. Toddler doll with vinyl head, arms, and legs, brown cloth body, rooted black hair, sleeping brown eyes, closed mouth. All original in blue and white striped dress with attached Kente cloth apron, white panties, shoes, and socks. Marks: OLMEC/1989, on head. Box is marked ©1991. Made in China. $25.00.

Plate 1095: Olmec. "Agent Telepathy," action figure from the "Bronze Bombers" series. 4" tall. ©1988. All vinyl, fully jointed, swivel waist, molded black hair, closed mouth, molded on black shirt with silver trim, fuchsia pants with silver cap molded on head. Unmarked. $10.00.

Plate 1096: Olmec. "A.J. Moon." Molded on black and silver outfit. Collection of Todd Perkins. $10.00.

Plate 1097: Olmec. "Mapman Jackson" from the "Bronze Bombers." 3¾". Jointed vinyl, molded on green outfit with orange spots, beard and mustache. Collection of Todd Perkins. $10.00.

Plate 1098: Olmec. "Sure Fire" from the "Bronze Bombers." Molded on brown clothes. Collection of Todd Perkins. $10.00.

Plate 1099: Olmec. "Wayne 'Golden' Alexander." Molded on blue and white navy outfit. Collection of Todd Perkins. $10.00.

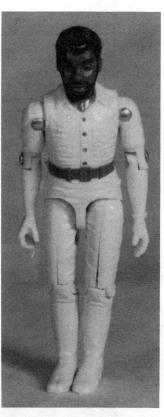

Plate 1100: Olmec. "Cool Breeze P.S.B. Enemy." Molded on white outfit trimmed in red. Collection of Todd Perkins. $10.00.

Plate 1101: Olmec. "Marc Kaboom Walters." Molded on navy blue outfit. Collection of Todd Perkins. $10.00.

Plate 1102: Olmec. "Hi Tech." Molded on orange outfit. Collection of Todd Perkins. $10.00.

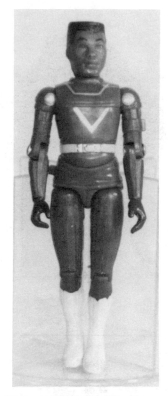

Plate 1103: Olmec. "The Baron P.S.B." Molded on purple outfit with yellow boots. Collection of Todd Perkins. $10.00.

Plate 1104: Olmec. "Arrow Hawk." Molded on olive top, gold pants. Collection of Todd Perkins. $10.00.

Plate 1105: Olmec. "Shaka Johnson." Molded on olive outfit with yellow spots. Collection of Todd Perkins. $10.00.

Plate 1106: Olmec. "Charles 'Chilly Pop' Battle P.S.B. Enemy." Mustache, molded on purple outfit with yellow boots. Collection of Todd Perkins. $10.00.

Left — Plate 1107: Vinyl teen doll from circa 1960. Rooted long black hair, sleeping amber eyes with one piece lashes, closed mouth, jointed hard vinyl body with high-heel feet. 9" tall. All original in dress with white batiste bodice and printed skirt, stapled on pink flannel panties and black plastic high-heeled shoes. Marks: P (in a circle), on head. High-heel fashion dolls are not commonly seen in this small size. $100.00.

Right — Plate 1108: PM Sales, Inc. "Ladies Boudoir Doll," #59592 612 28340. 23" tall. Vinyl head, rooted black hair, sleeping brown eyes, heavy painted on black eyeshadow, closed mouth, jointed vinyl body. All original in sewn and glued on long pink satin gown with pink lace trim. Original box says doll is fully jointed to sit on bed. Made in U.S.A. Marks: P M SALES INC/©1966/SD/13, on head. $60.00.

Plate 1109: Plastic Molded Arts. Walker doll. Hard plastic head, black glued on wig, sleeping amber eyes, open mouth with two upper teeth, red felt tongue, jointed hard plastic walker body. All original in Hawaiian outfit. 16" tall. Marks: PLASTIC MOLDED ARTS COL. L.I.C. NEW YORK, on body. $250.00.

Plate 1110: P.S.M.I. "Walter Payton." 7" tall. Jointed vinyl action figure of football player Walter Payton who played for the Chicago Bears. Molded on clothes, blue jersey, white pants, blue helmet. Marks: TAIWAN/©1977 P.S.M.I., inside right leg. Collection of Todd Perkins. $35.00.

Left — Plate 1111: Panosh Place. "Honey Combs," 1985. 18". Vinyl head, arms, and legs, hard plastic body, rooted black curly hair, painted eyes, open-closed mouth. All original doll came in several different outfits with different facial features. Marks: ©1985 PANOSH PLACE/27, on head; ©1985 PANOSH PLACE/CHINA, on body. $85.00.

Right — Plate 1112: Panosh. "Honey Combs" with a different facial expression and original outfit. Closed mouth, thick rooted black hair, painted eyes, ball jointed. Photograph courtesy of Phyllis Schlatter. $85.00.

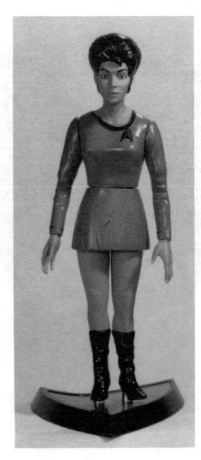

Left — Plate 1113: Another all original "Honey Combs." This one has hot pink sweater outfit. Marks: ©1985 PANOSH PLACE/14, on head; ©1985 PANOSH PLACE/CHINA, on body. $85.00.

Right — Plate 1114: Paramount Pictures. "Uhura." 10". Vinyl figure from "Star Trek" series. Molded hair, painted features, jointed at shoulders and waist, molded on high-heeled black boots, red dress. Marks: STAR TREK/™ ® & ©1991 PAR. PIC./HAMILTON AUTHORIZED USER/MADE IN CHINA, on back. $26.00.

Plate 1115: Dolls by Pauline. "Little Love," #38128. 8". Vinyl head, rooted curly black hair, stationary dark brown eyes, open-closed mouth, vinyl arms and legs, tan cloth body. All original in pink striped tagged dress. Marks: ©PBJ, on head. Available on the market in the early 1990's. Collection of Haille Nichole Perkins. $20.00.

Plate 1116: Dolls by Pauline. "Liza," #38115. 11" tall. Vinyl head, arms, and legs, rooted black curly hair, sleeping brown eyes, closed mouth, tan cloth body. All original in heart print dress with name embroidered on attached bib, pink leather-like slippers, white bloomers. Doll was designed by Pauline Bjonness-Jacobsen for "Applause, Inc." Made in the Philippines. Marks: PBJ (inside heart)/91984, on head. Collection of Mackenzie Gayle Scott. $45.00.

Plate 1118: Pedigree. "Sindy," 1980. 11½" tall. All vinyl, jointed waist, brown painted eyes with insert lashes, black rooted hair. All original. Marks: 033055X, on head. Photograph courtesy of Stephanie Lisoski. $25.00+.

Plate 1117: Dolls By Pauline. "Emily," #38187. 15" tall. Vinyl head, arms, and legs, tan cloth body, dark brown curly acrylic wig, stationary acrylic brown eyes with lashes, open-closed mouth. All original in lavender dotted dress with tagged floral print pinafore, lavender cloth shoes. Marks: © PBJ, on head. G1992, on box. $75.00.

Plate 1119: Phoenix. "Eclair" from the "Charlotte Russe" collection. ©1983, printed on the box. Vinyl head, painted black eyes, rooted brown hair, painted closed mouth and five red freckles, jointed hard vinyl body and limbs. 5" tall. All original in brown dotted long dress, white apron, and brown felt hat with white pompoms on the top. Marks: ©1962/PHOENIX TOTS, INC., on head; HONG KONG, on body. Doll came in a cup with a bottom like an ice cream on a push up stick. A hole in the shoes and the bottom of the feet can attach to the push up stick. Doll is said to have possibly been an advertising doll. $45.00.

Plate 1120: Play Vogue Ind. Co. Ltd. 14". Vinyl head, arms, and legs, pink cloth body, molded hair, painted eyes, open-closed mouth, redressed. Two fingers on right hand have been chewed off. Marks: 5140/HONG KONG, on head. Tag sewn to body: PL-V/.../PLAY VOGUE IND. CO. LTD./... . $20.00.

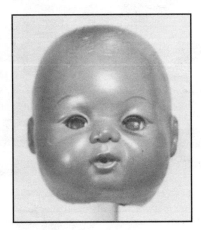

Plate 1121: Plated Moulds. Head only. Vinyl, sleeping amber eyes with one piece lashes, molded hair, nursing mouth. Head is 3½" tall. Marks: AE 37/ PLATED MOULDS/©1961. $15.00.

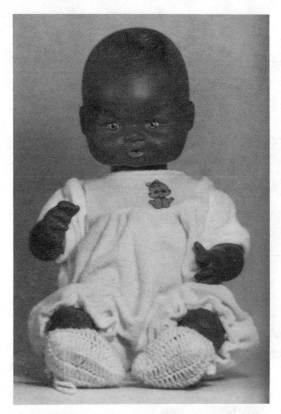

Plate 1122: Plated Moulds. "Baby." 16". Vinyl head, painted hair, stationary amber eyes, nursing mouth, bent-leg vinyl body. Redressed. Marks: PLATED MOULDS INC/© 1961, on head. $65.00.

Plate 1123: Playgroup (TCA Group Inc.). "Wendy Walka-long," 1991, #88043. Doll has realistic walking action, hold her hand and she will walk with you. Vinyl head, rooted reddish brown curly hair, sleeping amber eyes, open-closed mouth, jointed vinyl body with walking action. 28" tall. Doll is all original in print sundress trimmed in blue striped and yellow dotted fabrics. Doll came with child size flowered plastic shoulder bag. Marks: 1280, on head; MADE IN CHINA 1280, on back. $35.00.

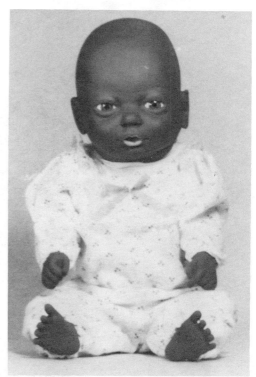

Plate 1124: Playgroup. "Care For Me Baby." 18" tall. Jointed vinyl baby, molded hair, stationary brown eyes, nursing mouth, dimpled chin. Doll cries and moves its body when "hungry" and stops when bottle is put into its mouth. Battery operated. All original in flannel pajamas. Marks: TCA/MADE IN CHINA, on head; pg (superimposed)/PLAYGROUP/MADE IN CHINA, on body. 1992. $30.00.

Plate 1125: Playmates. "Jill," #9405. 33" tall. Animated talking doll that moves her head, arms, and eyes when she talks. Vinyl head, hard plastic jointed body and limbs, rooted brown curly hair. Jill cassette comes with the doll, other cassettes and outfits are sold separately. 1987. $250.00.

Plate 1126: Playmate. "Little Baby Water Babies Doll," #1291. 10". You fill the doll with warm water and she feels like a real baby. Vinyl head, one piece vinyl body with plug to hold water in body, molded hair, painted eyes, closed mouth. All original in white printed bunting. Marks: ©LAUER TOYS, INC. 1991, on head. $13.00.

Plate 1127: Playmates. 12". Vinyl head, painted eyes, nursing mouth, painted sculptured hair, one-piece vinyl baby body. All original in long white cotton gown trimmed in white lace. Doll comes in a white plastic cradle, 13½" x 8" x 7" that chimes when rocked, pink flannel blanket. Marks: 8122 PLAYMATES (in logo) 1.4.77/HONG KONG, on head. First line of marks on body are not legible. Remainder are HONG KONG/42. Collection of the Museum of African American History (Detroit). $25.00.

Plate 1128: Playmates. "Lt. Com. Geordi La Forge" from "Star Trek: The Next Generation." 1992. Stock #6015. 4½". Jointed vinyl figure with molded on gold and black outfit. each figure is individually numbered. This one is #192597, on left foot. Marks on right foot: ©1992 PAR. PIC./PLAY-MATES TOYS. Role is played by actor LaVar Burton. $6.00.

Plate 1129: Playmates. "Lieutenant (JG) Geordi La Forge" in "Star Trek: The Next Generation" first season uniform. Stock number 6075. 1993. 4½". Molded on burgundy and black outfit. Individually numbered on left foot, this figure is #038930. $8.00.

Plate 1130: Playmates. "Lt. Commander Geordi La Forge" in dress uniform. Stock #6026. 1993. 4½". Molded on gold tunic with black trim and black pants. Number 026375 on left foot. $8.00.

Plate 1131: Playmates. "Guinan" from "Star Trek: The Next Generation." 4½". Stock #6020. Molded on red clothing. Role is played by actress Whoopi Goldberg. Figure is numbered 120523 on left foot. $20.00.

Left — Plate 1132: Playmates. "Lieutenant Worf" from "Star Trek: The Next Generation." 1992. 4½" tall. Jointed vinyl action figure with molded on gold and black outfit. Figures are individually numbered. This is #177785, on left foot. Right foot is marked: ©1992 PAR. PIC./ PLAYMATES. Role is played by actor Michael Dorn. $6.00.

Right — Plate 1133: Playmates. "Lieutenant (JG) Worf" in "Star Trek: The Next Generation" first season outfit. Figure is numbered 039128, on left foot. $8.00.

Plate 1134: Playmates. "Gowron the Klingon" from "Star Trek: The Next Generation." 5". Jointed vinyl action figure in molded on clothes in silver, black, and gray. Figure is individually numbered 145779 on left foot. Right is marked: ©1992 PAR. PIC./PLAYMATES. $6.00.

Plate 1135: Playmates. "Klingon Warrior Worf" from "Star Trek: The Next Generation." 1993. Action figure with molded on black clothing under long gray cape. Figures are individually number on the right foot. This figure is #028992. $6.00.

Plate 1136: Playtime. "Baby Crissy" from the "Ideal Nursery Classic Collection." 12". Other dolls in this collection are "Tiny Tears" and "Betsy Wetsy." Vinyl head, arms, and legs, cloth body, rooted brown hair, sleeping brown eyes, open-closed mouth with upper teeth. Doll has long pony tail but hair does not "grow" like the earlier "Baby Crissy" dolls by Ideal. All original. Marks: TALKING BABY CRISSY™/©1991 PLAYTIME PRODUCTS/INC/CHINA, on head. Although doll is marked Talking Baby Crissy, doll did not come with a talking mechanism and Talking Crissy is NOT marked on the box. $20.00.

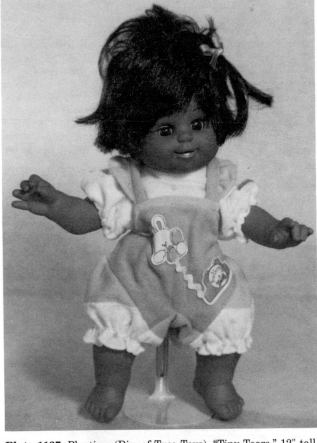

Plate 1137: Playtime (Div. of Tyco Toys). "Tiny Tears." 12" tall. Vinyl head, arms, and legs, brown cloth body, rooted brown hair, sleeping brown eyes with lashes, nursing mouth with two lower teeth. All original. Doll and outfit are marked "Talking Tiny Tears" but she does not talk and box is marked "Tiny Tears." Marks: TALKING TINY TEARS/© 1991 PLAYTIME PRODUCTS/INC/CHINA, on head. $20.00.

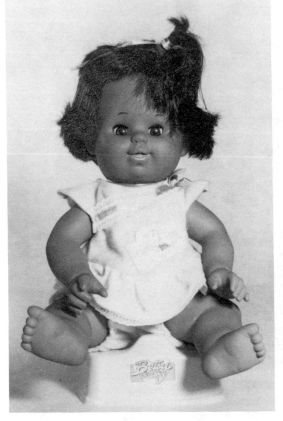

Plate 1138: Playtime. "Betsy Wetsy" from the "Ideal Nursery Classic Collection." 12". Vinyl head, jointed vinyl body, rooted brown hair, sleeping brown eyes, nursing mouth. Doll comes with a salmon colored plastic potty. All original. Marks: TALKING BETSY WETSY™/©1991 PLAYTIME PRODUCTS/CHINA, on head. Doll does not have talking mechanism and box does not indicate one should be present. Eyelids on all of the black dolls from the Ideal Nursery Classic collection for white dolls. $20.00.

288

Left — Plate 1139: Playskool. "Sweetie Pops," 7½" (standing up with clothes on), 5" (kneeling without clothes on). Doll comes in kneeling position with one set of clothes. Additional clothing sold separately. Just pop the kneeling doll into her clothing which comes with arms and legs, making the doll easy to dress. All vinyl with long brown rooted hair, painted features, molded on undies. Marks: 1986 PLAYSKOOL INC./MADE IN HONG KONG, on bottom of foot. $20.00.

Right — Plate 1140: Playskool. "Spring Fling Little Miss Dolly Surprise." 6½". All original in pink print dress with aqua bows at waist and in hair, painted on white tights and pink shoes. Jointed vinyl, rooted brown "growing" hair, painted eyes. Marks: U.S. PATENT NO. 4,801,286/1990 PLAYSKOOL, INC./MADE IN CHINA/H22, on back. $15.00.

Plate 1142: Playskool. "My Pretty Mermaids," 1991. Vinyl head, rooted long blue hair, painted eyes with pink eyeshadow, jointed vinyl body with molded on blue and yellow bikini top and pink mermaid bottom. When doll is dipped in ice water, her secret name design appears. 7" tall. Marks: ©1991 PLAYSKOOL INC./MADE IN CHINA, on body. This doll's name is "Water Lily." Other black dolls in the series are: "Sun Blossom" with pink hair and yellow mermaid bottom; "Sea Flower" with purple hair and pink mermaid bottom; and "Flower Dream" with lavender hair and aqua mermaid bottom. $10.00.

Plate 1141: Playskool. "Lolly Surprise," ©1987, from the "Dolly Surprise" series. Vinyl head, painted brown eyes, rooted dark brown curly hair with "growing" ponytail, blue plastic ring and green butterfly in hair, painted open smiling mouth, jointed vinyl body. 10½" tall. All original in aqua, pink, and yellow dress with striped tights in the same colors, blue plastic t-strap shoes. Marks: U.S. PATENT PENDING/©1987 PLAYSKOOL, INC/ MADE IN CHINA/H-22, on body. $20.00.

Plate 1143: Playskool. "Trendy Wendy" from the "Flip 'n Fancy" series. Vinyl doll that flips at neck, waist, and knees to mix and match fashions. 4" tall. Molded on clothing. One side has painted black hair, painted open mouth, white shirt printed "Flip 'n Fancy," aqua shorts, white shoes, and purple socks. This reverse side has red hair, closed mouth, aqua shirt, iridescent pink vest, purple dotted shorts, blue shoes, and white socks. Marks: ©1991/C-251/PLAYSKOOL, on bottom of feet. $5.00.

Plate 1144: Playskool. "Sweetheart Sadie" from "Flip 'n Fancy" series. One side is dressed in a sparkly pink and yellow dress, yellow hat, matching pink shoes, and has reddish brown hair. The reverse side has a sparkly aqua dress trimmed in pink and white, matching aqua shoes, yellow hat, and has black hair. Marks: ©1991/C-251/PLAYSKOOL, on bottom of feet. This doll is slightly different from some of the other "Flip 'n Fancy" dolls, her hat flips instead of her whole head. $5.00.

Plate 1145: Playskool. "Starry Stephanie" from the "Flip 'n Fancy" series. One side has red hair, green dress trimmed in yellow, white tights, yellow shoes. The other side has black hair, pink sparkle dress with green and white trim, green socks, white shoes. Marks: ©1991/C-251/PLAYSKOOL, on bottom of feet. $5.00.

Plate 1146: Playskool. "Rosey Renee" from the "Flip 'n Fancy" series. All vinyl doll that flips at the neck, waist, and just below knees. One side is wearing white shirt trimmed in aqua and pink, aqua pants, white socks, pink shoes and has dark brown hair. The reverse side is wearing white jumpsuit with blue print, pink blouse, blue shoes, and has red hair. Marks: ©1991/C-251/PLAYSKOOL, on bottom of feet. $5.00.

Plate 1147: Playskool. "Flip 'n Fancy Twins." All vinyl baby dolls that flip at the waist with molded hair and clothing. 2" tall. One doll is dressed in aqua with pink dots and has brown hair, the reverse side is dressed in baby blue with aqua dots and has black hair. The other twin has on a mauve outfit with aqua dots and has brown hair, the reverse side is dressed in pale green with pale blue dots and has black hair. Marks: ©1991/C-251/PLAYSKOOL, on feet. $10.00.

Plate 1148: Playskool. "Flip 'n Fancy Fun Friends," mix and match fashions with a flip. Two dolls came in this set, one is 3½" tall, the other is 4" tall. Also included is a white dog with black spots, a pink and white hat, and a white purse. Marks on both dolls are the same: ©1991/PLAYSKOOL/C-223, on bottom of feet. $15.00.

Plate 1149: Playskool. "Flip 'n Fancy Honeymoon Happiness." Bride and groom dolls. Groom is dressed in white on one side, black on the other. Bride is dressed in white on one side, pink on the other. Both dolls are 4" tall. Both dolls are marked the same: ©1991/PLAYSKOOL/C-223, on bottom of the feet. $15.00.

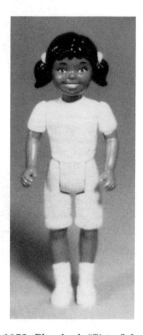

Plate 1150: Playskool. "Dollhouse Family," ©1991, #1551. Complete family of three included father, mother, and baby. Hard vinyl jointed dolls with molded on clothing. Father has on blue pants, yellow shirt, brown shoes, and belt. He is 6" tall and has the following marks: PLAYSKOOL, on belt in back. Mother has on pink blouse, aqua skirt, earrings, necklace, and pink shoes. She is 5½" tall and is marked PLAYSKOOL on her back. The baby is 2½" tall and has on a purple top, pink panties, and white booties, and is holding a baby bottle. She is marked the same as the mother and father. All three have black hair. $10.00.

Plate 1151: Playskool. "Brother" from "Dollhouse Wagon & Wheels Playroom." Set includes bed, wagon, and toy truck. Doll is hard vinyl with painted features, molded on green shirt and blue pants, fully jointed. 3" tall. Marks: ©PLAYSKOOL, on back. $10.00.

Plate 1152: Playskool. "Sister" from "Dollhouse Slumber Party Playroom," ©1991. Set includes sister, bed, tea table, and two round cushions. All vinyl doll is jointed at shoulders and waist with molded on pink shorts, white shirt with three pink hearts and aqua stripes, pink socks, and aqua shoes. 3¾" tall. Marks: © PLAYSKOOL, on back. $15.00.

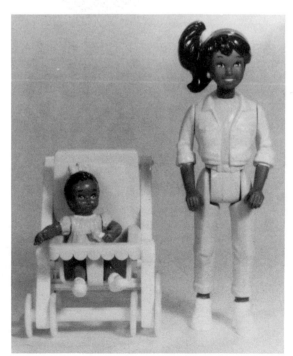

Plate 1153: Playskool. "Just for Baby Set," #1533, ©1992. Set includes babysitter, 5½" tall; baby, 2½"; stroller; potty-chair; rocking horse; and telephone. Dolls are fully jointed vinyl with molded on clothing. Marks: ©PLAYSKOOL, on both dolls. $10.00.

Plate 1154: Playskool. "Princess Krystal Stars" from the "Krystal Princess" series. 2½" tall. Vinyl head, jointed vinyl body, rooted purple hair, painted features, painted on blue swimsuit, removable blue skirt. Doll comes in plastic dome with purple base. Stars, moons, and glitter appear to fall around the doll when dome is shaken. Doll is unmarked. $10.00.

Plate 1155: Playskool. "Princess Krystal Diamonds" from the "Krystal Princess" series. 2½" tall. Vinyl head, jointed vinyl body, rooted pink hair, painted features, painted on white swimsuit, removable silver skirt. Doll comes in a plastic dome with a pink base. Unmarked. $10.00.

Plate 1156: Playskool. "Princess Krystal Hearts" from the "Krystal Princess" series. 2½" tall. Vinyl head, jointed vinyl body, rooted brown hair, painted features, painted on fuchsia swimsuit, removable pink skirt. Doll comes in a plastic dome with fuchsia base. Unmarked. $10.00.

Plate 1157: Playskool. "Cavester." 3½" tall. Jointed vinyl action figure from "Definitely Dinosaurs!" with painted molded hair, painted features, molded on caveman type orange outfit. Marks: ©1987/ PLAYSKOOL/INC., on left leg; MADE IN/CHINA H-15, on right leg. $5.00.

Plate 1158: Playskool. "Baby Doll," #5309. 13" tall. 1992. Vinyl head, slightly molded painted hair, painted eyes, open-closed mouth, cloth body and limbs with sewn on clothing. Doll has pacifier and baby bottle attached to hands with pink ribbons. Body is tagged. $16.00.

Below Left — Plate 1159: Playskool. "My Buddy," #1001. 20" tall. Vinyl head, painted eyes, rooted curly hair, cloth body and limbs. Sewn on clothing forms the body, hat is removable. Tagged body. This is the third "My Buddy" by Playskool. They are all very similar. The first one had glassine sleep eyes, 22" tall, removable clothing. The second one, shown in *Black Dolls, 1820–1991,* had painted eyes, 22" tall, removable clothing. $25.00.

Plate 1160: Playskool. "Kid Sister," #1008. 20" tall. Vinyl head, rooted black hair, painted eyes, cloth body and limbs. Sewn on clothing forms the body, only the visor is removable. Earlier "Kid Sister" doll with removable clothing and 22" tall is shown in author's previous book, *Black Dolls, 1820–1991,* page 233. Tagged body. $25.00.

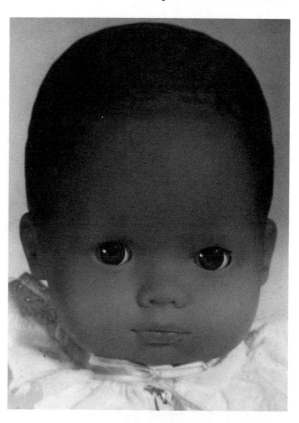

Plate 1161: Pleasant Company. "African-American," #20300 from "The New Baby Collection," 1991–92. Vinyl head, brown sleep eyes with lashes, sculptured hair, closed mouth, vinyl arms and legs, brown cloth body. 15" tall. All original in lace trimmed cotton sleeper with a matching undershirt and cloth diaper. Additional clothing sold separately. Marks: ©PLEAS-ANT COMPANY, on head. $60.00.

Plate 1162: Pleasant Company. "Addy." 18". Doll portrays a child in the mid 1800's and comes with a hardcover or paperback book with the doll as the main character. Vinyl head, arms, and legs, brown cloth body, sleeping brown eyes with lashes, open-closed mouth with two upper teeth, pierced ears with small goldtone hoop earrings. All original in pink dress with white stripes and tiny white buttons down the front, black stockings and shoes. Additional outfits and accessories sold separately. Marks: PLEASANT COMPANY/148 (SLASH) 16, on head. Doll is from "The American Girls Collection" and was released in 1993. $90.00.

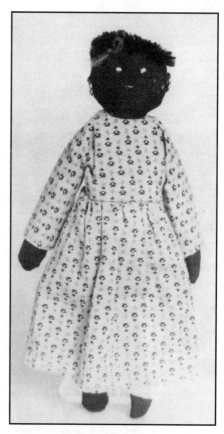

Plate 1163: Pleasant. "Ida Bean" doll. 6". Addy's rag doll. Black yarn hair, stitched features. Addy named her "Ida Bean" because she is stuffed with beans. All original in a purple print dress with tiny goldtone hoop earrings. $15.00.

Plate 1164: Positive Image Enterprises. "Baby Makeda" from the "Queen Makeda Doll Collection." 17" tall. Vinyl head, rooted black hair done up in many, many braids, sleeping brown eyes, closed mouth, vinyl arms and legs, white cloth body. Doll was designed by Makeda Muhammad. All original in African style print outfit. Unmarked. Courtesy of Susan Perkins. $60.00.

Plate 1165: Praise Unlimited Inc. "The Praise Doll." 14". Talking doll with vinyl head and hands, rooted black hair, painted eyes, open-closed mouth, pink cloth body with zippered back for batteries, cloth limbs. Tag sewn to body: .../THE PRAISE DOLL/ALL NEW MATERIALS/©1983 PRAISE UNLIMITED INC./ALL RIGHTS RESERVED/ MADE IN CHINA. Doll says the following phrases: "I'm a walkin' in faith and I love you"; "Did you know that Jesus loves you, and he is the Lord?"; "When I say my prayers I praise the Lord cause he loves me." Collection of Shirley Jackson. $65.00.

Plate 1166: Precious Moments. "Nurse" from the "Hi Babies." 5½" tall. Vinyl head, black yarn wig, painted features, vinyl body with movable arms, painted white panties, molded painted white shoes. All original in nurse's uniform with cap. Marks: HI BABIES/©1989 SAMUEL J. BUTCHER/ ALL RIGHTS RESERVED WORLDWIDE/LICENSEE ENESCO CORPORATION/ MADE IN THE PHILIPPINES, on right foot; THE/ ENESCO/PRECIOUS/ MOMENTS/COLLECTION, on left foot. $10.00.

Plate 1167: Precious Moments. "Mazie, American," February, 1989, from "Children of the World" collection. 9" tall. Vinyl head, painted eyes, rooted black hair, jointed vinyl body. All original in long blue print cotton dress. The inspiration behind the Children of the World collection is the song "Jesus Loves the Little Children." This is the only black doll in the collection. Other dolls are Filipino, Spanish, Eskimo, American Indian, Dutch, Swedish, German, Indian (East), Russian, Japanese, Irish, and a white American. Marks: MADE IN PHILIPPINES/PRECIOUS MOMENTS/BY SAMUEL/BUTCHER CO/USA, on body. $23.00.

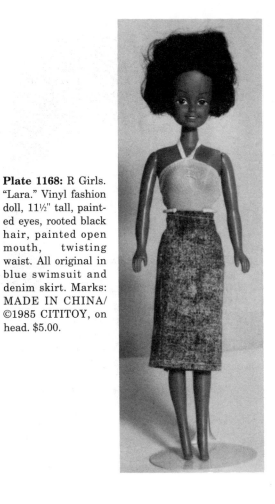

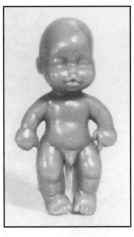

Plate 1168: R Girls. "Lara." Vinyl fashion doll, 11½" tall, painted eyes, rooted black hair, painted open mouth, twisting waist. All original in blue swimsuit and denim skirt. Marks: MADE IN CHINA/ ©1985 CITITOY, on head. $5.00.

Plate 1169: Raffoler, Ltd. "Karen," pregnant "mother-with-baby." 12" tall. Vinyl jointed doll, rooted black hair, side glancing painted eyes, closed mouth, doll comes "pregnant" with baby inside her stomach. When you remove the plastic cover from the doll's stomach, you can tell whether Karen has a new little girl or a boy. Baby is soft rubber/vinyl and is 2½" tall. After baby is removed from the stomach, a second flat cover fits onto the doll's stomach. Marks: MADE IN CHINA, on back. $10.00. **Right — Plate 1170:** Baby boy from "mother-to-be" doll Karen.

Plate 1171: Rainbow Classics. "Clown." 13½" tall. Vinyl head, painted clown face, round hole in the mouth similar to nurser hole, cloth body, hands, and feet, rooted blond hair, molded on black hair. All original. Doll was available in a variety of clown outfits. Marks: RAINBOW CLASSICS INC./CHICAGO, IL., 60603/..., on tag sewn to body. $15.00.

Plate 1172: Rainbow Classics. "Baby Doll," stock #15000. Vinyl head, arms, and legs, rooted black hair, sleeping amber eyes, brown cloth body, open-closed mouth. 15" tall. All original in blue print flannel sleeper. Marks: MADE IN CHINA, on head. Tag sewn to body: TCA GROUP INC./NATICK, MA 01760/R 1990... $15.00.

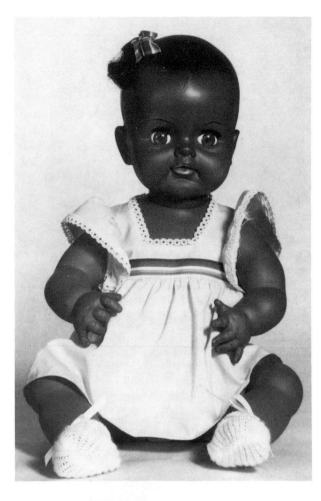

Left — Plate 1173: Regal. Baby doll, 20" long. Vinyl head, rooted tuft of black hair on right side of head, sleeping brown eyes, nursing mouth, jointed bent-leg vinyl body. Dressed in yellow sundress, white knit booties. Could be original. Marks: 4429/6/ REGAL/CANADA/200BDM, on head. $40.00.

Right — Plate 1174: Regal. "Kimmie." 10" tall. Vinyl head, painted eyes, rooted black hair, jointed vinyl body. Doll was originally dressed as an Indian. Marks: REGAL/ MADE IN CANADA, on head; REGAL/CANADA, on back. $35.00.

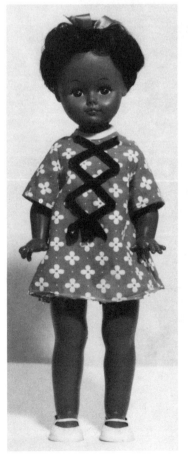

Plate 1175: Reliable. 1974. Vinyl head, painted eyes, rooted short black hair, jointed hard vinyl body. 16" tall. Dress seems appropriate to the period, could be original. Marks: RELIABLE TOY CO. LTD./MADE IN CANADA, on head. $65.00.

Plate 1176: Reliable. 13". 1960's. Vinyl head, rooted black hair, sleeping amber eyes, closed mouth, one piece stuffed vinyl body. Marks: RELIABLE, on head. $45.00.

Left — Plate 1177: Remco. "America's Kids Afro-American," #3588. Vinyl head, rooted short black curly hair, sleeping brown eyes, closed mouth with full lips, vinyl arms and legs, white cloth body. All original in printed African style dress with red hat. Doll came with an additional blue jean outfit. 16" tall. Marks: AFRO AMERICAN/REMCO TOYS/1991, on head. Doll was available through J.C. Penney catalog. $20.00.

Right — Plate 1178: Remco. "Baby Sitters Club, Jessi & Becca," ©1991. Jessi is 9½" tall, Becca is 6" tall. Both dolls have long rooted black hair, painted brown eyes, painted open mouth, soft vinyl head, jointed hard vinyl body. Jessi has pierced ears with earrings and is all original in pink leotards and tights with aqua skirt and leg warmers. Becca is all original in pink shirt and yellow jumper. The dolls are based upon Ann M. Martin's book series from Scholastic. Marks on Jessi: JESSE/©1991 REMCO, on head; ©REMCO 1991/MADE IN CHINA, on body. (Doll is marked "Jesse" but marketed as "Jessi," the character in the book.) Marks on Becca: BECCA/©1991 REMCO, head; ©REMCO 1991/MADE IN CHINA, on body. $35.00.

Plate 1179: Remco "Jessi & Becca" from the "Baby-Sitters Club Deluxe Gift Set Doll Collection," ©1992. The set includes six other white dolls, Kristy & Karen, Claudia & Jenny, and Stacey & Charlotte. Jessi and Becca are both jointed vinyl with rooted dark brown hair, painted eyes, and closed mouth. Jessi has pierced ears with pink dot earrings. Jessi is all original in a pink and aqua dress, Becca is all original in a pink blouse with black dots and a black and white skirt. The 1991 Jessi & Becca dolls had painted teeth showing. Dolls are 10" and 6" tall. Marks on Jessi: JESSI/©1992/REMCO, on head; ©REMCO 1991/MADE IN CHINA, on body. Marks on Becca: BECCA/1992 REMCO, on head; ©REMCO 1991/MADE IN CHINA, on body. $50.00.

Plate 1180: Remco. "Jessi & Becca," #9335 from the "Baby-Sitters Club" collection. 10" and 6" tall. The taller doll, Jessi has rooted dark brown hair, pink stud earrings, painted features, closed mouth. The smaller doll has rooted black hair, painted features, closed mouth. Both dolls are jointed vinyl. All original in ballet outfits. Dolls come with a How-to Guide for Baby-Sitters. Marks on Jessi: JESSI/1992/REMCO, on head; ©REMCO 1991/MADE IN CHINA, on body. Marks on Becca: BECCA/1992 REMCO, on head; ©REMCO 1991/MADE IN CHINA, on body. $20.00.

Plate 1182: Remco. "Baby Be Good." 13½". 1979. Vinyl head, rooted dark hair, painted eyes, vinyl hands. Pink dotted outfit with hood forms body and limbs. When you squeeze her tummy, doll will appear to kiss you; doll sucks her thumb. Doll comes with disappearing action milk bottle. No batteries required. Alden's 1979 catalog illustration. $40.00.

Plate 1181: Remco. Vinyl head, painted brown eyes, open-closed mouth with molded tongue, rooted black hair with bangs, vinyl hands, pink dotted cloth body and legs. 8½" tall. Marks: REMCO IND. INC./19©70, on head; ©1971/REMCO INDUSTRIES INC.,/..., on tag sewn to body. $20.00.

Plate 1183: Remco. "Monet" from "America's Kids" collection, 1991. Vinyl head, arms, and legs, sleeping brown eyes, rooted black hair, closed mouth, white cloth body. All original in red and yellow striped knit pants, pink shirt. Box lists doll as #3588, Afro-American. 16" tall. Marks: HISPANIC/REMCO TOYS/1991, on head. $16.00.

Plate 1184: Remco. "Jasmine" from "America's Kids" collection. Vinyl head, sleeping brown eyes, black hair, closed mouth, vinyl arms and legs, cloth body. 16" tall. All original in blue jean jumpsuit with orange trim. Marks: AFRO AMERICAN/REMCO TOYS/1991, on head. $16.00.

Left — Plate 1185: Remco. "Hi Heidi." 5½" tall. 1960's. Vinyl head, dimpled cheeks, painted side glancing eyes, open-closed mouth with hint of teeth, rooted black hair with bangs, jointed hard vinyl body. When small lever on the stomach is pushed, doll waves with her right hand. Blue cotton dress could be original. Marks: 15 ©1964 K/REMCO IND. INC., on head; ©/REMCO/INDUSTRIES/INC., on body. Courtesy of Michele Hill Grier. $100.00.

Right — Plate 1186: Remco. "Dune Buggy Baby." 11½" tall. Vinyl head, long back rooted hair with bangs, painted brown eyes, open-closed mouth, jointed vinyl body. When yellow plastic button in doll's back is pushed, doll waves "hi" with her right hand. All original in yellow plastic battery operated dune buggy. Redressed. Marks: REMCO IND. INC./19©72/HONG KONG, on head. $110.00.

Plate 1188: Remco. "Jiggly Jigglies." 1979. 11" tall. Vinyl head, molded brown hair, painted eyes, closed mouth, cloth body and limbs. Sewn on pink flannel outfit trimmed in yellow when you squeeze her. Marks: ©REMCO 1979/N.Y., N.Y. 10-8, on head. Name tag is sewn to back of cloth body. Collection of the Museum of African American History (Detroit). $45.00.

Plate 1189: Remco. "Baby This 'n That." 1976. 13" tall. Vinyl head, rooted curly black hair, painted eyes, closed mouth, vinyl arms and legs, hard plastic body. All original in cotton knit printed sunsuit. Doll moves her head in different directions when control on back is pushed, no batteries required. Comes with toothbrush and spoon. Marks: ©1978/REMCO N.Y., N.Y., on head; ©1978 REMCO TOYS INC./MADE IN HONG KONG/PRO, on body. Collection of the Museum of African American History (Detroit). $45.00.

Plate 1187: Remco. "Wake Up Sleepy Head." 13". 1979. Doll's eyes stay closed when her thumb or pacifier is in her mouth and open when not. Vinyl head, rooted brown hair around forehead, sewn on cap, open mouth, vinyl hands, white plastic body, cloth legs, feet, and arms, sewn on aqua romper. Her eyes also close when you squeeze her tummy. No batteries required. Marks: REMCO/WAKE UP!/SLEEPY HEAD/©REMCO 1979/PATENT PENDING/MADE IN HONG KONG..., tag sewn to body. Collection of the Museum of African American History (Detroit). $55.00.

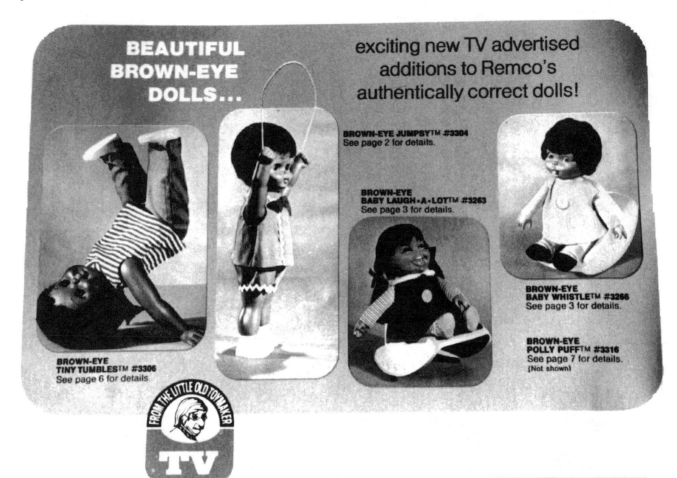

Plate 1190: Remco. "Brown-Eye Tiny Tumbles™," #3306, 8" tall; "Brown-Eye Jumpsy™," #3304, 13" tall; "Brown-Eye Baby Laugh-a-Lot™," #3263, 16" tall; "Brown-Eye Baby Whistle™," #3265, 15" tall; and "Brown-Eye Polly Puff™," #3316, 12" tall. Photograph of a page from Remco 1970 catalog courtesy of Frank Sposato.

Plate 1191: Remco. "Brown-Eye Tina." 15" tall. Vinyl head and arms, hard plastic body and legs, black rooted hair with long ponytail on left side, sleeping brown eyes with lashes, closed mouth. Doll was designed by black artist Annuel McBurroughs. Original green print cotton dress, attached white plastic shoes. Marks: E 6/REMCO IND. INC./19©68, on head. $95.00.

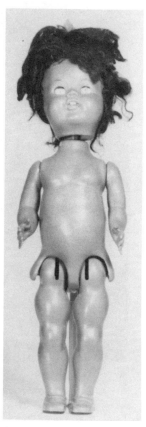

Plate 1192: Roberta Doll Co. 17½" tall. Hard plastic walker doll, black wig in original set, sleeping amber eyes, open mouth with four upper teeth, red felt tongue. All original in red plaid dress, red socks, white shoes, natural straw hat. Unmarked. 1950's. $300.00.

Plate 1193: Roddy. 12½". Hard plastic walking doll. 1940's. Glued on black wig that could be mohair, sleeping amber eyes with lashes, open-closed mouth with molded tongue and two upper teeth, molded unpainted shoes and socks. Daniel G. Todd, managing director of Toy Time Toys Ltd. of Lancashire, England, used the trademark "Roddy." The doll's neck sits up unusually high on the body. Marks: RODDY. MADE IN ENGLAND, on body. Roddy made a similar doll with a bent-leg baby body. $150.00.

Plate 1194: "Mr. T" from the TV series the "A-Team." 9½". Hard plastic head, rooted black hair, beard, mustache, and eyebrows. Painted eyes. Plastic dowel for body with mechanism for controlling boxing punches. Marks: ROJUS, on black mechanism. $20.00.

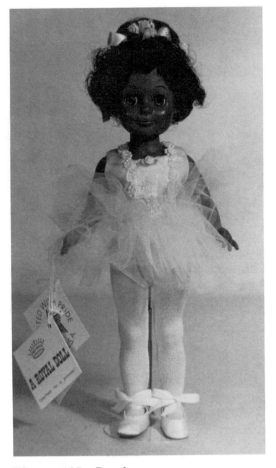

Plate 1195: Royal. "Brooke," 1991, #R88-1219, ballerina. Vinyl head, rooted black hair, sleeping amber eyes with real lashes, closed mouth, hard vinyl jointed body. 11½" tall. All original pink and white ballerina outfit trimmed with pearls, white tights, and pink slippers. Marks: ROYAL HOUSE/OF DOLLS INC./© 1985, on head, Made in U.S.A. $66.00.

Plate 1196: Royal. "Vintage Bride," ©1991, #R89-2531. Bride doll with the same face as the "Dallas Cheerleader" by Royal. Vinyl head, sleeping amber eyes with lashes, rooted black hair, painted open mouth, jointed hard vinyl body with high heel feet. All original in ivory bridal gown trimmed with pearls and lace. Marks: 7/ROYAL/©1982, on head. 15" tall. $85.00.

Plate 1197: Royal. "Winterbride," #R91-1233. Vinyl head, rooted black hair, sleeping amber eyes, closed mouth, jointed hard vinyl body. All original in white lace gown with feather boa trim around neck and on headpiece. 11½" tall. Marks: ROYAL HOUSE/OF DOLLS INC./©1985, on head. Made in U.S.A. $150.00.

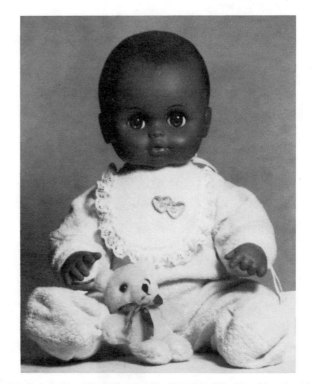

Plate 1199: Royal. "Angelique." 15" tall. #R88-346 Blk. Vinyl head with sculptured hair, sleeping brown eyes with lashes, open-closed mouth, jointed vinyl bent-leg baby body. All original in pink sleeper holding a 4" teddybear. Designed by Miss Elsa of Royal House of Dolls. Hang tag is hand signed: 6/30/91/WITH ALL MY/LOVE ELSA. MADE IN U.S.A. Marks: 4421/19/ROYAL HOUSE/OF DOLLS, INC./©1982, on head. Underneath these marks, doll is hand signed: 1991/ELSA. Courtesy of Xzena Moore of the Cubbyhole. $75.00.

Plate 1198: Royal. "Ashley," 1991, #R88-2509. Ballerina with vinyl head, sleeping amber eyes with real lashes, painted-open mouth, rooted black hair pulled back in a bun with braid trim over crown, jointed hard vinyl body with high heel feet. All original in white ballerina costume with sequin and pearl trim. 15" tall. Marks: 3/ROYAL/©1982, on head. Made in U.S.A. $80.00.

Plate 1200: Royal. "Communion," #R91-1235 Blk. 12" tall. Vinyl head, sleeping dark amber eyes with lashes, rooted long black curly hair, closed mouth, jointed hard vinyl body. All original in knee length white lace dress, white lace head cover, white tights and white tie slippers. Doll is carrying little bible and bouquet of pink rosebuds. Made in U.S.A. Designed by Miss Elsa of Royal. Marks: ROYAL HOUSE/OF DOLLS INC./©1985. Purchased new in early 1990's. $75.00.

Plate 1201: Rushton. "Coca-Cola Santa." 1956. 16½" tall. Doll is holding a Coke bottle in his right hand. Marked "The Rushton Co." on both boots. Photograph courtesy of Etta Houston. $300.00+.

Plate 1202: Schildkrot. 11" boy and girl. Jointed vinyl with sleeping amber eyes, nursing mouth. Boy has molded hair in tiny curls, girl has rooted black hair. Clothing is handmade, probably not original. Marks: (picture of a turtle inside a diamond)/ SHILDKROT/GERMANY, on body. $100.00 each.

Plate 1203: Schildkrot. "Cleodine." 12". Vinyl head, sleeping brown eyes with eyelashes, rooted black hair, nursing mouth, jointed vinyl baby body. Clothing does not look original. Doll has the "turtle" mark (a picture of a turtle inside of a diamond) on its head and body. Made in Germany. $30.00.

Plate 1204: Schildkrot. 18". Germany. Hard plastic open-crown head and ball jointed strung body, blue flirty eyes, closed mouth. Replaced wig. Redressed. Marks: (turtle)/46, on head; (turtle) T46, on back. $175.00.

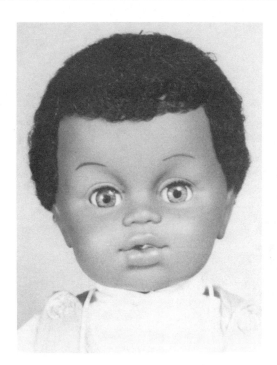

Plate 1205: Sebino. "Cicciobello." 19" tall. Vinyl head, rooted short black curly hair, sleeping brown eyes, opening in mouth for pacifier, vinyl arms and legs, tan cloth body. Doll sleeps when you lie him down and laughs when you pick him up. Batteries required. All original in red quilted jumpsuit, white shirt, brown and white vinyl saddle shoes. Marks: CICCIOBELLO/IL GICCO DELLAFFETTO/PRODOTTO ORIGINALE/©1979 SEBINO/MADE IN ITALY, printed on front of cloth body: SEBINO©/MADE IN ITALY, on head. Courtesy of Xzena Moore of the Cubbyhole. $150.00.

Plate 1206: Sharing. High-heeled fashion dolls, 14" tall. Vinyl head, painted eyes looking to the left, closed mouth, rooted black hair in original set, jointed hard vinyl bodies. Dolls are said to be from the 1960's. Clothing looks like it could be original. Marks: SHARING NO. 3001, on head. $35.00 each.

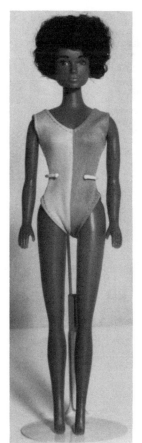

Plate 1207: Shillman. "Young & Lovely," No. 2007. Vinyl fashion doll with twisting waist, jointed arms and legs, rooted black hair, painted eyes, closed mouth. 11½" tall. All original in pink and purple swimsuit. Marks: ©88 SHILLMAN, on head; MADE IN CHINA, on body. M & S Shillman, Brooklyn, N.Y. $8.00.

Plate 1208: Shillman. "Bride," 1983. 11½" tall. All vinyl, brown painted eyes, black rooted hair. All original. Marks: SHILLMAN/ HONG KONG, on head; M & S SHILLMAN INC./ HONG KONG, on back. Photograph courtesy of Stephanie Lisoski. $25.00.

Plate 1209: Shindana. "Kim™" formal. 1975. #6000. 16" tall. Vinyl head, rooted black hair, painted eyes, closed mouth, jointed hard vinyl body. All original in long yellow formal gown with matching hat. Marks: 31/©1969/SHINDANA TOYS/DIV. OF OPERATION/BOOTSTRAP INC. U.S.A., on head. There are three different faces on Shindana Kim dolls. This is the earliest face. $125.00.

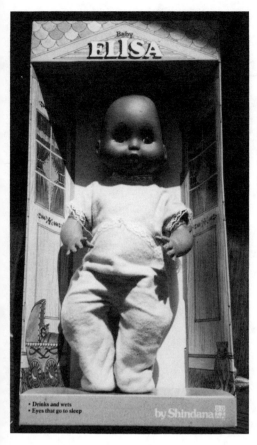

Plate 1210: Shindana. "Baby Elisa." 1977–1980+. 12". Jointed vinyl baby doll, sculpted hair, sleeping eyes, nursing mouth, All original. From the collection of and photograph courtesy of Dorothy E. Bordeaux. $55.00.

Plate 1211: Open letter to the public from back cover of Shindana Toys' 1973 catalog. Letter is from the late Louis S. Smith, the then president of Operation Bootstrap, Inc. of which Shindana Toys was a division. Letter demonstrates the involvement of Shindana Toys with the community.

Operation Bootstrap, Inc.

 LEARN BABY, LEARN

January 1, 1973

Dear Friend,

We at Operation Bootstrap, Inc., and especially the Shindana Toy Division, wish to take advantage of this, Shindana Toy's 5th anniversary, to share with you our feelings. Shindana has a dual purpose that is reflected in every product that we design and manufacture. Our goal is to produce products that educate children two ways.

We have attempted to produce dolls that children could relate to; fantasize with; and grow with. Hence we have stayed away from "gadgetry" dolls that "do for the child." It is our opinion that the toy should be a vehicle that helps the child use its imagination to grow, rather than the toy directing the child by its mechanical actions.

The second way our toys educate children is through the profits from our labor. Let me explain. Operation Bootstrap, Inc., which was founded in 1965, has a motto. "Learn, Baby, Learn." The profits from Shindana go to make that slogan, that dream, a reality. Thanks to all of you who have supported us in the past, we are now in a position to use our profits to build a pre-school in our community. "Learn, Baby, Learn." The Honeycomb Child Development Center, a project of Operation Bootstrap, will probably be open by the time you read this message. We are now able to get into pre-school education which is badly needed in this community.

Now you can see how our toys educate children in two ways. You have been a part of this self-help effort. Your continued support is needed to make this dream a reality.

Again, we at Operation Bootstrap thank you from the bottom of our hearts. Learn, Baby, Learn.

Yours for Brotherhood,

Louis S. Smith

Louis S. Smith
President, Operation Bootstrap, Inc.

Left — Plate 1212: Simba Dolls. "My Love," #2007. 16" tall. Vinyl head, arms, and legs, brown cloth body, rooted black hair, sleeping amber eyes, open-closed mouth. All original in blue striped cotton romper. Marks: SIMBA, on head. $30.00.

Right — Plate 1213: Simba. "My Love" #2003. 12½". Vinyl head, arms, and legs, brown cloth body, rooted black hair, sleeping brown eyes, open-closed mouth. All original in yellow dotted cotton dress. Unmarked. $25.00.

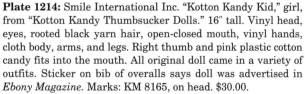

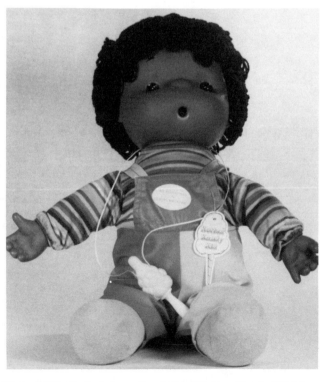

Plate 1214: Smile International Inc. "Kotton Kandy Kid," girl, from "Kotton Kandy Thumbsucker Dolls." 16" tall. Vinyl head, eyes, rooted black yarn hair, open-closed mouth, vinyl hands, cloth body, arms, and legs. Right thumb and pink plastic cotton candy fits into the mouth. All original doll came in a variety of outfits. Sticker on bib of overalls says doll was advertised in *Ebony Magazine*. Marks: KM 8165, on head. $30.00.

Plate 1215: Smile International Inc. "Kotton Kandy Kid," boy, from "Kotton Kandy Thumbsucker Dolls." 16" tall. Doll is similar to previous girl except for uncut looped yarn hair. Doll is unmarked. $30.00.

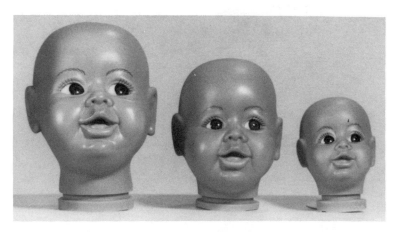

Plate 1217: Syndee's Crafts. Vinyl heads from 6" to 3½" to make baby dolls. Stationary brown eyes, painted eyelashes, open-closed mouth with molded tongue. Sold separately were vinyl limbs, cloth bodies, and wigs. Marks: SYN-DEE/MADE IN CHINA, on head of all three. Copyright 1990. $20.00.

Plate 1216: Soft-Luv Ltd. "Gentle Dreams." 13". Made exclusively for Kmart Corporation. Vinyl head, painted features, tuft of dark brown hair sewn under cap. Sewn on aqua and white print outfit forms body and limbs. Tag sewn to body: GENTLE/DREAMS, one side; ©1991 SOFT-LUV LTD. HONG KONG..., reverse side. $10.00.

Plate 1218: Super Doll Corp. Bed doll. 15" tall. Vinyl head, rooted black hair, sleeping brown eyes with lashes, closed mouth, jointed high-heeled vinyl body. All original in white lace with net veil. Marks: SUPER DOLL CORPORATION/MADE IN HONG KONG, on head. 1970's. $50.00.

Plate 1219: Super Doll Co. 12½". Jointed vinyl, molded hair, sleeping amber eyes, nursing mouth, Redressed. Marks: 12DM/SD/(last line is blurred), on head. Circa 1960. $45.00.

Plate 1220: Spatz. Sexed boy, 14½" tall. Vinyl head, rooted black hair, sleeping brown glassine eyes with lashes, nursing mouth, jointed vinyl anatomically correct body. All original in white flannel diapers. Marks: EK/(series of unidentified superimposed letters)/SPATZ, on head. Original red and gold tag attached to arm: ECHTES/KNOCH/ERZEUGNTS/EK/SEIT 1896. Collection of the Museum of African American History (Detroit). $95.00.

Plate 1221: Souvenir doll "Praline Mammy." 10" tall. Hard plastic head, black mohair wig, sleeping amber eyes, closed mouth, jointed hard plastic body. All original in red dotted dress, faded white apron, orange headwrap with goldtone earrings attached, molded on painted black shoes. Unmarked. Collection of the Museum of African American History (Detroit). $25.00.

Plate 1222: Haitian souvenir doll. Hard plastic shoulder head, molded painted black hair, side glancing painted eyes, cloth body and limbs with yellow felt sewn on shoes. All original. Marks: MADE IN HAITI, stamped on pantaloons. 15" tall. $55.00.

Plate 1223: Postcard from Freeport, Bahamas, showing the souvenir dolls for sale in the straw market. Postcard was sent to the author in 1991 by her son and daughter-in-law from the Bahamas.

Plate 1224: Vinyl souvenir doll from Nassau, Bahamas, 8" tall. Jointed vinyl, sleeping amber eyes, closed mouth. Doll has a skirt and underskirt made of straw, white cotton blouse, earrings attached to pink print headwrap (no hair is under headwrap), straw basket filled with plastic fruit attached to head. 1991. Courtesy of Susan Perkins. $20.00.

Plate 1225: Souvenir doll from Martinique or Guadeloupe. 12" tall. Vinyl head, jointed vinyl body, rooted black hair, closed mouth, sleeping brown eyes with lashes. All original in red and green print dress with Martinique and Guadeloupe as part of the print on the upper part of the skirt. Marks: 30/FRANCE/(unidentifiable logo inside a triangle)/MADE IN FRANCE, on body. $40.00.

The SYNIA line of dolls is the creation of a Jamaican brother and sister team, Carl and Adie McBean. The idea developed from the desire to see a true West Indian doll on the market. The name SYNIA was derived from Abyssinia, the former name of Ethiopia, the motherland of the Rastafarian movement. SYNIA represents a blend of the Caribbean, and places strong emphasis on the Rastafarian philosophy and reggae music, both originating in Jamaica. The Rastafarian movement began in Jamaica in the 1930's. Rastafarians emphasize strong ties with Africa, specifically Ethiopia. They regard Haile Selassie I, former Emperor of Ethiopia as a spiritual master. Marcus Garvey, who predicted Selassie's rise to the throne, is regarded as a prophet. The colors of the movement are red, green, black, and gold, which are also the colors of the Ethiopian flag. The clothing on all of the dolls is in these colors.

The dolls were sculptured by Fitz Harrack and Howard Kalish. Costumes on the dolls are designed by Adie McBean. SYNIA is a trademark of Parajjat International Inc. Following are photographs of the first two dolls in the line, "Johnny Cool" and "Nafti." Other dolls scheduled for addition to the line are "Queenie" and "Sammy Be Bop."

Plate 1226: Synia. "Johnny Cool." 18". Jointed vinyl male doll, rooted long dreadlocks, painted eyes. Johnny Cool represents the typical reggae star who overcame tremendous odds to become a success. All original in plastic sunglasses, green, black, and yellow shirt and knitted cap, black pants. Marks: SYNIA™ 1993, on head. $95.00.

Plate 1227: Synia. "Nafti." 7½". Jointed vinyl doll with rooted brown hair in long deadlocks, painted eyes. According to the creator of the doll, "Nafti is a source of strength to her family and her community. She is admired by the people who know her and she is viewed as a role model by all." All original in red, yellow, green, and black. Marks: SYNIA™ 1993, on head. $95.00.

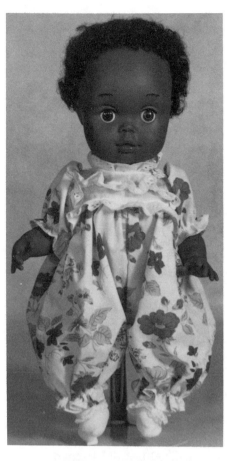

Left — Plate 1228: TCA Toy Corp. of America. "Cherise" from the "Oleg Cassini" collection. 13" tall. Vinyl head, arms, and legs, rooted brown hair, sleeping brown eyes, open-closed mouth, brown cloth body. All original outfit designed by Oleg Cassini. Marks: TCA/MADE IN CHINA, on head. $35.00.

Right — Plate 1229: TCA Toy Corporation of America. "Angelique." 16". Vinyl head, arms, and legs, brown cloth body, rooted dark brown curly hair, sleeping brown eyes, open-closed mouth. Designed by Oleg Cassini from the "Premier Collection." All original in burgundy velvet dress with white lace trim, white sateen pantaloons, white socks. Marks: 11TA16/PG/MADE IN CHINA, on head; TCA GROUP INC./NATICK, MA 01760/©1992 ALL RIGHTS RESERVED/... $35.00.

Plate 1230: Takara. "Lady Luminous." 17". Vinyl head, painted features, reddish brown hair, vinyl body jointed at the neck and arms, legs are poised in a fashion model's runway stance with one foot forward. All original in off-white two piece knit dress, white shoes, white earrings. Doll is available in a variety of outfits and hairstyles. $225.00.

Plate 1231: Takara. 17". Another "Lady Luminous" in a different all original outfit with different hair style. The Takara Toy Co. has changed the name of this doll line several time. In 1988, Takara introduced the line as "Petit Mannequin." The name was soon changed to "Deux-L" which means "Two L's" in French. The present name is "Lady Luminous" although "LL" is still written on the box. Collection of Jeff Sakarins. $275.00.

Plate 1232: TPI Distributing. "Mr. Track & Field," #P24, from the "Hi-5 Sports Stars" collection. Jointed vinyl action figure, swivel waist, painted features, molded on red and white striped shorts with blue waistband, molded on white socks and blue shoes, removable white shirt with #117 printed on. 6" tall. Marks: MADE IN CHINA/ ©EBONEEN/PRODUCTS 1987, on back. $5.00.

Plate 1233: "Mr. Basketball," #P21, from the "Hi-5 Sports Stars" collection. Painted on white shorts, yellow socks, and white shoes as well as removable white shorts and shirt imprinted 33. Removable pink basketball attached to left hand. Marks: MADE IN CHINA/©EBONEEN/PROD-UCTS 1987, on back. $5.00.

Plate 1234: TPI Distributing. "Mr. Football," #P23 from "Hi-5 Sports Stars." Painted on green jerseys, white socks, and black shoes, mold-ed on blue football helmet, remov-able pink football attached to left hand. Removable white shirt imprinted with number 72. Marks: MADE IN CHINA/©EBONEEN/ PRODUCTS 1987, on back. $5.00.

Plate 1235: TPI Distributing. "Mr. Baseball," #P22 from the "Hi-5 Sports Stars." Molded on blue cap with red bill imprinted Hi-5, white shorts, blue baseball pants, red socks, black shoes. Removable yellow shorts with white and red shirt. Removable baseball and glove. Marks: MADE IN CHINA/ ©EBONEEN/PRODUCTS 1987, on back. $5.00.

Plate 1236: TPI Distributing. "The Champ," #P25 from the "Hi-5 Sports Stars." Molded on white shorts, blue lace-up boots, and blue socks. Removable white shorts and pink plastic boxing gloves. Marks: MADE IN CHINA/©EBONEEN/ PRODUCTS 1987, on back. $5.00.

Plate 1237: TPI Distributing. "Mr. 'E' Wrestler," #P26 from the "Hi-5 Sports Stars." Molded beard, mustache, glasses, red, white, and blue shorts, red boots. Removable long baby blue cape with name printed on back. Marks: MADE IN CHINA/ ©EBONEEN/PRODUCTS 1987, on back. $5.00.

Plate 1238: Tara. "ABC Triplets." Vinyl head, rooted black hair, painted eyes, open-closed mouth, jointed baby body with molded on undies marked "A," "B," and "C." 3" tall. Blue plastic stroller for three was included with the dolls. Marks: ©TARA/CHINA, on head. Three dresses in pink, yellow, and blue came with the dolls. $8.00.

Plate 1239: Tara. "ABC Triplets." Similar to previous dolls except this set has straight vinyl toddler legs. Three gingham sleepers in pink, blue, and yellow came with the dolls. Dolls came in a purple crib made for three. Marks are the same. $8.00.

Plate 1240: Tara. "ABC Triplets" in a pink rocking horse for three. Dolls came with three romper sets in pink, yellow, and blue. This set also has straight toddler legs. $8.00.

Plate 1241: Tara. "Kuddlee Kids." 12" tall. Vinyl face, tuft of brown hair sewn under cap, painted features, cloth head, body, and limbs, sewn on clothing. Tag sewn to body: KUDDLEE KIDS/© TARA TOY CORP. HAUPPAUGE, N.Y. 11788/... $15.00.

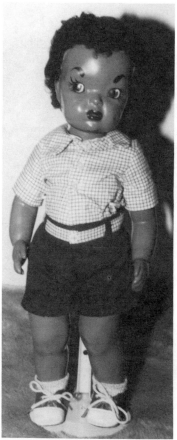

Plate 1243: Terri Lee. "Benjie" (black Jerri Lee boy). 16" tall. Painted hard plastic. All original. Tagged clothing. Courtesy of Susan Girardot. $750.00.

Plate 1242: Tanline. "Welcome Home Chubby." Vinyl head, rooted curly brown hair, sleeping brown eyes, open-closed mouth, vinyl arms and legs, brown cloth body. 18" tall. All original in white cotton and pink gingham dress with matching gingham bloomers, white booties. Except for marks on head, doll is identical to "Baby Chubby" by Tanline. This doll is one of the early Tanline dolls as box is marked Detroit, Michigan 48235. Later boxes are marked Southfield, Michigan. Marks: TANLINE PRODUCTS, on head. Tag sewn to body: TANLINE (inside logo)/TANLINE PRODUCTS INC./DETROIT, MICHIGAN 48235. $30.00.

Plate 1244: M.N. Thomas. Girl Cabbage Patch type, head only. Painted eyes, rooted black yarn hair in two ponytails, dimpled cheeks. Marks: CORP ©1984 M.N. THOMAS. Collection of the Museum of African American History (Detroit). $15.00.

Plate 1245: Thomas. Bald Cabbage Patch type, head only. Painted eyes, closed mouth, dimpled cheeks. Marks: CORP ©1984 M.N. THOMAS/8, on base. Collection of the Museum of African American History (Detroit). $10.00.

Plate 1246: M.N. THOMAS. Boy Cabbage Patch type head only. Painted eyes, closed mouth, dimpled cheeks, rooted cut loop yarn hair in black with green overtone. Marks: CORP/©1984 M.N. THOMAS, on base. Collection of the Museum of African American History (Detroit). $10.00.

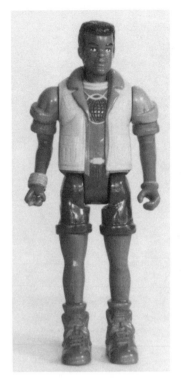

Plate 1248: Tiger. "Kwame," from "Captain Planet and the Planeteers." 5¼". ©1991. Jointed vinyl with molded on clothing, blue shirt, green and red vest, olive shorts, blue shoes and socks. ©1991. Sold in package with white doll "Ma-Ti." Marks: ™ ©1991 TBS PROD. & DIC Ent./TIGER ELECTRONICS INC/MADE IN CHINA, on back. Collection of Todd Perkins. $10.00.

Plate 1247: Tiger Toys. "Commander Clash" from "Captain Planet and the Planeteers." 1991. 5½" tall. Jointed vinyl action figure with molded on camouflage outfit. $5.00.

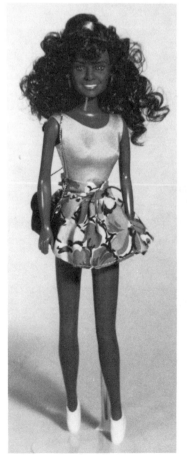

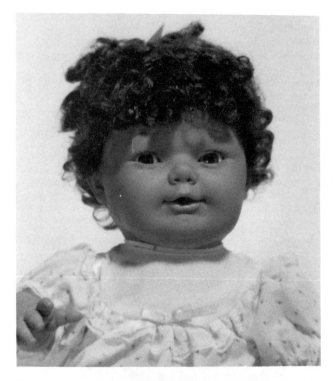

Plate 1249: Tiger Toys. "Lisa" as played by Lark from the TV series "Saved By the Bell." 11½". Jointed vinyl fashion doll, rooted dark brown hair, painted eyes, painted smiling mouth with teeth, swivel waist, pierced ears. All original in cotton floral print mini skirt over gold swimsuit. Marks: ©1992 N.B.C., on head; ©TIGER/MADE IN CHINA, on body. $25.00.

Plate 1250: Tonka. "Hush Little Baby," ©1990, #6991. Baby doll that responds to loving care by crying for her bottle, making sucking sounds when she is fed, moving her eyes back and forth when she is fed, moving her cheeks and mouth as she drinks her "milk," making happy cooing sounds and giggling. Requires four C alkaline batteries. Vinyl head with rooted dark curly brown hair, stationary brown eyes, open mouth, vinyl arms and legs, brown cloth body. All original in pink print romper suit with pacifier attached with pink ribbon. Comes with special baby bottle with "disappearing" milk. 21" long. Marks: ©IRWIN TOY LIMITED 1990/MADE IN CHINA/FAIT AU CHINE, on battery case in doll's back. $75.00.

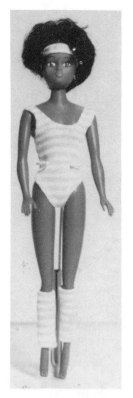

Plate 1251: Totsy. "Sandi Comb 'N Color." 1992. 11½" tall. All vinyl, brown painted eyes, black rooted hair. All original. Marks: TOTSY 1987, on head; MADE IN/ CHINA, on back. Photograph courtesy of Stephanie Lisoski. $20.00.

Plate 1252: Totsy. "Twistee." Fashion doll, 11½". Vinyl head, rooted black hair, painted eyes, closed mouth, jointed vinyl body with twisting waist. All original in pink striped swimsuit, headband, and leg warmers. Unmarked. On the market in the early 1990's. $5.00.

Plate 1253: Totsy. "Fiesta International," ©1991. Doll was available in several different outfits. Vinyl head, painted brown eyes with orange eyeshadow, rooted black hair, painted smiling mouth, jointed vinyl body with swivel waist 11½" tall. Marks: ©TOTSY 1987, on head; MADE IN CHINA, on back. $10.00.

Plate 1254: Totsy. "Maria," #6002. Vinyl head, sleeping brown eyes, closed mouth, rooted long black hair, jointed vinyl body. 19" tall. All original in striped pant outfit. This doll also appears to have been made with an old Beatrice Wright mold. Marks: BY TOTSY ©1988/MADE IN CHINA, on head. There are no marks on the body. $20.00.

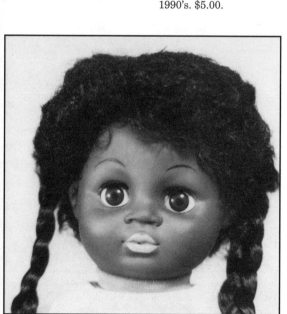

Plate 1256: Totsy. "Celebration Sandi," ©1989. Jointed 11½". Limited edition fashion doll. Vinyl head, painted brown eyes, long rooted black hair, painted smiling mouth with teeth, vinyl body with twisting waist and bendable knees. All original in white bridal gown. Marks: ©TOTSY 1987, on head. $15.00.

Plate 1255: Totsy. "Christine," #1003. Vinyl head, sleeping brown eyes, rooted black hair, jointed vinyl body. 18" tall. All original in pink shirt printed "Hot Stuff" and white stretch pants. Doll is like earlier Beatrice Wright dolls from 1960–70. Marks: BY TOTSY ©1988/MADE IN CHINA, on head; MADE IN CHINA, on body. $20.00.

Plate 1257: Totsy. "Miguel," #6001. Vinyl head, rooted short black hair, sleeping brown eyes, closed mouth, vinyl jointed body. 18½" tall. All original in red shirt and striped pants. The clothing as well as the doll is styled like the Beatrice Wright dolls. Marks: BY TOTSY ©1988/MADE IN CHINA, on head. Body is unmarked. $20.00.

Plate 1258: Totsy. "Ebony and Ivory" from the "Sandi" series. 11½" fashion doll. Vinyl head, painted brown eyes, rooted long curly reddish brown hair, painted mouth with teeth showing, pierced ears with silvertone drop earrings, jointed viny body with swivel waist. All original in long black and silver gown. Doll was available in a variety of formal outfits. Marks: ©TOTSY 1991, on head; MADE IN CHINA, on body. Nominated for 1992's DOTY award in Popularly Price Fashion Doll category. $15.00.

Plate 1259: Totsy. "Sharmell," #1962B from the "Fiesta International" collection, 1993. 11½". Jointed vinyl, bendable legs, twist waist, rooted brown curly hair, painted eyes, goldtone hoop earrings. All original doll was available in several outfits. Marks: © TOTSY 1991, on head; MADE IN CHINA, on body. $7.00.

Left — Plate 1260: Totsy. "Flower Festival Sandi." 11½". Vinyl with jointed body, bendable knees, swivel waist, rooted long black hair, painted open mouth. Doll was available in several different outfits. Marks: ©TOTSY 1987, on head; MADE IN CHINA, on body. $10.00.

Right — Plate 1261: Totsy. "Pretty in Pearls Sandi," 1993. 11½" tall. Vinyl jointed doll with swivel waist, rooted black hair that goes to the feet, painted eyes with pink eyeshadow, painted smiling mouth with teeth, goldtone drip earrings. Doll available in a variety of formal outfits. Marks: TOTSY 1992, on head; MADE IN CHINA, on back. $10.00.

Plate 1263: Toy Biz. "Storm," #4905. 5". Jointed vinyl action figure from "Marvel's X-Men" series. Molded on black outfit, white hair. Figure comes with "power glow action" chest activated by pressing button on Storm's back. Marks: TOY BIZ INC., left leg; ©MARVEL 1991/CHINA, right leg. $10.00.

Plate 1262: Toy Biz. "Baby Loves to Talk," electronic talking doll that can say over 250 words and phrases. 19" tall. Vinyl head, stationary brown eyes, real eyelashes, rooted black hair, open mouth with molded upper teeth, vinyl arms and legs, brown cloth body. All original in pink print romper with yellow trim. Batteries required. Marks: ©1992 TOY BIZ, INC. 24mm, on head. $50.00.

Plate 1264: Toy Biz. "G.W. Bridge," #4955 from "Marvel's X-Men X-Force" series. 5" tall. Jointed vinyl action figure with painted white hair, mustache and beard, molded on red shirt with gray sleeves, gray gloves, green pants, brown boots. Figure comes with rapid fire gun. Marks: TOY BIZ/INC., right leg; ©1992 MARVEL/CHINA, left leg. $8.00.

Plate 1265: Toy Biz. "Pretty and Me," 1993. 14". You can color her hair and yours with non-toxic color sticks. Vinyl head, rooted brown and blond hair, stationary brown eyes with lashes, closed mouth, pierced ears, jointed vinyl body. All original. Marks: ©1993 TOY BIZ INC./20, on head. $25.00.

Plate 1266: Toy Headquarters. "Orange Blossom Dancin' Berry Fun" from the "Strawberry Shortcake" series. ©1991 by Those Characters From Cleveland, Inc. Vinyl head, rooted brown hair, painted features including freckles, jointed vinyl body. 5½" tall. All original in orange print dress with orange net overlay, white tights with orange flowers, orange plastic shoes, green and white striped hair bow. Included with the doll is an extra outfit that was used on the earlier Orange Blossom dolls when they were made by Kenner and a two-sided play stage. The extra outfit is on a cardboard Orange Blossom doll. Marks: ©1991 TCFC INC, on head; CHINA, on body. $15.00.

Plate 1267: Toy Island. "Commando Ops, Chief" from the Tiger team of "Fighting Talk!" © 1991. 3¾". Jointed vinyl action figure with "talking" back pack that says: "open fire" and makes two different battle sounds. Molded on beige outfit with brown camouflage marks, orange vest, and brown boots. Batteries required. Marks: CHINA, on lower back. $8.00.

Plate 1268: Toy Island. "Special Ops, Cmdr." from the Eagle Team of "Fighting Talk!" 3¾". Jointed vinyl action figure in molded forest green clothing with black belt, boots, and holster strap. He says "C'mon, let's go!" and makes battle sounds with battery operated blue plastic backpack. Marks: CHINA, on lower back. $8.00.

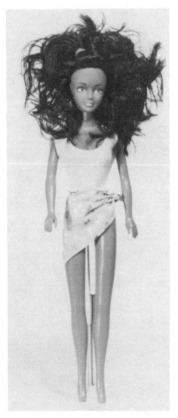

Plate 1269: Toys N' Things. "Glamour Girl," fashion doll. 11½" tall. Vinyl head, rooted black hair, painted eyes, aqua eyeshadow, painted open mouth, hard vinyl body with twisting waist, hard vinyl arms, and bendable legs. All original in lime green swimsuit and pink scarf tied around waist. Marks: BARTER, on head; MADE IN CHINA, on body. Available 1990. $15.00.

Plate 1270: Toys N' Things. "Sweet Scents," #4240B. 5½". Candy scented posable vinyl doll. Rooted black hair, painted features. Doll is grape scented. All original in purple and white striped cotton dress, purple tights, and hairbows. Marks: © T N T/ MADE IN CHINA, on head; MADE/ IN CHINA, on body. $5.00.

Plate 1271: Toy-O-Rama. "My Crawling Baby." 7" long. Battery operated crawling doll. Vinyl head, molded hair, painted eyes, closed mouth, hard plastic body and limbs. All original. Battery case opens on the tummy. Unmarked. $7.00.

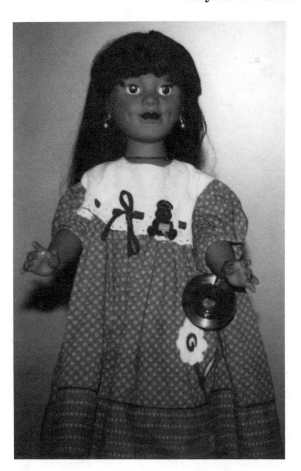

Plate 1272: TreBelle. "Shining Star." Approx. 22". Talking doll. Vinyl head and arms, hard plastic body and legs, sleeping brown eyes, pierced ears, closed mouth, dimpled cheeks, rooted black hair. Doll talks by using small plastic records. All original. Marks: MADE IN JAPAN/DTD/6/ PAT. P., on battery case in back. Collection of Tanya Mitchell Charles. $75.00.

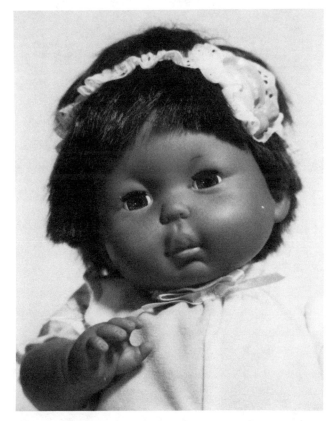

Plate 1273: Tyco. "Twinkling Thumbelina," ©1991, #5641 from the "Ideal Nursery" series of dolls. Doll moves like a real baby and twinkles with lights. Batteries required. Vinyl head, arms, and legs, rooted brown hair with plastic hair bauble that is not removable, stationary brown eyes with real lashes, closed mouth, brown cloth body. All original in pastel romper with sewn on name patch, white lace headband, yellow booties, and pink plastic rattle that attaches to her left hand. 16½" tall. Marks: THUMBELINA®/©1991 TYCO/MADE IN CHINA, on head. $35.00.

Plate 1274: Tyco. "Little Oopsie Daisy." She crawls, falls down, cries, and gets back up. Batteries required. Vinyl head, rooted dark brown hair, stationary brown eyes with lashes, closed mouth, hard vinyl body. All original in lavender romper and matching booties. 12" long in crawling position. Marks: ©IRWIN TOY LIMITED 1991/U.S. PATENT NO.4.878.87/MADE IN CHINA/FAIT AU CHINE, on back. $25.00.

Plate 1275: Tyco. "Potty Time Drink and Wet Quints," ©1991, #1548. They wet in their potty for five. Jointed vinyl bent leg baby bodies, rooted dark brown hair, painted eyes, nursing mouths. 2½" tall. Set includes five quints, (three girls, two boys,) nursing bottles, training pants, potty chair and baby powder for five. Marks: ©TYCO/1990, on head. $20.00.

Plate 1276: Tyco. "Thirsty Quints," #1568, ©1991. Their milk disappears like magic in their milk bottle for five. Quints come with molded on diapers in pink, blue, green, yellow, and purple with matching barettes for the girls. Dolls have painted open mouths with painted teeth. Marks: TYCO/1990, head. $15.00.

Plate 1277: Tyco. "Quints Cousins," #1587, ©1992. Triplet babysitters for the quints. Vinyl heads, rooted dark brown hair, painted eyes, closed mouths, jointed hard vinyl bodies with painted on underclothes in pink, green, and purple. Removable plastic shoes match the underclothes in coloring with matching print dresses. 5" tall. Marks: ©1991 TYCO INC., on head. One piece mint green doll stand comes with the dolls. $16.00.

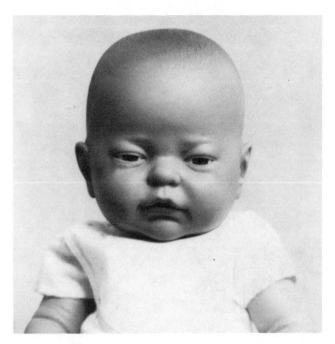

Plate 1278: Tyco. "Newborn Baby Shivers." ©1990. She really shivers when you take her clothes off. Batteries required. 17" long. Vinyl head, brown stationary eyes, sculptured hair, open-closed mouth, jointed vinyl baby body. All original in diapers and yellow flannel dress with bib sewn on. Doll's head screws off to insert battery. Unmarked. $40.00.

Plate 1279: Tyco. "Magic Bottle Baby Newborn," ©1991. A baby doll with a 6½" magic bottle that makes real baby sounds. Battery required. Vinyl head and hands, painted eyes, tuft of rooted dark brown hair, open-closed mouth, sewn on pink outfit with bib with doll's name. 13" tall. Marks: ©1990 TYCO/MADE IN CHINA/A28, on head. Tag sewn to body: TYCO/MAGIC BOTTLE BABY NEWBORN/... Collection of Leanne Nicole Johnson. $26.00.

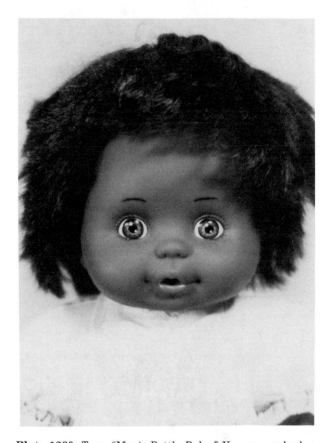

Plate 1280: Tyco. "Magic Bottle Baby." You can make her laugh, cry, drink, and burp, all with her "magic" electronic bottle. Batteries required. Vinyl head, arms, and legs, painted brown eyes, rooted brown hair, open-closed mouth, sewn on pink outfit for body, removable yellow bib with name printed on, white knit booties. 14½". Marks: ©1990 TYCO/MADE IN CHINA/38, on head. Name tag sewn to body. $35.00.

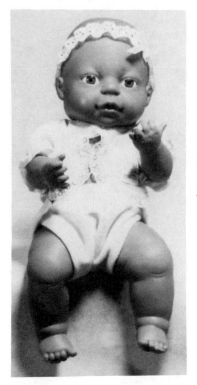

Plate 1281: Tyco. "Baby Feels So Real," from the "Ideal Nursery" series. 13" tall. Doll feels like a real baby with soft skin and tiny bones. Vinyl head, stationary brown eyes, open-closed mouth, jointed vinyl baby body. All original in lavender top, white diapers, and headband. Marks: BABY FEELS SO REAL/©1991 TYCO IND., INC/CHINA, on body. $25.00.

Plate 1282: Tyco. "Kenya," hairstyling doll. Vinyl head, rooted dark brown hair (also available with reddish brown or black hair), stationary brown eyes with real eyelashes, closed mouth, pierced ears with goldtone stud earrings, jointed vinyl body. Doll comes with hair pick, hair beads, rubber bands, curlers, bottle of styling lotion by Pro-Line, and hairstyling guide book. All original in pink print jumpsuit outfit. 13" tall. Marks: ©1991 TYCO IND., INC./MADE IN CHINA, on head. Doll was available in three different skintones. $30.00.

Plate 1283: Tyco. Outfit for "Kenya" with "magic" hair lotion. The dress is fuchsia. $10.00.

Plate 1284: Another outfit sold separately for "Kenya." $10.00.

Left — Plate 1285: Tyco. "Baby Giggles 'n Go." 14". Doll comes with motorized walker. Batteries required. When you tickle her tummy, she giggles. In her walker, she bumps, turns, giggles, and goes. Vinyl head and arms, rooted brown hair, painted eyes, open-closed mouth with two upper and two lower teeth, clothing forms the body. Marks: © 1992 TYCO IND. INC./ MADE IN CHINA, on head. Tagged body. $35.00.

Right — Plate 1286: Tyco. "California Roller Baby." 16" (including skates). Doll moves her head as she skates on roller blades. Vinyl head and arms, hard plastic body and legs, rooted dark brown hair, painted eyes, earrings. All original. Marks: ©1991 TYCO/MADE IN CHINA/ U.S. PAT. 4,507,098/J, on head. $35.00.

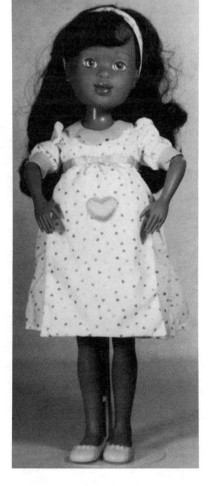

Plate 1287: Tyco. "Mommy's Having a Baby." 18" tall. Baby is 4½" tall. Mommy is a fully jointed vinyl doll, rooted long black hair, painted eyes, closed mouth. Baby comes inside the maternity dress and is all vinyl, jointed body, molded hair, painted features. Marks on mommy: ©1992 TYCO IND. INC./MADE IN CHINA, on head. Marks on baby: © TYCO IND. INC./CHINA, on head. $30.00.

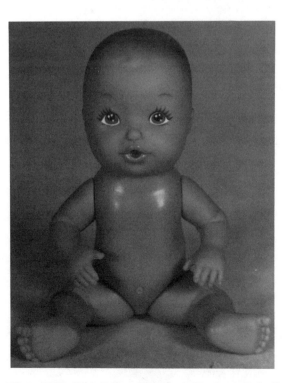

Plate 1288: "Baby" from "Mommy's Having a Baby." Baby has an open nursing mouth, and wets and drinks.

Plate 1289: Uneeda. "Whispy Walker," 32", life size walking doll. All original. Vinyl head, black rooted hair, sleeping dark brown eyes, jointed vinyl body. Marks: 3178/UNEEDA DOLL CO. INC./MCMLXXVI, on head. MADE IN CHINA, on body. Purchased new in 1989. $40.00.

Plate 1290: Uneeda. 36", walking doll. All vinyl, sleeping amber eyes, rooted black hair. Marked: UNEE-DA DOLL, on head. 1968. #3268. Collection of and photograph courtesy of Shirley Jackson. $175.00.

Plate 1291: Uneeda. "Jelly Jeans," 10", vinyl doll with black yarn rooted hair, painted features, open-closed mouth, jointed vinyl body. All original in pink jeans with blue shirt. Marks: MADE IN HONG KONG, on back. Box is marked MCM-LXXXIV. $15.00.

Left — Plate 1292: Uneeda. "Chubby Tub-a-Tot and her duckie." 14" tall. Vinyl head, sculptured hair, sleeping brown eyes, open mouth for pacifier, jointed vinyl toddler body. All original in blue terrycloth sunsuit and matching bonnet. Doll comes with a yellow rubber duck, pink terrycloth babies bath sponge, green face cloth, and pacifier. Marks: UNEEDA DOLL CO INC./MCMLXXXIV, on head; MADE IN CHINA, on body. $12.00.

Right — Plate 1293: Uneeda. "Little Treasure." 8" tall. Vinyl head and hands, rooted long black hair, painted eyes, closed mouth, brown cloth body. All original pink and purple outfit. Marks: MADE IN CHINA, on head; UNEEDA DOLL CO INC, tag sewn to body. $5.00.

Plate 1294: Uneeda. "Tummy Talks," vinyl baby doll. Press her tummy and she laughs, giggles, and cries for mama. Batteries required. Vinyl head, sculpted hair, sleeping brown eyes, open mouth, vinyl hands, brown cloth body with zipper opening for battery. All original in blue print sleeper and matching hat. 14" tall. Marks: UD CO. INC., on head. Available in a variety of outfits. $20.00.

Plate 1295: Uneeda. "Baby Tummy Talks," ©1990. When you squeeze her tummy, she cries. No batteries needed. Vinyl head, arms, and legs, brown cloth body, sculptured hair, sleeping brown eyes, open-closed mouth. All original in pink dotted romper outfit with name on the bib and matching bonnet. 10" tall. Marks: U.D.CO INC 1990/MADE IN CHINA, on head. $15.00.

Plate 1296: Uneeda. 11". Vinyl head and hands, cloth body, legs, and arms, rooted black hair, sleeping brown eyes with lashes, closed mouth. Original clothes. Marks: © UNEEDA DOLL INC. (rest of marks are unclear), on head. Tag sewn to body: UNEEDA DOLL CO. INC. MCMLXXIX ©KFS 1979/... $15.00.

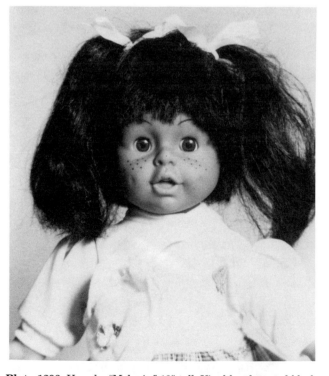

Plate 1297: Uneeda. "Brittany." 11½" vinyl fashion doll marketed by F.W. Woolworth Co. Rooted long black hair, painted eyes, closed mouth, jointed vinyl body with bendable knees, swivel waist. All original doll was available in a variety of formal outfits. Marks: MADE IN CHINA, on head. Box is marked ASSTMT. NO. 6920 and is dated MCMLXXXIX. $15.00.

Plate 1298: Uneeda. "Melanie." 12" tall. Vinyl head, rooted black hair with bangs, sleeping brown eyes with lashes, freckles, slightly dimpled cheeks, open-closed mouth with two upper teeth, vinyl hands, brown cloth body and limbs, white cloth feet for shoes. All original in plaid dress with yellow bodice, long pink pants. Marks: ©1986 UNEEDA DOLL CO. INC./MADE IN CHINA, on head. Courtesy of Xzena Moore of the Cubbyhole. $20.00.

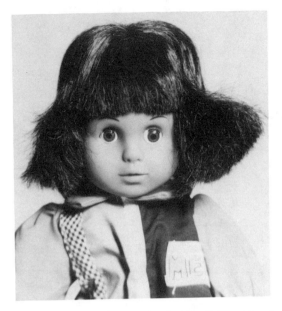

Plate 1300: Uneeda. "Touch n' Talk." 14". Vinyl head, hands, and feet, brown cloth body, arms, and legs, rooted black hair, sleeping brown eyes, open-closed mouth. Talking doll can say five phrases when hands, feet, and stomach are pressed: "Please pick me up and hold me tight"; "I love you Mommy. Will you play with me?"; "I love you Mommy"; "Tell me a story before I go to sleep"; and "Mommy please let's play house." All original in pink print romper with blue sleeves. Marks: U.D. CO. INC./MADE IN CHINA, on head. $25.00.

Plate 1299: Uneeda. "Debbie." 12" tall. Vinyl head and hands, rooted black hair, sleeping brown eyes with bangs, closed mouth, brown cloth body and limbs, white cloth feet for shoes. All original in green, black, and red jumpsuit. Marks: U.D. INC/MADE IN CHINA, on head. Early 1990's. Courtesy of Xzena Moore of the Cubbyhole. $20.00.

Plate 1301: Uneeda. "Tiny Powder Puff." ©1992. 6" tall. Vinyl face, tuft of black hair sewn under cap, painted eyes, freckled cheeks. Clothing forms the body, back of head, and limbs, cloth hands. Body is tagged UNEEDA. Doll was marketed by R.W. Woolworth Co. Outfit came in a variety of pastel colors. This one is aqua and lavender. $5.00.

Plate 1302: Uneeda. "I say Da Da." 6½". Vinyl head and arms, blue cloth body and legs, molded hair, painted eyes. Doll says "Da Da" like a real baby when you press the tummy. Non-replaceable battery. All original in blue print sleeper and bonnet. Marks: CHINA, on head; © UNEEDA DOLL CO., INC. MCMLXXXXI BROOKLYN N.Y. 11232/..., on tag sewn to body. $7.00.

Plate 1303: Uneeda. "I Say Ma Ma." 6½" tall. Identical to previous doll except doll says "Ma Ma." Body is yellow cloth and outfit is pastel print. $7.00.

Plate 1304: Uneeda. 17". Vinyl head, arms, and legs, brown cloth body, sleeping brown eyes with lashes, open-closed mouth with two upper teeth. Collection of Valerie Burbank-Pugh. $55.00.

Plate 1305: Uneeda. "Whispy Walker." 24" tall. Jointed vinyl, amber sleep eyes, painted closed mouth, pale green rooted saran hair. All original in white dress with green bodice. Marks: © UNEEDA DOLL CO INC. 1962, on head. Collection of Emma Ransom Howard. $85.00.

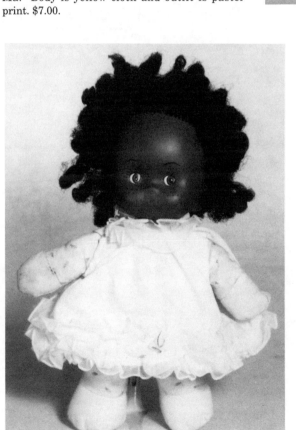

Plate 1307: Uneeda. "Magic Talker." 13". Doll "talks" when you pull her thumb from her mouth. Vinyl head, hands and legs, cloth body and arms, rooted black hair, brown sleep eyes with lashes, open talking mouth. Original clothes. Marks: 7 14/U.D. CO. INC./MADE IN CHINA, on head. Body is tagged UNEEDA. $17.00.

Plate 1306: Uneeda. 10". 1979. Vinyl head, rooted black hair, painted eyes, six freckles on each cheek, yellow rosebud print body and limbs, removable yellow dress with white ruffle trim. Marks: UNEEDA DOLL CO. INC. MCM-LXXIX KFS 1979/..., tag sewn to body. $20.00.

Left — Plate 1308: Vogue Dolls (a subsidiary of Tonka Corp.). "Littlest Angel," #6559. 15". All original in a calico nightie and cap. Vinyl jointed doll, rooted brown hair in bangs with two long braids, sleeping amber/brown eyes with lashes, closed mouth. 1976. Marks: VOGUE DOLL/©1965, on head. $75.00.

Right — Plate 1309: Vogue. "Soft-n-Wet." 1978. 19" tall. Vinyl head, rooted brown hair, sleeping brown eyes with lashes, wide-open nursing mouth, vinyl arms and legs, brown cloth body. All original in long white floral print gown with matching bonnet. Marks: LESNEY PROD. CORP./1978/41879, on head. Tag sewn to body: MADE BY VOGUE DOLLS INC./495 RIVER ST./ PATERSON, N.J. 07524... Collection of the Museum of African American History (Detroit). $95.00.

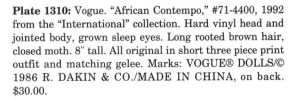

Plate 1310: Vogue. "African Contempo," #71-4400, 1992 from the "International" collection. Hard vinyl head and jointed body, grown sleep eyes. Long rooted brown hair, closed moth. 8" tall. All original in short three piece print outfit and matching gelee. Marks: VOGUE® DOLLS/© 1986 R. DAKIN & CO./MADE IN CHINA, on back. $30.00.

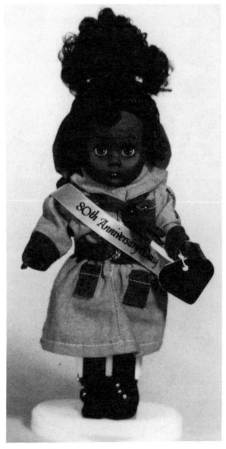

Plate 1311: Vogue Dolls, Division of Dakin, Inc., 1992. "G.S. 80th Anniversary Daisy," #78647. 8" tall. Numbered edition of 2016 dolls dressed by the Senior Girl Scout Troop 1595 of the Girl Scout Council of NW Georgia, to commemorate the 80th anniversary. The basic doll is "Dress Me Black Ginny," #71-0070. The anniversary outfit was manufactured by Vogue and placed over the pink "dress me" outfit originally worn by the doll. Doll comes with a miniature box of cookies and scout handbook and a certificate of authenticity signed by the executive director of NW Georgia Girl Scout Council. This is issue number 870. Jointed vinyl, rooted brown hair, sleeping amber eyes with molded lashes, closed mouth. Marks: ®/ VOGUE DOLLS/© 1984 DAKIN INC./MADE IN CHINA, head. Doll is dressed in an authentic 1912 uniform of blue. $50.00.

Left — Plate 1312: Vogue. "Ginny," 8", classic ballerina, #71-3260 from the "Classics" collection. The box reads: "This design, based on a ballerina costume from the mid 50's, uses pink satin, ribbons and lace to achieve a dancing success." Doll is all hard vinyl with brown sleeping eyes, lashes, rooted brown hair. Marks: VOGUE®/©1986 R. DAKIN & CO./MADE IN CHINA, back of doll. All original. $35.00.

Right — Plate 1313: Vogue. "Ginette," #30193, ©1978. 8" tall. Vinyl head, rooted black hair, brown sleep eyes, closed mouth, jointed vinyl body with bendable knees. All original in blue dotted dress with white lace and appliqué trim, white socks and shoes. The same doll is shown in two other all original outfits in author's book *Black Dolls, 1820–1991*. Marks: GINNY®/VOGUE DOLLS/1977, on head; 1978 VOGUE DOLLS INC./MOONACHIE, N.J./MADE IN HONG KONG, on body. $45.00.

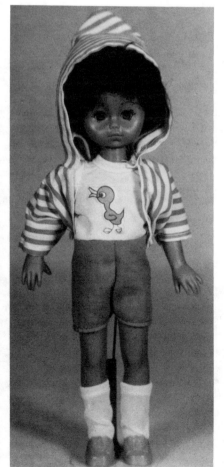

Left — Plate 1314: Vogue. "Ginny" or "Ginnette," #301944. 8" tall. Vinyl head, rooted black hair, sleep eyes, closed mouth, jointed vinyl body. All original in red and white outfit with hooded striped jacket. Doll came in a green and white striped box. Marks: GINNY®/VOGUE DOLLS/1977, on head; ©1978 VOGUE DOLLS INC./MONACHIE, N.J./MADE IN HONG KONG, on body. $45.00.

Right — Plate 1315: Vogue. "Ginny" (Ginette). 8". Special edition for Sears. Vinyl head, rooted black hair, sleeping amber eyes with lashes, closed mouth, jointed body. All original in green velveteen dress with attached white eyelet pinafore. Marks: GINNY®/VOGUE DOLLS/1977, on head; ©1978 VOGUE DOLLS INC./MOONACHIE, N.J./MADE IN HONG KONG, on body.

Plate 1316: Wilco. "Tina," 11½" fashion doll. Vinyl head, arms, and legs, hard plastic body with three screw holes in the back, rooted black hair, painted brown eyes, closed mouth, bendable legs. All original in denim pants and vest with red mock turtle neck sweater. Doll is unmarked. Doll was distributed by Montgomery Ward & Co. $25.00.

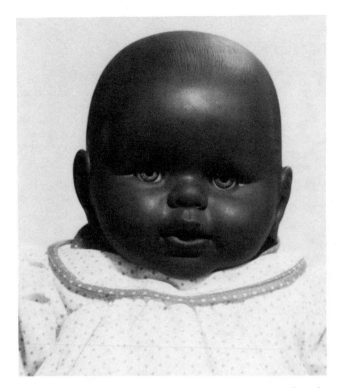

Plate 1317: Star-Doll Division of Wis-Ton Mfg. Co. Ltd., Canada. "Baby Cuddle Soft." 25" long. Vinyl head, faintly molded hair, sleeping amber eyes, open-closed mouth with molded tongue and two lower teeth, vinyl arms and legs, white cloth body. All original in white and red print dress. Marks: M 3(upside down) N B 2 7/HONG KONG/1983/1, on head. $65.00.

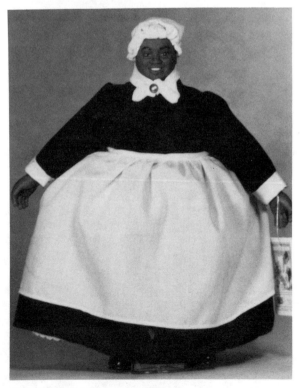

Plate 1318: World Doll. "Mammy," #61061 from "Gone With the Wind" mini-series collection. Limited to one production year. 11" tall. Mammy was played by actress Hattie McDaniel. Vinyl head, painted features, vinyl arms and legs, brown cloth body. All original in long black dress, white apron, and famous red petticoat. Marks: ©1939 SELZNICK, REN/1987 MGM, on head. $50.00.

Plate 1319: Zambardon Corp. "The One & Only." 19". Talking doll made in the image of the Tamika Martin, daughter of the chairman of the Zambardon Corp., Don Martin. Vinyl head, arms, and lower legs, painted eyes, rooted hair, closed mouth, brown cloth body and upper legs. Doll available in a variety of outfits. Battery operated doll talks in Tamika's voice saying the following phrases: "What is your phone number?"; "Have you done your homework today?"; "What is your address?"; "Can you count to twenty?"; "Please read me a favorite story." Marks: ©1988 MARTIN/ZAMBARDON, on head. (Zambardon is very faint.) Photograph courtesy of Zambardon Corp. $70.00.

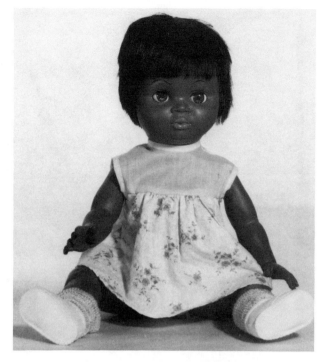

Plate 1320: Wright. Girl from "The Ethnic Doll People" series. 19" tall. All original in dress with print skirt and pink top trimmed in lace. Doll has straight legs, not the toddler as on some Wright dolls. Marks: 1/B. Wright, on head. $75.00.

Plate 1321: Wright. "Patricia," 17". Vinyl baby doll with slightly bent legs, rooted black hair in straight style, sleeping amber eyes with lashes, closed mouth. All original in blue print dress with matching panties. Marks: 1967/BEATRICE WRIGHT, on head. $75.00.

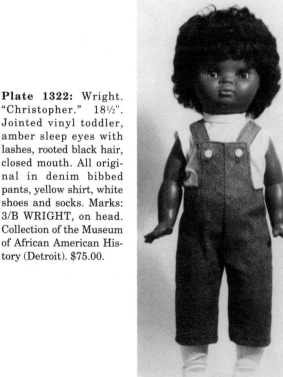

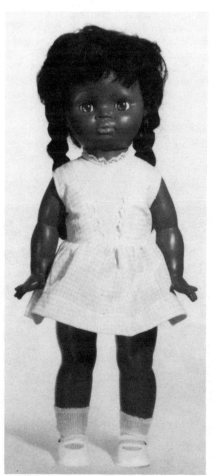

Plate 1322: Wright. "Christopher." 18½". Jointed vinyl toddler, amber sleep eyes with lashes, rooted black hair, closed mouth. All original in denim bibbed pants, yellow shirt, white shoes and socks. Marks: 3/B WRIGHT, on head. Collection of the Museum of African American History (Detroit). $75.00.

Plate 1323: Wright. "Christine." Vinyl head, sleeping brown eyes, rooted black hair with two long braids, closed mouth, jointed hard plastic body. 19" tall. Marks: B. WRIGHT, on head. $75.00.

Plate 1324: YDC (Gigo Toy). "Betty's Gift Set" from the "Dream Collection." 14". Vinyl head, arms, and legs, brown cloth body, rooted black hair, sleeping brown eyes, closed mouth with lips slightly partly. Dressed. Marks: GI-GO FTY LTD/..., tag sewn to body. $15.00.

Plate 1325: YDC. "Baby Gift Set" from the "Dream Collection." 16". Vinyl head, arms, and legs, cloth body, black rooted hair, sleeping brown eyes with lashes, open-closed mouth. Doll comes with seven outfits. Marks: MADE IN CHINA, on head; GI-GO TOYS FTY. LTD./... , tag sewn to body. $22.00.

Plate 1326: Zaninni & Zambelli. "Twins." 26" tall. Vinyl head, arms, and legs, cloth body, open-closed mouth, black sleep pupil-less eyes, thick rooted hair. All original. Girl is wearing red gingham dress under striped pinafore. Boy has on white and yellow outfit. Photograph courtesy of Phyllis Schlatter. $85.00 each.

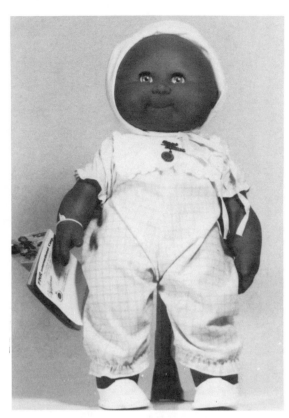

Plate 1328: Zapf. "Sauerkraut Bunch." 1984. 18" tall. Bald vinyl head, sleeping amber eyes, closed mouth, vinyl arms and legs, brown cloth body. All original in pink checkered jumpsuit and white bonnet. Doll was one of four black dolls available in the Sauerkraut Bunch collection of 26 dolls. Two of the black dolls were babies and the other two were a boy and a girl with rooted hair. Clothing is tagged Sauerkraut Bunch. Made in Western Germany. Marks: Z (inside circle), on head. $150.00.

Plate 1327: Zapf. "Denise" from "Balica Dolls." 20½" tall. Vinyl head, rooted short curly back hair, sleeping brown eyes, closed mouth, vinyl arms and legs, brown cloth body. All original in two piece denim and blue print pant set with "Zapf Creation" label on front of blouse. Doll was designed and created in Europe by Bridgette Zapf who designed the entire line for Balica Dolls. Marks: ©MAX ZAPF/1985/ALL RIGHTS RESERVED/17 (logo). Balica dolls is a division of Tiger Toys. Dolls from other divisions of Tiger Toys are pictured under Tiger Toys. Made in Yugoslavia. $50.00.

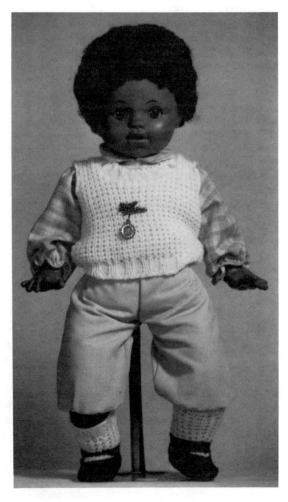

Left — Plate 1329: Zapf. "Jonina," 1982 or 1983. 19" tall. Vinyl head and limbs, cloth body. All original in black velvet dress. Pin on dress reads "Exclusive Collette." Hang tag on wrist reads "Jonina Exclusive Collette." Marks on doll: Z (in circle) 50-17, on head. Collette dolls are a collection of dolls in the Zapf line. Photograph courtesy of Etta Houston. $200.00.

Right — Plate 1330: Zapf. "Basile." 19" tall. Vinyl head and limbs, cloth body, rooted hair, sleep eyes. All original in knitted vest and socks, plaid shirt, cotton pants. Marks: Z/50 (slash) 18, on head. Collection of Reevah Turner. $150.00.

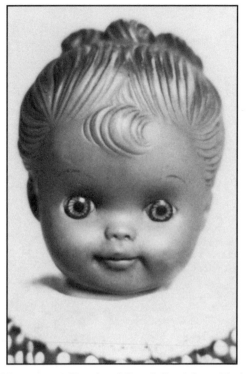

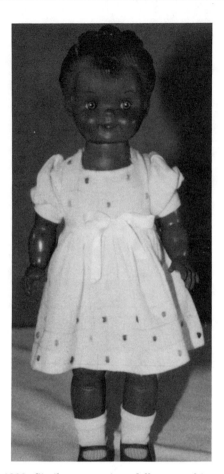

Plate 1332: Vinyl toddler doll with molded upsweep hairdo and tiny bangs on the forehead, brown glassine eyes, closed mouth, one-piece vinyl body, movable head. 12" tall. Marks: 4131/K16, on head. Redressed in blue and white dotted dress. $50.00.

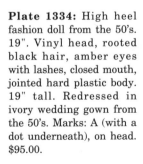

Plate 1331: 19½" fashion doll from the 1950's. Vinyl head, open-shut amber eyes with real lashes, rooted black hair, closed mouth, jointed hard vinyl body with high heel feet. Redressed in Madam Alexander coat. Marks: P-21, on head; AE (superimposed backward), on body. $95.00.

Plate 1333: Similar to previous doll except this one is larger, 16" tall, and is unmarked. Hard vinyl body and legs, rubber head and arms, molded hair in upsweep with nine curls on top of head and curl on forehead, inset eyes, closed mouth smile. Clothes may be original. 1950's. Photograph courtesy of Etta Houston. $60.00.

Plate 1334: High heel fashion doll from the 50's. 19". Vinyl head, rooted black hair, amber eyes with lashes, closed mouth, jointed hard plastic body. 19" tall. Redressed in ivory wedding gown from the 50's. Marks: A (with a dot underneath), on head. $95.00.

Plate 1335: High-heeled fashion doll. 1960's. Vinyl head, sleeping amber eyes, rooted black hair, closed mouth, pierced ears with pearlike earrings, jointed vinyl body. 20" tall. Dressed in long yellow gown that looks old but might not be original. Marks: 18, on head. $95.00.

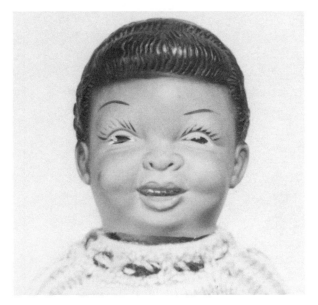

Plate 1337: "Polly" with a head that seems to have been attached to another body. 13½" tall. Marks: PULLAN, on head; 8/V-4, on body. $75.00.

Plate 1336: 13" tall. Jointed vinyl doll, rooted black hair, sleeping amber/brown eyes with lashes, closed mouth. All original in native-type outfit made of bark cloth. Marks: MADE IN ENGLAND, on head; MADE/IN/ENGLAND, on body. $45.00.

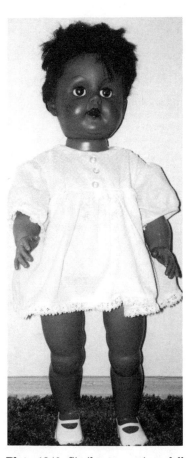

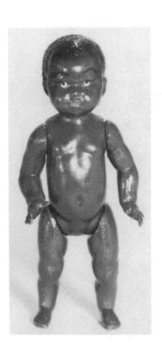

Plate 1338: Hard vinyl toddler doll. 3½" tall. Molded kinky hair, painted features, closed mouth, movable arms and legs. Doll was given to Bobbie Wilhite by the late fashion designer Willie Smith. It was reported that he had a collection of over 6000 black dolls. Whenever visitors came to see his collection he gave them one of these dolls. A pin was glued to the back of the doll so that it could be worn as a doll pin. Doll is unmarked. $20.00.

Plate 1339: Vinyl toddler, 1950-1960. 24" tall. Rooted reddish brown hair over sculptured hair, sleeping brown eyes with real lashes, open-closed mouth with molded tongue, jointed vinyl toddler body. Redressed. Marks: AE (superimposed), on head; 25-5/AE (superimposed), on body. $95.00.

Plate 1340: Similar to previous doll except this one has black hair and is 24". Vinyl head, rooted black hair, sleeping brown eyes with lashes, open-close mouth with molded tongue, hard vinyl jointed body. Redressed. Marks: 25-5/AE, on body. Collection of Shirley Jackson. $50.00.

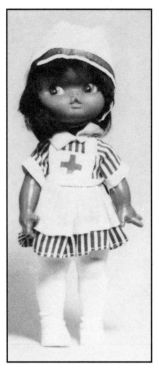

Plate 1341: Vinyl girl. 7". Painted eyes, rooted black hair, jointed vinyl body, closed mouth. All original in print flannel nightgown and matching bonnet. Marks: MADE IN JAPAN, on body. $15.00.

Plate 1342: Vinyl character face doll. 9" tall. Painted side-glancing eyes, open-closed mouth, black rooted hair, jointed vinyl body. All original in blue and white striped Red Cross outfit. 1970's Marks: HONG KONG, on body. $20.00.

Plate 1343: "Combat Man." 12" vinyl doll. Painted eyes, molded black hair, open-closed mouth with painted teeth, jointed body. All original in army outfit. Manufacturer or distributor was not noted on the package, only the doll's name and SKU NO. S315812. Marks: MADE IN CHINA, on body. $5.00.

Plate 1345: Vinyl "Kewpie-like" jointed doll. 14" tall. Rooted black curly hair, painted eyes, closed mouth, molded "wings" on back shoulders, molded "knot" under rooted hair on top of the head. The same "knot" is on the back of the head near the neckline. Marks: K (in a diamond)/TAIWAN, on back. Courtesy of Joya Mallory. $20.00.

Plate 1344: "It's a Small World." 10" tall. Vinyl head, rooted black hair, sleeping brown eyes, closed mouth, jointed vinyl bent-leg body. All original in red print two-piece swimsuit from Disneyworld in the 1970's. Marks: U, on head. $50.00.

Plate 1346: Vinyl character face doll. 10" tall. Vinyl head, rooted brown hair, painted eyes, closed smiling mouth, jointed vinyl body. All original in jumper outfit with red and white striped top, blue felt bottom. 1970's. Marks: 3, on head and body. $30.00.

Plate 1347: Toddler doll. 11" tall. 1958. Vinyl head, rooted black synthetic hair, sleeping amber eyes with one-piece lashes, closed mouth, jointed vinyl body. All original in red velveteen dress with matching headscarf. Marks: 4092/K53, on head. $50.00.

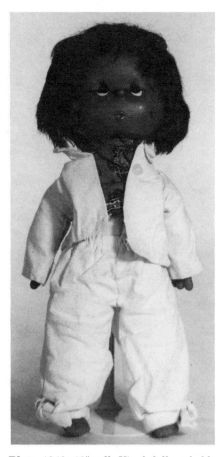

Plate 1348: 12" tall. Vinyl doll probably made from a kit. Rooted black hair, painted eyes, freckles, open-closed mouth. Unmarked. Collection of Valerie Burbank-Pugh. $25.00.

Plate 1349: "Susan." 11½" vinyl fashion dolls. Very inexpensive dolls that were on the market in the early 1990's. Rooted black hair, jointed vinyl arms and legs. Dolls came in a variety of inexpensively made outfits. Doll on the left has a closed mouth, the one on the right has painted open mouth. Identical packages are marked "Susan" with no indication of the manufacturer. Unmarked. $5.00.

Plate 1350: 10", seated. Vinyl head, tuft of black synthetic hair sewn under cap, painted features. Beige clothing forms the body. Doll looks very much like the "Eskimo Pie" logo. Unmarked. $25.00.

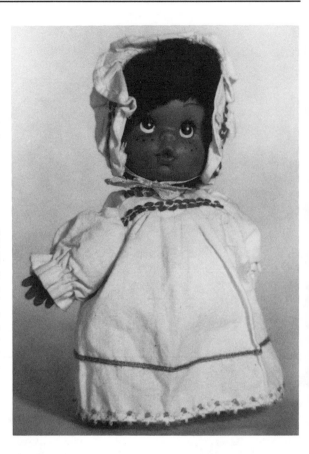

Left — Plate 1351: 10" vinyl doll. Rooted dark brown hair, sleep brown eyes, closed mouth, jointed vinyl body. Unmarked. Collection of Valerie Burbank-Pugh. $20.00.

Right — Plate 1352: 9" tall. Vinyl head, hands, and feet, cloth body, rooted black hair, painted eyes, open-closed mouth, freckled cheeks. Unmarked. Collection of Valerie Burbank-Pugh. $20.00.

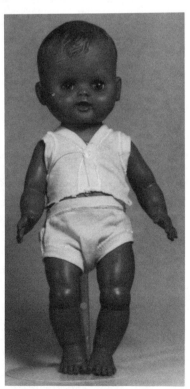

Plate 1353: Vinyl baby. 12". Molded hair, sleeping amber eyes, nursing mouth, jointed vinyl body. All original in pink cotton knit undies. Marks: 4161/K53, on head; K12-5, on body. $25.00.

Plate 1354: 1970's. 11½". Vinyl head, rooted black hair, painted eyes, open-closed mouth, jointed vinyl body. Redressed. Original hair set. Marks: MADE IN HONG KONG, on head; HONG KONG/MADE IN, on body. $25.00.

Plate 1355: 24" tall. Vinyl head, rooted black hair, sleeping amber eyes with real lashes, closed mouth, jointed vinyl body. Unmarked. Redressed. $55.00.

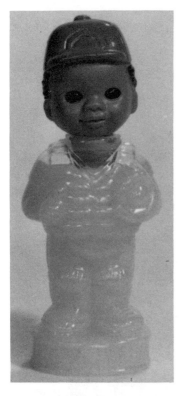

Plate 1356: "Baseball Kids." Candy container boy doll. 4½" tall. Plastic head with molded on baseball cap, painted black eyes, molded black hair in tight curls, one piece clear plastic body with molded on baseball outfit. Body came filled with candy, removable head is the top. Doll came in either a red or blue cap. Marks: CHINA, on back of cap. Distributed by the E. Rosen Company. $5.00.

Plate 1357: 14" toddler doll. Vinyl head, rooted black hair, sleeping amber eyes, nursing mouth, jointed vinyl toddler body. All original in dress with print cotton bodice, pink organza skirt. Doll was purchased in New Mexico in the late 1950's for Beverly A. Hill. Marks: AE278, on head. Courtesy of Beverly Alison Hill. $50.00.

Plate 1358: "Jaci." 11". Vinyl head, rooted black hair, sleeping brown eyes, closed mouth, jointed vinyl toddler body. Doll was purchased as a Christmas gift for Beverly A. Hill in 1956. Doll was ordered from Montgomery Ward's *Christmas Book, 1956*, page 163. The collection was called "Miss America Miniatures." The doll was advertised as ready-to-dress and came wearing a pair of white underpants. Doll was dressed in 1957 by Beverly's mother, Verna Hill. She made a complete wardrobe for Beverly's Jaci doll. Additional outfits were also sold separately from the Ward's catalog. Marks: VM, on body. Courtesy of Beverly Alison Hill. $95.00.

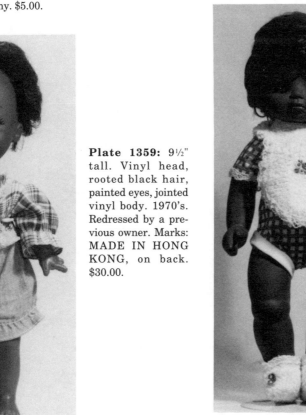

Plate 1359: 9½" tall. Vinyl head, rooted black hair, painted eyes, jointed vinyl body. 1970's. Redressed by a previous owner. Marks: MADE IN HONG KONG, on back. $30.00.

Plate 1360: 15½" tall. Vinyl head and jointed body, sleeping brown eyes with lashes, rooted black hair, painted closed mouth. All original in blue checkered romper, white terrycloth bib and booties. Marks: B40/156, on head. Collection of the Museum of African History (Detroit). $75.00.

Plate 1361: 6" vinyl baby doll. 1970's. Painted eyes, sculptured hair, nursing mouth, jointed body. Marks: Made in Hong Kong, on body. Collection of the Museum of African American History (Detroit). $15.00.

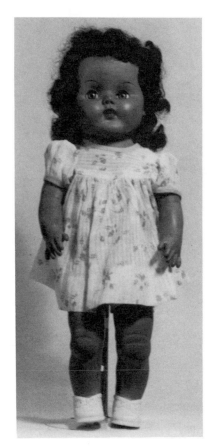

Plate 1362: 16" tall. Vinyl head with molded hair under a glued on black wig, sleeping amber eyes with lashes, closed mouth, stuffed one-piece vinyl body. Marks: MRP, on head. Circa 1955. Collection of the Museum of African American History (Detroit). $125.00.

Plate 1363: "Baby-Sitter." 31" tall. Vinyl head, rooted black hair, sleeping brown eyes, closed mouth, jointed vinyl body. All original in striped body suit, red skirt, red head scarf, black patent boots. Marks: 9/19©61, on head. Collection of the Museum of African American History (Detroit). $125.00.

Plate 1364: Hard vinyl doll, 7½" tall. Rooted black hair, painted side-glancing eyes, painted mouth with tongue curled over upper lip, jointed body. Dressed in magenta two piece crocheted outfit with matching bonnet and booties. Marks on back are unreadable. Collection of the Museum of African American History (Detroit). $40.00.

Plate 1365: "Baby Pele." Approximately 2½" tall. Vinyl head, stationary amber plastic eyes, white tuft of hair, cloth body. Sewn on blue flannel outfit. Doll comes inside a box with similar doll pictured on the outside. Manufacturer unknown. Collection of the Museum of African American History (Detroit). $20.00.

Plate 1366: Toddler girl. 11" tall. Circa 1965. Vinyl head, replaced wig, original hair was rooted, sleeping amber eyes, closed mouth, jointed vinyl body. Marks: AE10F, on head. Collection of the Museum of African American History (Detroit). $50.00.

Plate 1367: "Terry." 16" tall. Vinyl head, rooted black hair, sleeping brown eyes with lashes, closed mouth, jointed vinyl body. Redressed in an Ideal "Crissy" outfit. 1970's. Marks: MADE IN/HONG KONG, on body. Collection of the Museum of African American History (Detroit). $65.00.

Plate 1368: 5" vinyl doll with movable head and arms, rooted black hair, painted features, molded on white socks and red shoes. Marks: JAPAN, on back. $20.00.

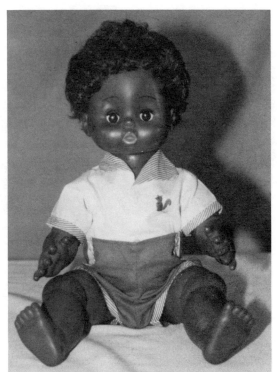

Left — Plate 1369: 21" unmarked sexed boy. All hard vinyl, rooted hair, sleep eyes. All original. Collection of and photo courtesy of Etta Houston. $150.00.

Right — Plate 1370: 8" tall. Vinyl head, rooted black hair, sleeping amber eyes, closed mouth, one-piece body with movable arms. All original and unmarked. Collection of Reevah Turner. $40.00.

Plate 1371: 17" hard plastic walker, 1950's. Brown sleep eyes, black wig, open mouth with four teeth, felt tongue. Unmarked. Probably redressed. Photograph courtesy of Stephanie Lisoski. $165.00.

Plate 1372: "Cheer Girl" advertising doll, early 1960's. 10". All vinyl, brown painted eyes, black rooted hair. All original in two piece orange outfit, white boots. These dolls were attached to King-sized boxes of All-Temperature Cheer detergent. Photograph courtesy of Stephanie Lisoski. $85.00.

Plate 1373: "Tina Fashion" dolls distributed by Montgomery Ward & Co., 1980. 11½" tall. All vinyl, blue painted eyes with insert eyelashes. Doll on left has dark red rooted hair, light skin tone, and is wearing a blue jumpsuit. Doll on right has black rooted hair, darker skin tone, and is dressed in a yellow outfit. Marks are the same: MADE IN/ HONG KONG, on back. Photograph courtesy of Stephanie Lisoski. $25.00.

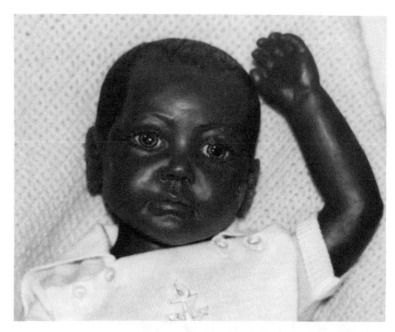

Plate 1374: "Comfy Karen." 8" tall. Jointed vinyl, molded hair, nursing mouth, painted eyes. All original in yellow blanket with bottle. Purchased new in 1991. Made in China. Photograph courtesy of Faith Wyse. $5.00.

Plate 1375: "Anthony," hospital mannequin baby. 21" tall. All vinyl, closed mouth, painted eyes, molded and painted hair, anatomically correct boy, open nostrils and ear canals, soft spot in head, ball jointed water tight body. Photograph courtesy of Phyllis Schlatter. $400.00+.

Plate 1376: "Baby John." 17" all vinyl medical model. Anatomically correct baby boy preemie. Not jointed, eyes closed. Photograph courtesy of Phyllis Schlatter. $300.00+.

Plate 1377: "Rockabye Lullabye." 19". Key wound vinyl musical doll plays a lullabye and holds a baby doll as body moves from side to side and eyes slowly close. Rooted black hair, closed mouth. Vinyl baby has painted eyes and is 6½". Both dolls are all original. Marks: MADE IN HONG KONG, on neck and back. Collection of Shirley Jackson. Sebino Doll Company, Italy, made a similar doll called "Titti With her Baby," #02400, ©1980. The doll plays "Lullaby and Good Night" and is 21" tall. The baby is 7" and named "Cialdino." Original clothing on Titti was a plaid dress with pantaloons. $100.00.

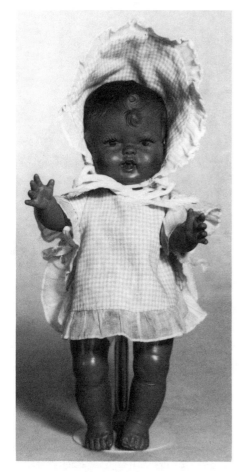

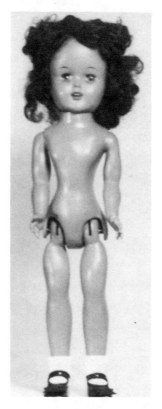

Plate 1378: 10" tall. Soft vinyl head and arms, molded curly hair, painted eyes, open-closed mouth with two upper teeth, hard vinyl body and legs. 1950–60. Clothing could be original. Marks: 12, on head. $30.00.

Plate 1379: 1950's walker doll. 16" tall. Hard plastic head, black glued on synthetic wig, sleeping amber eyes, open mouth with four upper teeth, red felt-like tongue, jointed hard plastic body. Unmarked. $125.00.

Plate 1380: Bottle doll, 12" tall. Head is hard vinyl, painted eyes, brown yarn hair. Body is a plastic bottle filled with sand, clothing forms arms, brown felt hands. Dressed in old plaid skirt, white apron, shawl, and kerchief. Unmarked. $20.00.

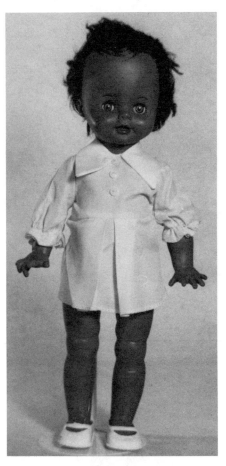

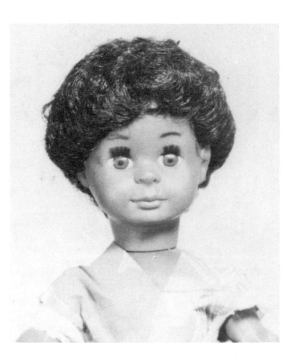

Left — Plate 1381: 16". 1950–60. Vinyl head, rooted black hair (badly damaged), sleeping amber/brown eyes, open-closed mouth with molded in tongue, jointed vinyl body. Three fingers on right hand are in curled position. Marks: AE 1505/12, on head. Redressed. $20.00.

Right — Plate 1382: Vinyl doll made in France. 12". Vinyl head, sleeping brown eyes with lashes, rooted black hair, closed mouth, jointed vinyl body (one replaced leg). Doll was an island souvenir from either Guadeloupe or Martinique as both names are printed on original clothing. Marks: 30/ FRANCE/(a triangle logo with a figure inside that cannot be identified)/ MADE/IN/FRANCE, on body. $40.00.

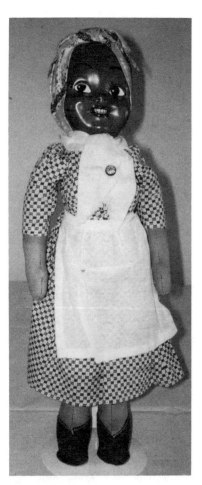

Plate 1383: 12" tall. Hard plastic face, back of head is cloth, painted features, brown cloth body with legs attached by using metal fasteners. All original in striped dress, blue apron, and white neck scarf. Unmarked. Doll was probably made in Poland. $65.00.

Plate 1384: 17". Vinyl face over cloth head, cloth body with jointed legs, painted features. All original in mammy outfit. Marks: POLAND, stamped on right upper leg. Collection of Emma Ransom Hayward. $75.00.

Plate 1385: 16", mask face. Plastic face with painted features. All original. Photograph courtesy of Susan Girardot. $75.00.

Plate 1386: 10½" boy and girl inflatable vinyl dolls with "blinky" eyes. Collection of Emma Ransom Hayward. $100.00.

Plate 1387: 7½" hard plastic doll. 1950's–1960's. Dark brown glued on wig, sleeping brown eyes, closed mouth, jointed body, painted on black shoes over molded toes (unusual as shoes are not molded). Redressed. Unmarked. $45.00.

Plate 1388: Hard plastic walker. 27" tall. Glued on wig, sleep eyes, four teeth, felt tongue. Doll is wearing an original Saucy Walker dress that is not original to this doll. Hat and shoes are not original. Unmarked. Photograph courtesy of Etta Houston. $350.00.

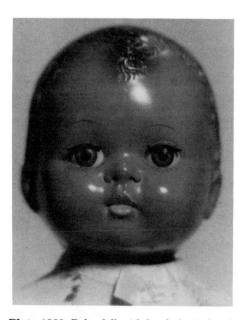

Plate 1389: Baby doll with hard plastic head, molded hair, sleeping brown eyes with lashes, closed mouth, "real skin" one piece brown vinyl body. 13½" tall. Redressed in white flower print dress with long sleeves and white tights to keep the body from deteriorating. Unmarked, early 1950's. $125.00.

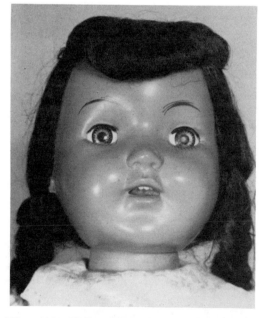

Plate 1390: Walker doll, 1940's. Hard plastic head, sleeping brown eyes, open mouth with four upper teeth and felt tongue, walking hard plastic body. Black synthetic wig in bangs and two braids, a style that was very popular during that period. 27" tall. Shoes and socks look original. Replaced dress. Unmarked. $350.00.

Plate 1391: 9½" baby. Hard plastic head and five piece jointed body, lamb's wool wig, black sleep eyes, closed mouth with Negroid features. Marks: MADE IN/ENGLAND, on body. $250.00.

Plate 1392: Plastic marionette. 10" tall. Unmarked. Photograph courtesy of Virginia Kiley. $50.00.

Plate 1393: Plastic marionette. 10" tall. The two balls rattle when shake them. Unmarked. Collection of and photograph courtesy of Virginia Kiley. $75.00.

Plate 1394: 7½" tall. Hard plastic, movable arms and head, molded hair with loop for ribbon, painted eyes, closed mouth. Molded on shorts with suspenders. Painted socks, painted black shoes. Marks: CIPSA (or GIPSA), on back. $65.00.

Plate 1395: Topsy-turvy doll from Brazil. Hard plastic heads in one piece with hard plastic body, movable hard plastic arms, painted eyes, glued on black wigs. One head is painted brown, the other is painted black. 6" tall. Marks: TR (inside triangle) INC A, on back of both bodies. $20.00.

Plate 1396: Souvenir type doll. 7". Hard plastic head and jointed body, sleeping amber eyes with one piece lashes, black lamb's wool wig, closed mouth. All original in clothing made of bark-type material. Marks: MADE IN ENGLAND, on body. Courtesy of Patricia B. Whittler-Martin. $35.00.

Plate 1398: Souvenir type doll. 6½" tall. Hard plastic "Native Man." All original in loincloth, fur headdress, and fur ankle pieces. Arms are strung, one piece body, legs, and head. Unmarked. Photograph courtesy of Etta Houston. $35.00.

Plate 1397: Souvenir type doll. 7". Hard plastic head, closed mouth, amber sleep eyes with one piece lashes, jointed hard plastic limbs, lamb's wool hair. All original in beaded red leather two-piece outfit. Marks: MADE IN ENGLAND, on body. Courtesy of Patricia Whittler-Martin. $35.00.

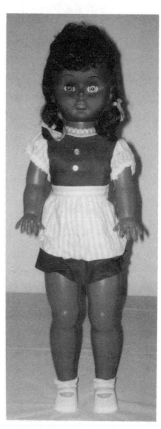

Plate 1399: 14" tall. Vinyl head and jointed body, sleeping amber eyes with lashes, closed mouth. All original in red outfit with white shoes and socks. Marks: © 1963/A-E 154, on head. Courtesy of Lillian J. Ransom. $55.00.

Plate 1400: 12". Movable vinyl head, molded hair, stationary amber/brown eyes, open-closed mouth, hard vinyl body with movable arms. Unmarked. $40.00.

Plate 1401: 23" tall. 1970's. Vinyl head and body, rooted black hair, sleeping brown eyes, closed mouth. Original clothing. Marks: HONG KONG, on head. Collection of Emma Ransom Hayward. $75.00.

CHAPTER SIX
ARTIST AND REPRODUCTION DOLLS

Plate 1402: Anguish. "Rachel." Original mold by Vickie Anguish. ©1988. Makes a 25" lady doll. Mold is a shoulder head with stationary eyes, closed mouth. Also available was a mold to make "Small Rachel," a 20" doll. Both molds were on the market available to doll-makers. Photograph courtesy of Vickie Anguish Originals. $150.00+.

Plate 1403: Anguish. "Melody." Original mold by doll artist Vickie Anguish. ©1986. 16". Socket head, porcelain body, closed mouth, stationary brown eyes, black wig. Mold was sold on the market to doll-makers. Cost of the mold, when issued, was approximately $65.00. Photograph courtesy of Vickie Anguish of Vickie Anguish Originals. $150.00+.

Plate 1404: Artchees. "Gen. Colin Powell." All cloth. Soft-sculptured painted face, cloth sculptured body. All original. Gen. Powell was appointed Joint-Chiefs-of-Staff by the George Bush administration. He was the first African American to be appointed to this position. 21" tall. Courtesy of Artchees. $650.00.

Plate 1405: Artchees. "Rosa Parks." 17" tall. Soft sculpture. Rosa Parks is known as the "Little Heroine of Montgomery" because she refused to give up her seat on a bus after a day's work. This began the bus boycott in Montgomery, Alabama, 1955–56 and the Civil Rights Movement. Collection of the Museum of African American History (Detroit). $650.00.

Left — Plate 1406: Avon. "Adama." 8" tall. Porcelain shoulder head, arms, and legs, cloth body, painted features and hair, molded on sandals, molded on jewelry with real beads added to neck and right arm, holding a porcelain jug. All original in African style clothing. Doll is from the "International Porcelain Doll Collection" and represents Nigeria. $75.00.

Right — Plate 1407: Avon. "Sunday Best." 9" tall. 1993. Porcelain head and limbs, cloth body, brown painted eyes, black wig. From the "Childhood Dreams" series. Doll is unmarked but dress is tagged Avon. Photograph courtesy of Stephanie Lisoski. $45.00.

Barray (a combination of Barry and Ray) is the trade name of a line of hand-crafted dolls made by artists Barry McLeod and Ray Compos. Each Barray doll is 29" tall, stamped with the BARRAY logo, and hand signed behind the right ear indicating name of doll, artist, and date completed. The medium used for each BARRAY doll is hand painted papier-maché head, leather or fabric ears, synthetic hand sewn hair, soft sculptured body of canvas, leather, or assorted fabric. All dolls are anatomically correct. Clothing and shoes are removable and are hand made by BARRAY. Following are photographs of BARRAY dolls.

Plate 1408: Barray. "Anisha and Forest." Handmade one-of-a-kind. Made in 1993. Second place winners in the couples competition at the Dark Images 1993 convention in Philadelphia. Private collection. Photograph courtesy of Barray. $600.00+.

Plate 1409: Barray. "Skipper." One-of-a-kind, made in 1993. Photograph courtesy of Barray. $600.00+.

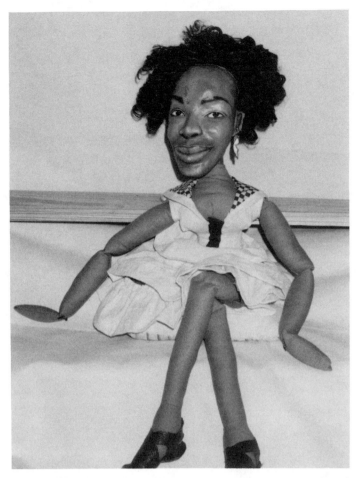

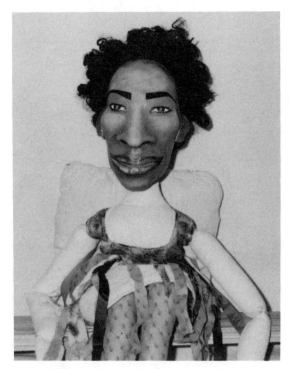

Plate 1411: Barray. "Maddie." One-of-a-kind in a series made in 1993. Private collection. Photograph courtesy of Barray. $600.00+.

Plate 1410: Barray. "Fern." One-of-a-kind, made in 1993. Private collection. Photograph courtesy of Barray. $600.00+.

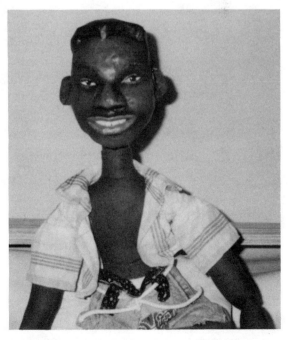

Plate 1412: Barray "Alton." One-of-a-kind made in May, 1993. Private collection. Photograph courtesy of Barray. $600.00+.

Plate 1413: Barray. "Mike." One-of-a-kind made in 1993. Private collection. Photograph courtesy of Barray. $600.00+.

Plate 1414: Artist Floyd Bell at work in his studio in 1988. Bell is the second black artist elected into the prestigious doll association, NIADA (National Institute of American Doll Artists). He was inducted into the association in 1992. The first black member was the late I. Roberta Bell of Bertabel's Dolls. The two are not related. Floyd Bell's dolls have been on display in the U.S. and Europe and have won numerous awards. Mr. Bell is a teacher in the Los Angeles public schools.

Plate 1415: Floyd Bell. "Benjamin Bannecker." 1983. 14" tall. One-of-a-kind, handcarved head and hands, cloth body. Photograph courtesy of Floyd Bell. $750.00.

Plate 1416: F. Bell. "Dr. Ralph Bunch." 15" tall. One-of-a-kind doll was carved from basswood in 1981. Dr. Ralph Bunche was the first black person to receive the Nobel Peace Prize. Photograph courtesy of Floyd Bell. $1,000.00.

Plate 1417: F. Bell. "Cabaret Dancer" by artist Floyd Bell. 16". Porcelain head, composition body. Edition of 20, 1983. Photograph courtesy of Floyd Bell. $500.00.

Plate 1418: Bell, F. "Booker T. Washington." 23" tall. Hand carved from basswood by Floyd Bell, 1988. Edition of four. Photograph courtesy of Floyd Bell. $2,000.00.

Left — Plate 1419: Bell, F. "Fredrick Douglass." 18" tall. Hand carved from basswood by Floyd Bell, 1990. Edition of three. Photograph courtesy of Floyd Bell. $2,000.00.

Right — Plate 1420: Bell, F. "Mary McLeod Bethune." 18" tall. Hand carved from basswood by Floyd Bell. 1989. Limited edition of five. From the collection of the Wanke Museum, Germany. Photograph courtesy of Floyd Bell. $2,000.00.

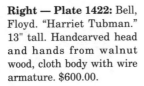

Left — Plate 1421: Bell, F. "Matthew Henson." 19" tall. Limited edition of 24 dolls, carved from alderwood by artist Floyd Bell. Doll was shown at the Louvre Museum in Paris, France, 1991. Photograph courtesy of Floyd Bell. $2,000.00.

Right — Plate 1422: Bell, Floyd. "Harriet Tubman." 13" tall. Handcarved head and hands from walnut wood, cloth body with wire armature. $600.00.

Plate 1423: Floyd Bell. "Southern Gentlemen." 12" tall. Porcelain head, composition body. Edition of 10, 1983. Photograph courtesy of Floyd Bell. $500.00.

Plate 1424: Bell, F. "Mary McLeod Bethune." 19" tall. Hand carved by artist Floyd Bell in 1988. Head and limbs are alderwood, molded painted hair, cloth body with wire armature. Photograph courtesy of Floyd Bell. $2,000.00.

Plate 1425: Bell, Floyd. "Jane Pittman." 17". Hand-carved one-of-a-kind from walnut wood. Doll is based on character from the movie "Miss Jane Pittman." Marks: ©FLOYD BELL/1992, on back of shoulder head. $1,000.00.

Plate 1426: Floyd Bell, doll artist, with "Scott Joplin" doll, 1992. Doll, 18", and piano are one-of-a-kind, hand carved from walnut wood, cloth body with wire armature, painted eyes, carved hair. Photograph of Floyd Bell. $2,500.00.

Plate 1427: Bell, F. "John Henry" by Floyd Bell, 1982. 21" tall. Head and hands carved from mahogany wood, cloth body, carved hair, painted eyes. One-of-a-kind. An edition of five was also created. Photograph courtesy of Floyd Bell. $1,500.00.

Plate 1428: Bell, F. "Tap Dance Twins," 1985, by Floyd Bell. Hand carved from walnut wood. One-of-a-kind. 12" tall. Photograph courtesy of Floyd Bell. $1,500.00 pair.

Plate 1429: Bell, F. "Sojourner Truth" by Floyd Bell. 1987. 13". Head hand carved from walnut wood with cloth body. $500.00.

Plate 1430: Bell, F. "Dr. George Washington Carver." 16". Handcarved head and limbs, cloth body with wire armature. Edition of five. Photograph courtesy of Floyd Bell. $2,000.00.

Plate 1431: Bell. "Leroy on a Carousel Horse." 1988. Doll is 6" tall and made of composition. Carousel horse is hand carved from basswood. One-of-a-kind by artist Floyd Bell. Photograph courtesy of Floyd Bell.
Leroy, $150.00.
Horse, $1,200.00.

Ida Roberta Bell, 1904–1992, was the first black American elected into the prestigious organization of doll artists, NIADA, (National Institute of American Doll Artists.) She was inducted into the organization in 1970 as a result of the excellence of her Dr. George Washington Carver doll. She is primarily known for her portrait dolls of famous black Americans. Professionally, she was an educator and used the dolls to impart her knowledge of black history to her students. Her dolls include the following: George Washington Carver; Mary McLeod Bethune; Paul Lawrence Dunbar; Harriet Tubman; Crispus Attucks; Jean Baptiste Point du Sable; W.C. Handy; Dr. Daniel Hale Williams; Frederick Douglass; Anna Murray Douglass, Fredrick Douglass' wife; Elizabeth Keckley, dressmaker and confidante to Mary Todd Lincoln; Ashanti Queen Mother, queen of Ashanti (Ghana); a black Madonna and child; Solon C. Bell, (her husband) labor leader, first to establish a union among dining-car employees in the 1930's; Matthew Henson; Harold Washington, first black mayor of Chicago; and Annie Davis Frierson, her maternal grandmother. Her dolls are in museums and private collections all over the country.

Bell was born in Nashville, Tennessee. At the the age of eleven, she moved with her family to Kansas City, and was educated in the elementary and high schools of Topeka, Kansas, and Kansas City, Missouri. She received a bachelor's degree from Kansas University in Lawrence, Kansas, and master's degree from Northwestern University in Evanston, Illinois. She taught elementary school in Kansas City, Missouri, and Chicago, Illinois, and retired in 1969 from the Chicago public schools.

Ida Roberta Bell came from an artistic background. Her father, Robert Eugene Bell, was an artist and sculptor, as was his brother, Walter Bell. When Roberts, as she preferred to be called, was a young child, her father was upset at the fact that she had only white dolls to play with and once removed the pink and white bisque head and hands from a doll and sculpted black ones to replace them. Mrs. Bell later won a black bisque headed doll at a church raffle. The doll was ordered from a catalog by the National Negro Doll Co. in Nashville, Tennessee.

Bell first began making dolls in the early 1940's. She used papier-maché, oven-hardening clay, and cloth. Wanting to perfect her craft, she took classes in mold making and painting facial features. Her famous black Americans series were made by first modeling the head in plastilene. A mold was then made and the head and hands were poured with brown porcelain slip (liquid porcelain). The bodies are stuffed with sawdust. All costuming was done by Mrs. Bell and was thoroughly researched for detail.

Although I. Roberta Bell had a full and rich life as a professional, her avocation was her first love. She was involved for some years with the United Federation of Doll Clubs and was the founder of the Guys and Gals Funtastique Doll Club in Chicago. Presently, a doll club named in her honor is in operation in Cincinnati, Ohio.

Plate 1432: Photograph of I. Roberta Bell with three of her dolls. Dolls are, left to right: W.C. Handy, the "Father of the Blues," famous for "The St. Louis Blues"; Jean Baptiste Pointe du Sable, first citizen of Chicago and a wealthy trapper and fur trader; and Dr. Daniel Hale Williams, the first open heart surgeon and founder of the Provident Hospital and School of Nurse Training. $425.00 each doll.

Plate 1434: Bell, I. Roberta. "Dr. George Washington Carver," eminent scientist. Porcelain shoulder head, flocked gray hair, eyebrows, and mustache, painted eyes and mouth, porcelain hands, cloth body and legs. All original in white shirt, black pants, red plaid tie, tan felt scientist's apron. 17½" tall. Marks: DR. G.W. CARVER/ "BERTABEL"/©1969, on head. $425.00.

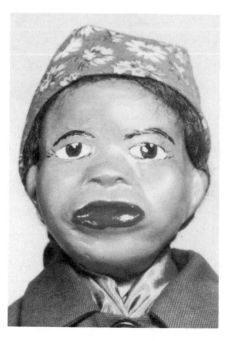

Plate 1433: Bell, I.R. "Harriet Tubman." Abolitionist — "Moses of her People." 16" tall. Porcelain shoulder head, gray wavy hair, painted features, closed mouth, porcelain hands and feet, one hand is holding a gun, brown cloth body. All original in long black cotton skirt, navy blue jacket, navy neck scarf, red calico kerchief, and carrying a knapsack made of cotton ticking. Marks: HARRIET TUBMAN/"BERTABEL"/©1969, on head. $425.00.

Left — Plate 1435: Bell, I.R. "Mary McLeod Bethune." Educator, humanitarian, advisor to President Franklin Delano Roosevelt. 18" tall. Porcelain head and hands, gray wig, painted features, brown cloth body, legs, feet, and arms. All original in two piece gray flannel suit, tan cotton stockings, black vinyl shoes. Marks: MARY MC. BETHUNE/ "BERTABEL"/©1969, on head: MARY MCLEOD BETHUNE/BY "BERTABEL"/ (I. ROBERTA BELL), on label sewn to left leg. $425.00.

Right — Plate 1436: I. Roberta Bell. Prototype of "Gay Nineties Picnic Costume," made in early 1940's. 17½" tall. Porcelain shoulder head, molded painted hair and facial features, closed mouth, brown felt body and limbs. All original in long sleeved white cotton blouse, ankle length orange skirt, white slip and pantaloons, black felt high-button shoes. Unmarked. $500.00.

Plate 1437: Bell, I.R. "Annie Davis Frierson." 16". A "Bertabel" doll by I. Roberta Bell. Annie Frierson was the maternal grandmother of Roberta Bell. Head and hands are porcelain, body is cloth stuffed with sawdust. This doll was part of a series of portrait dolls of Mrs. Bell's family members. She wears a black silk dress with a white collar trimmed with lace. A cameo pin is at her neck. The dress is buttoned down the back with five black jet beads. Under the dress, she wears a cotton slip and pantaloons. Her gray mohair wig is parted down the center and is styled in a bun on the back of her head. It is believed that the doll was made in an edition of 60.

The doll's Bertabel hand tag tells of Mrs. Frierson's life as follow: "1859-1939. She was about seven years old when slavery ended. She never knew her parents and had no last name. She was adopted, reared, and educated by a family named Davis. She graduated from what later became Fisk University in Nashville, Tennessee. She married a schoolmate, the Reverend Robert Frierson and bore 12 children, one of whom was I. Roberta Bell's mother. Mrs. Frierson also taught school in rural Tennessee." Collection of and photograph and information courtesy of Frances L. Smith. $500.00.

Plate 1438: I. Roberta Bell. "Matthew Henson" and "Harold Washington" by artist I. Roberta Bell. Both dolls are 18" tall with porcelain heads and hands, cloth bodies. Matthew Henson was the first black American to reach the North Pole. Harold Washington was Chicago's first black mayor and was the last doll designed and created by Bell. He was made in 1988. Collection of and photo courtesy of Frances L. Smith. $425.00 each.

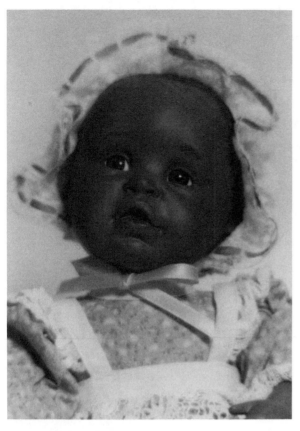

Plate 1439: Yolanda Bello. "Danielle" from Yolanda's "Picture Perfect Babies Collection." Porcelain head, arms, and legs; cloth body; stationary brown eyes, open-closed mouth, painted black hair. All original in aqua print dress and pink print bloomers and cap, ecru lace apron. 9½" tall when seated. ©1991 by Knowles, makers of fine china. Dolls in this series are numbered. This is number 8743E. Marks: YOLANDA BELLO/8743E, on head. Doll was marketed by the Ashton Drake Galleries and a nominee for the 1992 "Dolls" Award of Excellence in the porcelain: Under $100 category. $75.00.

Plate 1440: Yolanda Bello. "David," the first issue in the "Yolanda's Precious Playmates" collection, 1992. Porcelain head, arms, and legs, white cloth body, stationary brown eyes, closed moth. All original in burgundy plaid cap. This is doll #5634 A. The edition ended on December 31, 1993. At that time the molds for this doll were broken and no more porcelain will be cast. 9½" in seated position. Marks: 5634A (handwritten)/YOLANDA BELLO, on head. $75.00.

Plate 1442: Blake. "My Little Mahji." 9½". Original all porcelain doll by artist Sandra Blake. The doll is a portrait doll of LaVerne Hall's daughter Mahji. (LaVerne is the producer of the traveling doll show "Holiday Festival of Black Dolls" and the publisher of the *Doll-E-Gram*.) Edition of 250 Mahji dolls. This is doll number 20. Black wig, painted eyes, painted smiling mouth with teeth, molded painted black shoes, and white socks. Marks: ©/SANDRA M./BLAKE/20/250. $260.00.

Plate 1441: Bello. "Jolie." Artist doll by Yolanda Bello. Available in 1989. Represents a Haitian baby. Issue price was approximately $600.00. 21" tall. Porcelain and cloth. Edition of 250. Photograph Courtesy of Phyllis Schlatter. $800.00.

Plate 1445: Brewington. 14½" tall. Original doll by artist Beatrice Wright Brewington. All porcelain, painted eyes, black wig, painted black shoes. Beatrice Wright (Brewington) designed and marketed vinyl dolls as playthings for children in the 1960's. The dolls had Negroid features. This doll was made in the late 1980's or early 1990's. Unmarked. Collection of Emma Ransom Hayward. $150.00.

Plate 1443: Billie Peppers. "The School Teacher" from the "Old Friends Collection." 30" tall. Fibre-craft head and hands, cloth body, arms, legs, and feet. Painted molded white hair, painted eyes. All original in blue plaid blouse, burgundy skirt, black shoes, eyeglasses. Marks: ©BILLIE PEPPERS 1987, on head. $110.00.

Plate 1444: Billie Peppers. "The Entertainer" from "Old Friends Collection." 30" tall. Fibre-craft head and hands, remainder is cloth. Painted, molded balding hair, painted eyes. All original in black tuxedo, bowtie, and shoes, white shirt. Marks: ©BILLIE PEPPERS 1987, on head. $110.00.

Plate 1447: Lois Bro. "Julie." 14" tall. 1982. Porcelain head, arms, and legs, cloth body, stationary brown glass eyes, black mohair wig. Limited edition of 250 dolls. Marks: (incised heart)/L. BRO/JULIE/1982, on head. Photograph courtesy of Lois Bro. $350.00.

Plate 1446: Brinn. "Maxine." 14". Porcelain head, arms, and legs, cloth body, brown googley eyes, black curly wig. All original in floral print dress. Hang tag reads "Authentic Collectible by Brinn 1992." Photograph courtesy of Darlene Luther. $50.00.

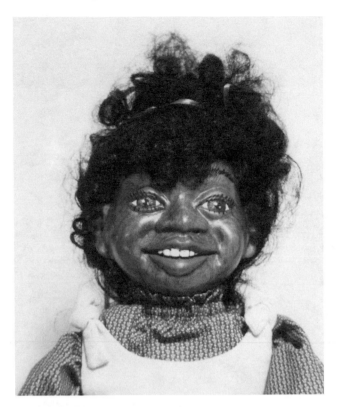

Plate 1448: Nancy Bruns. "Yolanda" from the "Brunswood Doll" collection. Head, arms, and legs are hand carved and polished from walnut, painted features, black curly wig, white cloth body. 24" tall. All original in red print dress with off-white pinafore and pantaloons. Marks: NANCY L. BRUNS/1988, handwritten on back of the body. Pinafore is tagged "Yolanda" next to the pocket. $700.00.

Plate 1449: Bruns. "Tim." 24" tall. Head, arms, and legs are hand carved from cherry wood, dark brown curly hair, painted eyes, cloth body. Made by doll artist Nancy Bruns for Brunswood Dolls. All original in tan knickers, cotton print shirt, black lined vest, checkered bowtie, cap. Cap and knickers are tagged. Marks: ©1986/NANCY L. BRUNS/CHERRY/TIM/35, handwritten on head. $500.00.

Plate 1451: Bruns. "Polly." Kit to make a reproduction doll by artist Nancy Bruns. Head is cast molded wood with the grain and texture of hardwood. Features are handpainted on head with directions included for a body and dress pattern. Completed doll is 21" tall. $45.00.

Plate 1450: Bruns. "Maurice Andre Dubos." 23" tall. Carved wood head and limbs, cloth body. Limited edition of 100. Courtesy of Linda Boulware of Dolls of Color, Inc. $600.00.

Left — Plate 1452: Barbara Buysse of Johanna Art Dolls. 10". All cloth, oil painted face and lower arms, white unpainted cloth body and legs, violet wool yarn hair. Made in 1993. Dressed in clothing made of antique fabrics. Collection of Michael Wolk-Laniewski. $175.00.

Right — Plate 1453: Barbara Buysse. 10". Black fabric body, oil painted face, black stitched on synthetic hair. Dressed in red print dress made of antique fabrics. Collection of Michael Wolk-Laniewski. $175.00.

Plate 1454: Cavel-Greant. "Benny." 32" composition and cloth portrait doll by Canadian artist Deborah Cavel-Greant. Composition hands, felt, and mask face, glass eyes. Collection of and photograph courtesy of Phyllis Schlatter. $300.00+.

Plate 1455: "Raggedy Ann & Andy." 8½" tall. Clay type shoulder heads, arms, and legs, cloth body, black yarn hair, painted features. All original. Marks: K. EAVENSON ©'91, on leg. Collection of Michael Wolk-Laniewski. $200.00 pair.

Plate 1456: Camelot. "Odette." 20" porcelain doll. Available exclusively from TV shopping club QVC. Limited edition of 2500 worldwide. Porcelain socket head, breast plate, arms, and legs, white cloth body, brown stationary eyes with lashes, black synthetic wig, closed mouth. All original in long cotton print dress. Replaced head wrap. The only mark is a large, fancy letter "U" on the back shoulder-plate. Courtesy of Xzena Moore. $125.00.

Plate 1457: Camelot. "Rose." 16". Porcelain head, arms, and legs, white cloth body, stationary brown eyes, black wig, closed mouth. All original in pink silk dress and white pantaloons. Camelot dolls are available exclusively through QVC, a home shopping organization. Unmarked. $75.00.

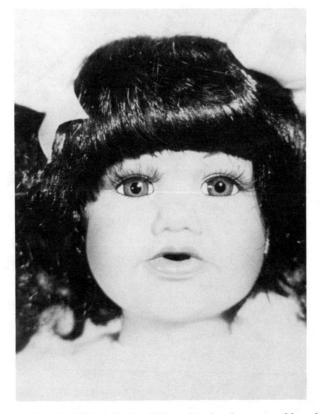

Plate 1458: Camelot. "Melody." 16" tall. Porcelain head, arms, and legs, black wig, stationary brown eyes with "real" upper eyelashes, open mouth, white cloth body. All original in pink faille dress, pantaloons, and matching purse. Available exclusively from QVC, home shopping TV club. Unmarked. $60.00.

Plate 1459: Camelot. "Naomi." 14" musical mechanical doll. Her head and arms move when she plays "You Light Up My Life." Porcelain head, arms, and legs, brown wig, stationary brown eyes, closed mouth, white cloth body with key-wound mechanism in back. All original in baby blue dress with matching pantaloons. Available exclusively through QVC home shopping. Marks: 2106, on head. $65.00.

Plate 1460: Camelot. "Sharon." 14" tall. Porcelain head, arms, and legs, white cloth body, black wig with bangs and two long braids, stationary dark brown eyes with painted eyelashes, open-closed moth with painted lower teeth. All original in red print dress, white pantaloons, red shoes, and white socks. Marks: CAMELOT, on head. $60.00.

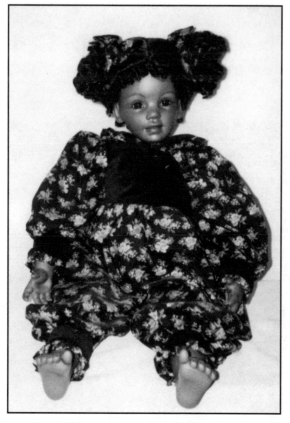

Plate 1461: Reproduction. "Tamika" from mold set designed by artist Laura Cobabe. 20" seated toddler. Porcelain head, hands, and feet, cloth body. Doll was made and dressed by Clara Clark. $200.00+.

Plate 1462: Crunkleton. "Jasmine & Izahia." 37". Limited edition of 150 each by doll artist Marge Crunkleton. Heads, hands, and feet are wood resin, bodies are stuffed flour sacks. Individually created, each is a signed and dated. Photograph courtesy of Marge Crunkleton. $375.00 each.

Plate 1463: Crunkleton Dolls. "Teri Saturday/Sunday." 15". Limited edition of 200 by doll artist Marge Crunkleton. Wood resin heads and limbs, flour sack bodies. Doll on left is dressed in play clothes for Saturday. Doll on the right is in a dress for Sunday. Dolls are signed and dated. Photograph courtesy of Marge Crunkleton. $200.00 each.

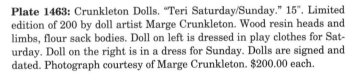

Plate 1464: Crunkleton. "Rosa." 10". Limited edition of 250 dolls by artist Marge Crunkleton. Wood resin head and limbs, flour sack body. All original in red print dress with lace trim. Photograph courtesy of Marge Crunkleton. $185.00.

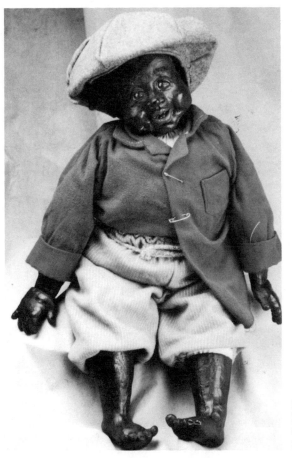

Plate 1466: Crunkleton. "Luvy." 14". Limited edition of 250 by doll artist Marge Crunkleton. Head, hands, and feet are wood resin, body is cloth. Photograph courtesy of Marge Crunkleton. $185.00.

Plate 1465: Crunkleton. "Sharley 'Tom Boy.'" Sharley is a girl and her hair is under her cap. Limited edition of 150 by doll artist Marge Crunkleton. Wood resin head, arms, and legs, flour sack body. Dressed in red shirt, blue pants, and cap. Photograph courtesy of Marge Crunkleton. $375.00.

Plate 1467: Cunningham. "Ty & Pup." 22". All cloth one-of-a-kind by cloth doll artist Cynethea Cunningham. Photograph courtesy of Cynethea Cunningham. $45.00 for both.

Plate 1468: Cunningham. "Lionel." 25". All cloth by doll artist Cynethea Cunningham. Photograph courtesy of Cynethea Cunningham. $50.00.

History of Daddy's Long Legs, quoted from brochure that comes in the box with each doll:

"Karen Germany, designer of Daddy's Long Legs, was born and raised in Dallas, Texas. She first began making dolls as a hobby in 1979, and was pleased to sell them at local arts & craft shows. Using her experience in interior decorating, Karen began designing accessories which could readily be reproduced in wood resin. After she and her husband had established a successful manufacturing business in the wholesale industry, Karen began working closely with the KVK staff artists to design a doll which would enhance any decor. 'Daddy's Long Legs' was conceived in 1989 and was immediately recognized as an American made collectible doll. Since then, Daddy's Long Legs has become known internationally and collected by many celebrities and other notable individuals. Karen says, 'The real fun is in creating a certain appeal with the doll's image, the clothing, the tiny accessories and especially his or her name.' Some of the earlier dolls are signed by Pat Weeks. Some of the later ones are signed by Karen Germany. The vast majority are unsigned."

Plate 1469: Daddy's Long Legs. "Santa," #DLS02B from the "Daddy's Long Legs" collection, 1992. 28" tall. Wood resin head and torso, lower arms and hands, lower legs and feet; cloth upper arms and upper legs; painted eyes; gray wig and beard. All original in red and white Santa Claus coat with matching cap and black pants. Introduced July 1, 1992, retired June 30, 1993. Total quantity produced was 511. Bench not included. $225.00.

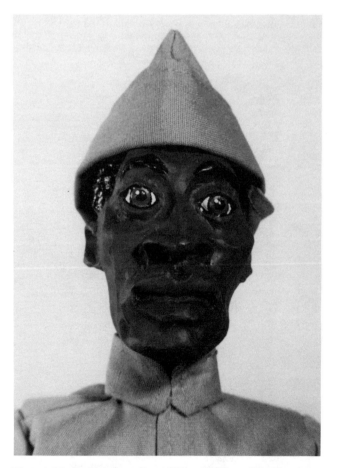

Plate 1470: Daddy's Long Legs. "Jeremiah" from "The Homecoming." Apx. 26" tall. All original in soldier's uniform. Released January, 1992, #Dl10N. Marks: K. Germany/©1991, handwritten on right spat of uniform. Courtesy of Joan Banks. Retired March 30, 1994. $100.00.

Plate 1471: Daddy's Long Legs. "Jasmine." Jeremiah's bride from "The Homecoming." Apx. 24" tall. All original in floral print dress with chunky lace collar, natural straw hat decorated with flowers, bead necklace, brown gloves, and shoes. Released January, 1992, #DL10P. Retired March 30, 1994. Marks: DLL ©1991, incised on right leg; K GERMANY/©1991, handwritten on right leg. Courtesy of Joan Banks. $100.00.

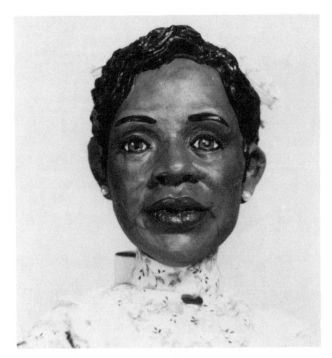

Plate 1472: Daddy's Long Legs. "Ruth," #DL33E. 21" tall. Wood resin head, torso, lower arms, and legs; cloth upper arms and legs; molded black hair; painted eyes; closed mouth; pearl earrings. All original in long sleeve floral print blouse, blue skirt, carrying a small black bible, molded on white shoes. Marks: DLL/©1992, on right leg. Released January, 1993. Courtesy of Xzena Moore of the Cubbyhole. $100.00.

Plate 1473: Daddy's Long Legs. "Nettie," DL10. 24". Released January, 1990. First African-American doll in the family of Daddy's Long Legs, wife of Tobias (sometimes called Toby). All original in long floral print duster over white dress with white pantaloons and headwrap, natural straw hat. Marks: WEEKS ©1990, handwritten on right leg. Courtesy of Joan Banks. $80.00.

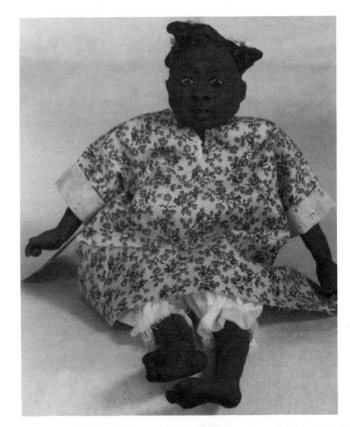

Plate 1474: Daddy's Long Legs. "Sofie," #DL10C, released July, 1990. Retired June, 1992, first black character to retire. 10½" tall. All original in beige floral print dress, white undies, barefoot, four white cotton hairbows. Marks: WEEKS ©1990, on inside calf of right leg. Hangtag: … "This unique work of art by Pat Weeks will become a treasured keepsake in you own private collection" …/KAREN'S VINTAGE KOLLEC-TIONS. Courtesy of Patricia Whittler Martin. Total dolls produced 5,548. $400.00+.

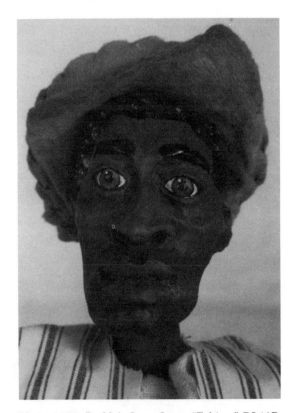

Plate 1475: Daddy's Long Legs. "Tobias," DL10B, released July, 1990. Striped cotton jacket, tweed pants, white shirt, tan flannel cap. Tobias, husband of Nettie, is sometimes called "Toby." 26" tall. Marks: WEEKS ©1990, on right leg. All Tobias dolls were not signed by Weeks. Courtesy of Joan Banks. $80.00.

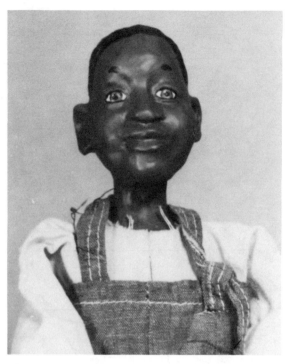

Plate 1476: Daddy's Long Legs. "Junior," #DL10F. Released January, 1991. 16" tall. All original in denim overalls, beige shirt. Junior is Miss Hattie's grandson. Unmarked. Courtesy of Xzena Moore of the Cubbyhole. Doll comes with a sling shot. $70.00.

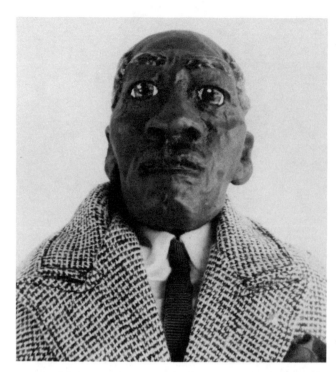

Plate 1477: Daddy's Long Legs. "Rev. Johnson," #DL10D. Released January, 1991. Approx. 28" tall. Wears gray tweed suit, white shirt, red tie. Courtesy of Xzena Moore of the Cubbyhole. $100.00.

Plate 1478: Daddy's Long Legs. "Miss Hattie," #DL10E. Released January, 1991. Dark print dress, white scarf at neckline, hat. Miss Hattie is Junior's grandmother. 22" tall. Courtesy of Xzena Moore Dolls the Cubbyhole. $90.00.

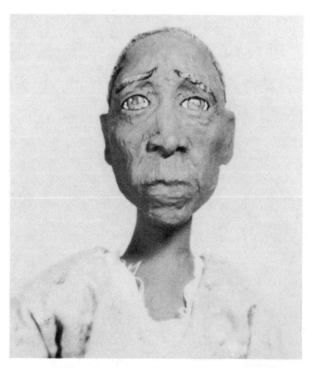

Plate 1479: Daddy's Long Legs. "Oma Green," #DL10G. 20" tall. The great grandmother from the "Baby Sitting Collection." Released July, 1991. Dressed in blue print dress with painted gray hair and eyebrows. Marks: WEEKS ©1991, on right leg. Courtesy of Joan Banks. $95.00.

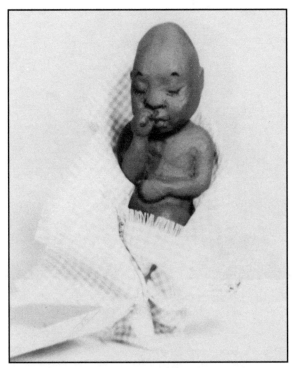

Plate 1480: Daddy's Long Legs. "Baby Jesse," DL10J. 4½" tall. From the "Baby Sitting" collection. Baby is nude wrapped in blue cotton gingham cloth. Marks: Weeks ©1991/DLL ©1991, on upper right leg. Courtesy of Joan Banks. $20.00.

Plate 1481: Daddy's Long Legs. "Ezra," #DL10H, Oma's husband from the "Baby Sitting" collection. 22". Released January, 1992. Dressed in denim overalls, plaid shirt, straw hat. Marks: DLL ©1991, on right leg. Courtesy of Joan Banks. $90.00.

Plate 1482: Daddy's Long Legs. "Sister Mary Kathleen," #DL10S, released January, 1992. Dressed in black nun's habit. 20" tall. Marks: K. GERMANY/©1991, on right stocking. Courtesy of Joan Banks. $100.00.

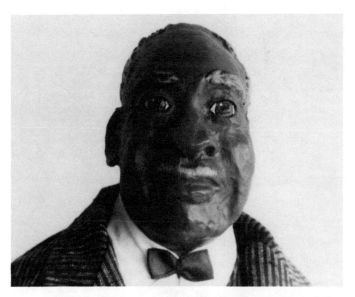

Plate 1483: Daddy's Long Legs. "Doc Moses," #DL10M. Released January, 1992, retired September 30, 1993. Quantity produced was 2,494. 20" tall. Nominated for 1992 "Dolls" Award of Excellence, a nominee in All Prices. Majority were issued wearing a brown suit. Due to exhausted supply of fabric, approximately 200 were issued wearing a gray suit. Courtesy of Xzena Moore of the Cubbyhole. $150.00+.

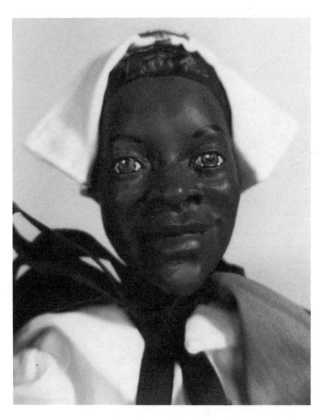

Plate 1485: Daddy's Long Legs. "Judge," #DL33C. 22" tall. Issued January 1, 1993. Courtesy of Xzena Moore of the Cubbyhole. $100.00.

Plate 1484: Daddy's Long Legs. "Nurse Garnet," #DL32C. 22" tall. Released July, 1992. Retired September 30, 1993. Quantity produced was 1,415. All original in white uniform and cap, navy cape lined in red. Marks: DLL © 1991, on right leg. $100.00.

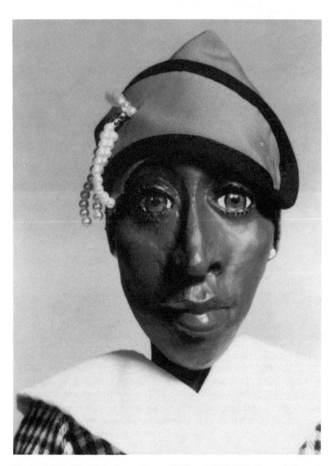

Plate 1486: Daddy's Long Legs. "Billye," #DL33B. Issued Jan. 1, 1993. 22" tall. $100.00.

Plate 1487: Daddy's Long Legs. "Babe Bouchard," #DL10K. Issued January 1, 1992. Courtesy of Xzena Moore of the Cubbyhole. $100.00.

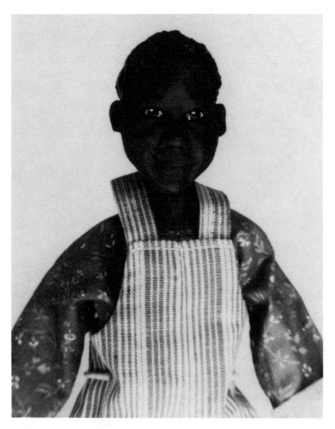

Plate 1488: Daddy's Long Legs. "Choo-Choo" from "Baby Sitting" collection. Issued Jan. 1, 1992, retired Sept 30, 1993. 11½" tall. Total issued 3,618. Courtesy of Xzena Moore of the Cubbyhole. $75.00.

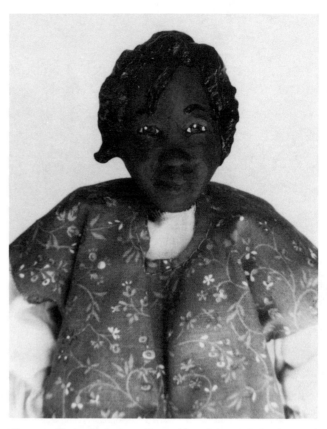

Plate 1489: Daddy's Long Legs. "Josie" from "Baby Sitting." 11½" tall. Issued January 1, 1992, retired September 30, 1993. Total quantity produced was 4,132. Courtesy of Xzena Moore of the Cubbyhole. $75.00.

Plate 1490: Daddy's Long Legs. "Micah," #DL32A, dressed in Sunday best. Introduced June, 1992. 14" tall. All original in brown pants, white shirt, and black bowtie. Marks: DLL ©1991, on right leg. Courtesy of Joan Banks. $70.00.

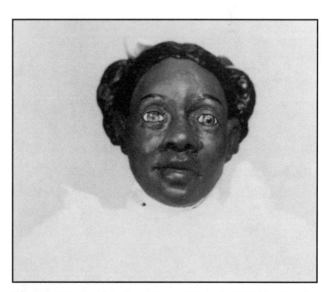

Plate 1491: Daddy's Long Legs. "Katy," #DL32B, Micah's sweetheart. Introduced June, 1992. 12½" tall. Molded hair is parted in the center with two braids, pink ribbon is attached to the top of each braid. All original in white eyelet dress, white pantaloons, carrying basket of flowers. Marks: CLL ©1991, on right leg. Courtesy of Joan Banks. $70.00.

Plate 1492: Daddy's Long Legs. "Santa," 1991. 26". Wood resin head, lower arms, legs, and body, cloth upper arms and legs, brown painted eyes, mixed gray beard and mustache, black gloves and boots. Issued July, 1991; retired December, 1991. Dressed in deep burgundy felt outfit. Marks: WEEKS ©1991, hand signed on right leg. Total produced 1,101. Courtesy of Patricia B. Whittler-Martin. $400.00.

Plate 1493: Daddy's Long Legs. "Bessie," #DL32E. Approx 17". Issued July, 1992. All original in black skirt, white blouse, green jacket, plaid scarf and cap. Portion of sales go to the homeless. Courtesy of Cultural Accents (Detroit). $100.00.

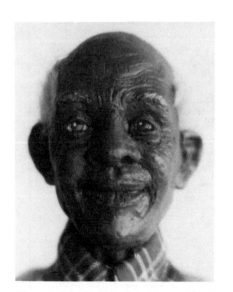

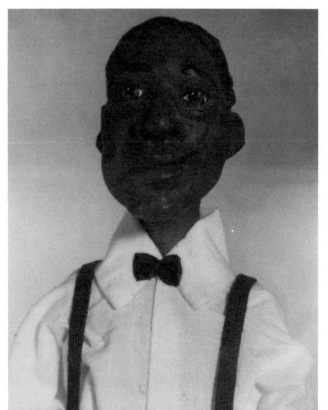

Plate 1494: Daddy's Long Legs. "Abe," #DL33A, released January, 1993. 18" tall. Gray trousers, plaid shirt, red cardigan sweater. Doll comes with a newspaper and brown paper wrapped package. Courtesy of Xzena Moore of the Cubbyhole. $100.00.

Plate 1495: Daddy's Long Legs. "James" the groom, #DL102. 20" tall. Limited edition for 1992. Dressed in black pants, white shirt, and bowtie. Courtesy of Xzena Moore of the Cubbyhole. Total amount produced 1,268. James was sold along with "Olivia," the bride. $150.00.

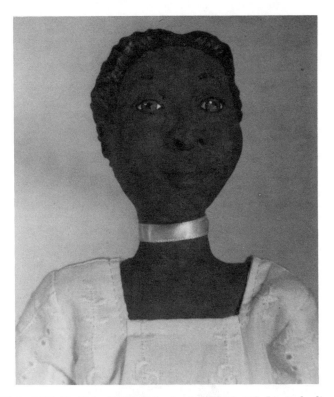

Plate 1496: Daddy's. "Olivia," the bride, #DL03. 18". Limited edition for 1992. Sold with previous doll James. Total produced 1,268. Courtesy of Xzena Moore of the Cubbyhole. $200.00+.

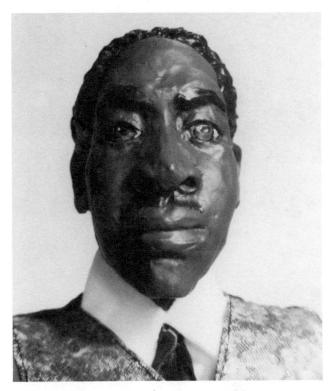

Plate 1497: Daddy's. "Lucky the Gambler," #DL10L. 26". Doll wears gray pants, white shirt, tapestry print vest, black tie, and black felt hat. Doll was released January, 1991, and retired December, 1992. Marks: DLL 1991, left boot. Courtesy of Xzena Moore of the Cubbyhole. Total produced 939. $150.00–200.00.

Plate 1498: Daddy's. "Esther," #DLL93A. 22". Dressed in long white cotton dress with lace trim and pearl earrings, hair molded into a bun. Released January, 1993. Limited edition of 3000. Marks: K. GERMANY/#271 (slash) 3000 ©1993 LIM. ED., on right boot. Courtesy of Xzena Moore of the Cubbyhole. $200.00+.

Plate 1499: Daddy's. "Phoebe," #DL33D. 12". Dressed in navy blue floral print. Hair in molded braids with two pink ribbons attached. Released January, 1993. Unmarked. Courtesy of Xzena Moore of the Cubbyhole. $65.00.

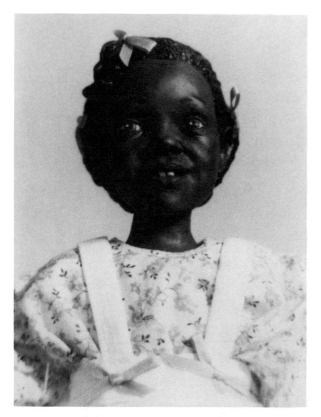

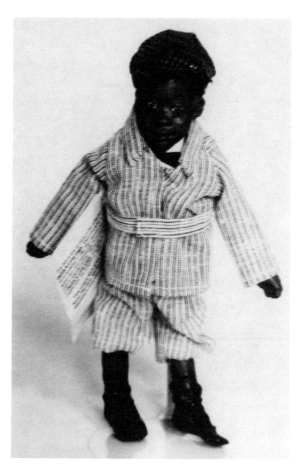

Plate 1500: Daddy's Long Legs. "Faith," #DLM93A. 14". Released January, 1993. The first members edition doll. She was available to each member who joined the Daddy's Long Legs Collector's Club in 1993. Marks: K. GERMANY/#177 G1993 MEM. ED./LDD, on right leg. Edition of 2,250. Courtesy of Xzena Moore of the Cubbyhole. $125.00.

Plate 1501: Daddy's Long Legs. "Timothy." 8". Limited edition of 750 dolls. All original in brown striped suit with knickered pants, brown houndtooth cap. Marks: K. GERMANY/#417 (slash) 750./1993/LTD ED, handwritten on left foot. Collection of Patricia Banks-Tyson. $400.00.

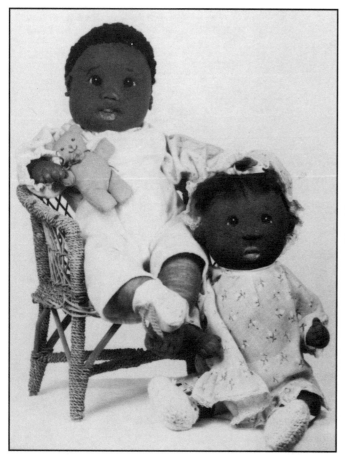

Plate 1502: Cloth dolls made by doll artist Diane Dengel. 14" tall. 1970's. Photograph courtesy of Frasher's Auctions. No price available.

Plate 1503: Design Debut. "Consuela." 20" tall. Porcelain shoulder head, arms, and legs; cloth body; stationary brown eyes; dark brown crimped styled wig; closed mouth. All original in pink dress with pale blue trim, white pantaloons and barefoot. Flowers are glued on her right temple and she is carrying a small bouquet of flowers. Marks: 0050 (slash) 3360, painted in gold on head. $55.00.

Plate 1504: Design Debut. "Carmen," 1992. Porcelain head, black short curly synthetic wig, stationary brown eyes, closed mouth, porcelain arms and legs, white cloth body. 16½" tall. All original in pink floral print dress. Unmarked. Purchased from Home Shopping Club on cable TV. $45.00.

Plate 1505: Design Debut. "Paulette." 16". Porcelain head, arms, and legs, stationary brown eyes, molded hair, closed mouth, white cloth body. All original in pink eyelet dress trimmed with white eyelet with matching pantaloons and bonnet. Marks: 23 (slash) 13, very faintly on head. $45.00.

Plate 1506: Design Debut. "Rebecca," #4097. 9" in sitting position. Porcelain head, black curly wig, stationary brown eyes with painted lashes, closed mouth, porcelain arms and legs, white cloth body. All original in blue strap shoes. Marks: DESIGN/DEBUT/LIMITED EDITION, on head. $60.00.

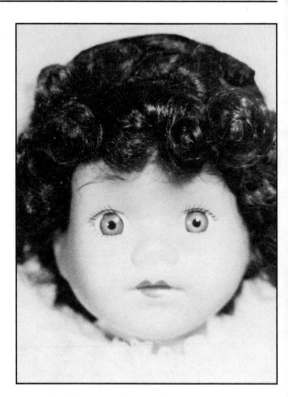

Plate 1507: Designer Row Dolls. "Tina Berry." Home Shopping Club doll molded after show host Tina Berry. Porcelain shoulder head, arms, and legs; cloth body; stationary brown eyes; closed mouth; black curly synthetic wig; earrings. All original in white sweater with black trim. Leather like black skirt and black molded on boots. 16" tall. Marks: 7721, on back. $75.00.

Plate 1508: Doll Collectors. "Julie." Porcelain head, closed mouth, dark brown synthetic wig, gray eyes, porcelain arms and legs, cloth body. All original in ivory satin dress trimmed in lace with pink ribbon around waist. White bloomers, white stockings and shoes, matching cap. Doll is unmarked. 15" tall. $30.00.

Plate 1509: Dream Dolls. 15" tall. Porcelain head, hands, and feet, cloth body, black wig, brown stationary eyes, closed pouty mouth. All original in blue print dress with white bodice. Unmarked. $30.00.

Plate 1510: Duck House. "Deserie." Porcelain head, hands, and legs, brown stationary glass eyes with real lashes, black synthetic curly wig, closed mouth, cloth body. This is doll #498 of limited edition of 5,000 dolls. All original in white pique romper trimmed with white eyelet. 20" tall. Doll was sold on TV Home Shopping Club as "Dumplin." Marks: 0498, on head. Doll was designed by artist Holly Hunt. $150.00.

Plate 1511: Dynasty. "Kesia." 14". Porcelain head, arms, and legs, white cloth body, black wig, stationary brown eyes, closed mouth. All original in dark blue print dress with white collar and red bow, white hat. Marks: DYNASTY/DOLL (a dolls face is inside the letter "O"/COLLECTION/DESIGN COPYRIGHT/CARDINAL, INC., stamped on head; ©CARDINAL, INC./1989, incised on head. $80.00.

Plate 1512: Dynasty. "Shannon," 14" doll from the "Anna" collection limited to a maximum production of 3500 dolls worldwide. Porcelain head, arms, and legs; cloth body; stationary brown eyes; glued on black wig. All original in red and black checked dress with red hat. Marks: DYNASTY DOLL/COLLECTION/DESIGN COPYRIGHT/CARDINAL INC. (stamped on head); CARDINAL 1989 (incised on head). $80.00.

Plate 1513: Dynasty. "Audrey." Porcelain head, black curly synthetic wig, stationary brown eyes, closed mouth, porcelain arms and legs, cloth body. All original in off-white lace dress with white pantaloons and stockings. 14" tall. Marks: © CARDINAL, INC./1989, on head. $85.00.

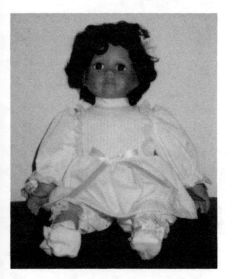

Plate 1515: Dynasty. "Cory." Porcelain head, stationary brown eyes, curly black wig, closed mouth, porcelain arms and legs, white cloth body. 14" tall. All original in red watchplaid dress with white cotton skirt, navy blue hooded cap lined in the same watchplaid, red socks, and black t-strap shoes. Marks: DYNASTY/DOLL/COLLECTION/DESIGN COPYRIGHT/CARDINAL, INC, printed on head; ©CARDINAL/1989, incised on head. $85.00.

Plate 1514: Dynasty. "Jessica." 15". Porcelain head, arms, and legs, stationary brown eyes with eyelashes, closed mouth, curly wig, cloth body. All original in a pink outfit with aqua and pink trim, white lace, pink hairbow and booties. Collection of and photograph courtesy of Mary June Hill. $125.00.

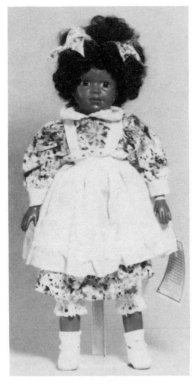

Plate 1516: Dynasty. "Felicia," #D858.60. 16". Musical doll plays "Moon River." Porcelain head, arms, and legs, white cloth body, stationary brown eyes, black wig, closed mouth. All original in calico dress and matching hairbow, white pinafore, and pantaloons. Marks: DYNASTY/DOLL/COLLECTION/DESIGN COPYRIGHT/CARDINAL INC., stamped on head. Identical mold was used for a Treasures in Lace doll. $60.00.

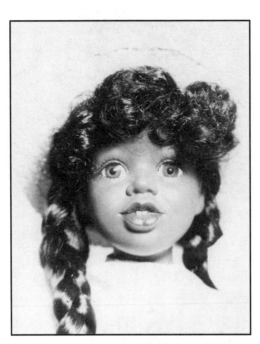

Plate 1517: Dynasty. "Felicia," from the "Anna Collection." 17". Porcelain head, black wig styled in two long braids with curly bangs, stationary brown eyes, open-closed mouth, porcelain arms and legs, white cloth body. All original in pink cotton dress with attached print pinafore, natural straw hat. Marks: DYNASTY/DOLL/COLLECTION/DESIGN COPYRIGHT/CARDINAL INC., on head. $100.00.

Plate 1518: Dynasty. "Modern Bride" from the "Anna Collection." 18" tall. Porcelain head, arms, and legs, black wig, stationary brown eyes, closed mouth. All original in white gown and brimmed white straw hat trimmed with netting and gown fabric. Marks: DYNASTY/DOLL/COLLECTION/DESIGN COPYRIGHT/CARDINAL, INC., on head. $120.00.

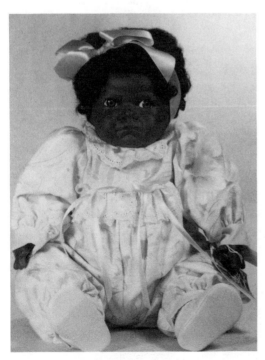

Plate 1519: Dynasty. "Annie At Play," #D766. 18" tall. Porcelain head and hands, cloth body, arms, legs, and feet, black curly wig, stationary amber/brown eyes with upper lashes, pouty mouth. All original in pastel floral print romper trimmed with pink ribbon and white lace, pink hairbow, white shoes and socks. Glued on wig covers most of the marks on back of head. $150.00.

Plate 1520: Dynasty. "Poppy." 18". Porcelain head, arms, and legs, cloth body, stationary brown glass eyes, mouth open so that she can suck her left thumb, black curly wig, long eyelashes. All original in aqua dress trimmed in white lace, white pinafore trimmed with aqua ribbons, aqua ribbons in her hair, white shoes and socks. Doll comes with certificate of authenticity. Collection of and photograph courtesy of Mary June Hill. $175.00.

Plate 1521: Reproduction. "Hilary." 24". Original mold made by Dianna Effner. Mold came in sizes to make an 18" and a 24" doll. Marks: HILARY/BY DIANNA EFFNER. Made by Clara Clark. $150.00.

Plate 1522: Embry. Cloth doll by artist Jacqueline Embry. Collection of Zenobia Holiday. $90.00.

Plate 1523: Embry. Handcrafted cloth doll by doll artist Jackie Embry. Brown yarn hair, painted features, dressed in print dress with matching headbow. Courtesy of Xzena Moore of the Cubbyhole. $90.00.

Plate 1524: Ernest Enterprises. "Uhura" from the "Star Trek Doll collection." 13" tall. Porcelain head and upper body, porcelain arms from the elbows, porcelain legs from the hips, cloth lower body and upper arms, molded painted black boots, molded painted hair and facial features, pierced ears with goldtone hoop earrings. All original in red tunic and black shorts. Marks: ©1990 PARAMOUNT PIC-/TURES CORPORATION. ALL/RIGHTS RESERVED, at waist. $100.00.

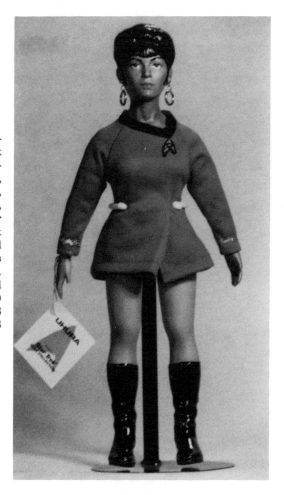

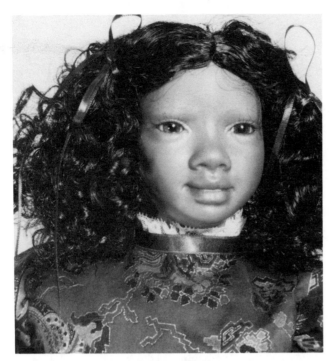

Plate 1525: Reproduction. "Cleo." 26" tall. Reproduced from a mold sculpted by artist Jennifer Esteban. Porcelain head, arms, and legs, cloth body. Made by Clara Clark. Courtesy of Clara Clark. $200.00.

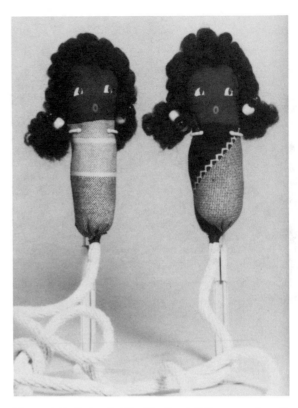

Plate 1526: Eubank. "Double Dutch." Jumprope handle dolls design by doll artist E'dee Eubank. Dolls are 5" long, all cloth, black yarn hair, painted features. $12.00.

Plate 1527: Eubank. "Creative Story Puppets." Approx. 10" tall. Cloth puppet comes with a pad so children can write their own story. Attached braided yarn hair, painted features. Also available as boys. Courtesy of E'dee Eubank. $13.00.

Plate 1528: E'dee Eubank. "Proud Couple." All cloth with painted features. Pair won a blue ribbon at the "Michigan Doll Makers Guild" show, 1993. Courtesy of E'dee Eubank of Art Deco Designs. $100.00.

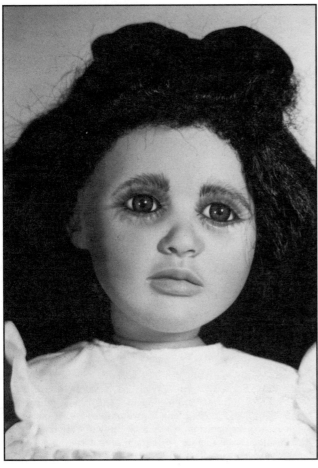

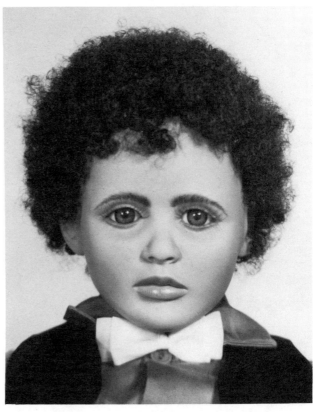

Plate 1529: Federica. "Kamiko." 25" tall. Vinyl jointed head, shoulder-plate, arms, and legs, white cloth body, black wig, stationary brown glassine eyes with upper and lower lashes, closed mouth. Dressed in purple cotton dress with white upper bodice, white tights, and black patent shoes. Marks: ©1993/FEDERICA, on head. Courtesy of Xzena Moore of the Cubbyhole. $375.00.

Plate 1530: Federica. "Kito." 26" tall. Vinyl movable head, shoulder-plate, arms, and legs, white cloth body, dark brown curly wig, brown stationary glassine eyes with upper and lower eyelashes, closed mouth. All original in black velvet pants and vest, purple shirt, white bow tie and socks, black shoes. Marks: ©1993/FEDERICA, on head. Courtesy of Xzena Moore of the Cubbyhole. $375.00.

Plate 1531: Flory. "The Saloon Girl." Approx. 10". Clay shoulder head, arms, and legs, painted eyes, black wig, molded on shoes, cloth body. One-of-a-kind by doll artist Anita Flory. Marks: A. FLORY/83, on head. Courtesy of Xzena Moore of the Cubbyhole. $130.00.

Plate 1532: Formaz, Betty. "Rodney Allen Rippy" by doll artist Betty Formaz. Porcelain shoulder head; stationary brown glass eyes; open-mouth with molded, painted teeth; molded hair with black flocking added; porcelain arms and legs; cloth body. All original in black pants and vest, black bow tie, white shirt. 12½" tall. Marks: BETTY FORMAZ. 1970's. $150.00.

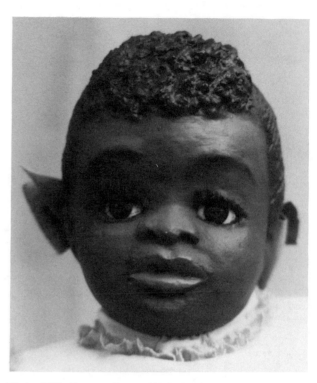

Plate 1533: Formaz, Betty. "Myla." 23". One of a kind artist doll by Betty Formaz. Papier-maché head, arms, and legs, brown cloth body, molded hair in two braided corn rows with molded holes for ribbons at the neck, brown stationary eyes with lashes, closed mouth. Dressed in blue dotted dress with muslin yoke. Marks: BY/BETTY FORMAZ/ONE OF A KIND/ "MYLA" 1992, on cloth sewn to chest. $600.00.

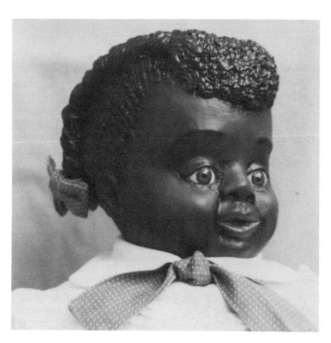

Plate 1534: Formaz, Betty. Approximately 28" tall. One-of-a-kind. Papier-maché head, arms, and legs, brown cloth body, stationary brown eyes, molded hair. Collection of Patricia Martin. $700.00.

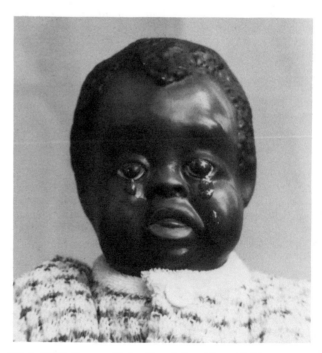

Plate 1535: Formaz, Betty. Porcelain with molded hair, tears, glass eyes. Approximately 20" tall. Made in the late 1980's or early 1990's. Collection of Patricia Martin. $300.00.

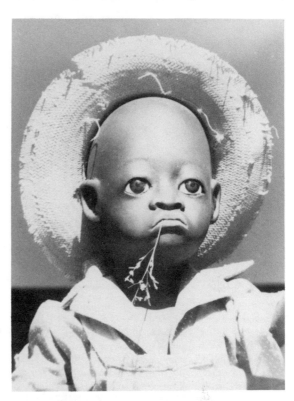

Left — Plate 1536: Formaz, Betty. "Willie." 16" tall. Papier-maché head, molded hair, brown glass eyes with real lashes, closed mouth, vinyl arms and legs, cloth body. Unmarked. 1988. Courtesy of Betty Formaz. $500.00.

Right — Plate 1537: Formaz, Tony. One of a kind boy. 19" tall. Doll is made of a type of self-hardening modeling clay (mixture of papier-maché and composition). Head and body are all in one piece, brown glass eyes, closed mouth with a tiny opening for a piece of weed or straw. Unmarked. 1992. Courtesy of Tony Formaz. $1,000.00.

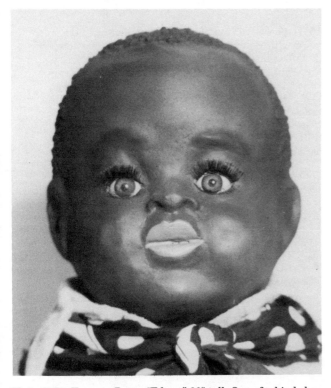

Plate 1538: Formaz, Betty. "Edgar." 28" tall. One of a kind character face made by artist Betty Formaz and named for author's husband. Papier-maché head, composition arms and legs, brown cloth body, stationary brown eyes with real lashes, closed mouth, molded hair. All original in old blue jeans and plaid flannel shirt with neck bandanna. Marks: 4MAZ, on head. $600.00.

Plate 1539: Galperin. "Grace." 17". An original design from the "Hearts in Song" collection by doll artist Jan Galperin. Doll is available exclusively from the Georgetown Collection and is limited to 100 firing days. Porcelain shoulder head, arms, and legs, cloth body, dark brown wig, stationary brown eyes with upper lashes, open-closed mouth with molded tongue. All original in long red velvet dress with short white lace choir robe. Doll is also referred to as "Amazing Grace" as she represents a choir girl and that is her favorite song. $150.00.

Plate 1540: Goebel. "Tanya." Limited edition of 1000 dolls, doll #746. Designed by Bette Ball for the "Carol Anne Dolls Collection." Musical doll plays "Love Makes the World Go Round." Porcelain head, dark brown curly wig, stationary brown eyes, closed mouth, porcelain arms and legs, white cloth body. 16" tall. All original in floral print dress with brown background with white bib trim, white pantaloons, white lace stockings, white shoes. Marks: CAROL ANNE DOLLS/DESIGNED BY BETTE BALL/LIMITED EDITION 746 (slash) 1000(numerals written by hand)/©GOEBEL INC., 1989, on head. $125.00.

Plate 1541 : Goebel. "Shana." Doll #800 from limited edition of 1000, designed by Bette Ball for the "Betty Jane Carter Collection." 18" tall. Doll is musical and plays "Younger Than Springtime." Porcelain head, dark brown wig, stationary brown eyes with painted eyelashes, closed mouth, porcelain arms and legs, white cloth body. All original in turquoise print dress with white eyelet apron, white pantaloons. Doll has a cloth cat made of the same fabric as her dress. Marks: BETTY JANE CARTER DOLLS/DESIGNED BY BETTE BALL/LIMITED EDITION 800 (slash) 1000/©GOEBEL INC. 1989, on head. $180.00.

Plate 1542: Goebel. "Gloria." 12". Porcelain musical doll designed by Bette Ball for the "Carol Anne Dolls Collection." Limited edition of 1000 dolls. This is #562. Doll plays "Hark! The Harold Angels Sing." Porcelain head, dark brown synthetic wig, stationary brown eyes, closed mouth, porcelain arms and legs, white cloth body. All original in white lace angel costume accentuated with gold, gold angel wings with faux pearl trim. Marks: CAROL ANNE DOLLS/ DESIGNED BY BETTE BALL/LIMITED EDITION 562/1000 (written by hand)/G1992 GOEBEL UNITED STATES, on head. $130.00.

Plate 1543: Goebel. "Deana," musical collector doll designed by Bette Ball for the "Betty Jane Carter Dolls Collection." 20" tall. Doll #389 in a limited edition of 1000 dolls. Porcelain head, arms, and legs, dark brown wig, stationary brown eyes, closed mouth, cloth body. Musical doll plays "We Wish You a Merry Christmas." All original in red print dress, holding an embroidery hoop. Marks: BETTY JANE CARTER DOLLS/ DESIGNED BY BETTE BALL/LIMITED EDITION 389 (slash) 1000/©1992 GOEBEL U.S., on head. $150.00.

Plate 1544: Goebel. "Monica," #912336 from the "Victoria Ashlea Originals." Porcelain head, arms, and legs, stationary brown eyes, closed mouth, brown wig. Musical doll plays "Honey." Limited edition of 1000. All original in print dress with white pinafore. Marks: VICTORIA ASHLEA ORIGINALS/DESIGNED BY KAREN KENNEDY/LIMITED EDITION 499 (handwritten) 1000/G GOEBEL INC. 1989, on head. Courtesy of Xzena Moore of the Cubbyhole. $100.00.

Plate 1545: Goebel. "Sheena" from the "Victoria Ashlea Originals." Musical doll plays "Sing." Number 196 from a limited edition of 1000. Approx. 16". Porcelain head, arms, and legs, brown wig, stationary brown eyes, cloth body. All original in dress with white eyelet bodice and striped skirt. Marks: VICTORIA ASHLEA ORIGINALS/DESIGNED BY BETTY BALL/LIMITED EDITION 196 (slash) 1000/GOEBEL INC. 1989, on head. Courtesy of Xzena Moore of the Cubbyhole. $100.00.

Plate 1546: Goebel. Porcelain musical dolls from the "Victoria Ashlea originals" collection. ©1992. Dolls are from left, "Denise," #912362, 16", plays "Someday My Prince Will Come"; "Cassandra," #912355, 18", plays "Try to Remember"; and "Noelle," #912360, plays "The First Noel." The first two dolls were designed by Karen Kennedy, the one on the right by Bette Ball. All are in editions of 1000. Photograph courtesy of Victoria Ashlea Originals®. ©Goebel United States 1993. $100.00 each.

Plate 1547: Goss. "Hockey Players." 18" tall. One-of-a-kind made in the images of Faith Wyse's sons Julian and Caleb. Dolls were made in the early 1980's by Dee Goss, Craft Collage. Papier-maché with cotton pants, yellow knit jersey with names (Wyse) and numbers on back. Photograph courtesy of Faith Wyse. No price available.

Plate 1548: Haas. 28" girl by artist Ella Haas of Denmark. Painted cloth over clay head, mohair wig, weighted cloth body similar to Kathe Kruse mannikin babies. Collection of and photograph courtesy of Phyllis Schlatter. $500.00.

Plate 1549: Gotz. "Joy." #40330, 1991. Vinyl head, painted eyes, rooted long black hair in straight style with curly wisps of hair for bangs, closed mouth, jointed hard vinyl body. 18" tall. All original in white embossed cotton dress with tucks in skirt, trimmed with pink rickrack and pink buttons on bodice, white sandals. Marks: Gotz/131SN (superimposed), on head. $250.00.

Plate 1550: Gotz. "Kemba and Bintu." 1992/1993, the third limited edition of "Fanouche and Her Friends" by Sylvia Natterer. Kemba is handsigned and numbered in an edition limited to 1500 pieces worldwide. This is #193. Kemba is 18" tall, Bintu is 8" tall. Bintu has painted black hair, both dolls have painted eyes and closed mouths. Marks: GOTZ/131/SN (superimposed), on Kemba; SN (superimposed) 169, Gotz, on Binty. $500.00.

Plate 1551: Heath. "Allesandra" from "A World of Children" collection designed by Philip S. Heath. 24" tall. Vinyl head in light brown coloring, vinyl half-body, vinyl arms from the elbows to hands, vinyl legs from mid-thigh to feet, tan cloth stuffed body, stationary brown glass crystal eyes, open-closed mouth with two upper teeth, curly red kanekalon wig. All original in red striped sundress with orange overskirt in front and matching jacket and shorts, string tied sandals. Marks: PSH/792-20, on head; PSH, on back. Nominated for *Doll Reader's* 1992 DOTY award. Allesandra was also issued in a very limited edition in porcelain. $500.00.

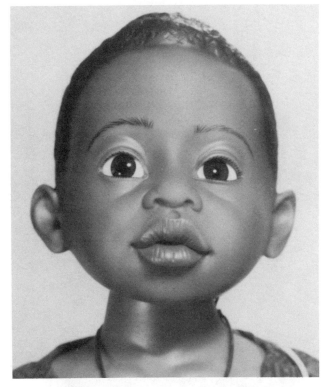

Plate 1552: Heath. "Ami," 1992. Vinyl head, black kanekalon wig, glass eyes, closed mouth, vinyl arms and legs, cloth body. 24" tall. All original in blue pants with white shirt, beads around her wrist and ankle, white band in her hair. She has a gourd on a string around her neck, used as a water jug. Doll is designed by Philip S. Heath. Signed with artist initial "PSH." The box states that this doll, along with Yoromong and Allesandra, are folklore-designer dolls and are not suitable as play dolls. Limited to one year's production. Nominated for *Doll Readers* 1992 DOTY Award in the manufacturer's artist doll category. "Ami" was also made in porcelain in an edition of 25. 10" tall, 1992. Collection of Beverly Dooms. $500.00.

Plate 1553: Heath. "Yoromong," 1992. Vinyl head, molded hair, glass eyes, vinyl arms and legs, cloth body. 24" tall. All original in a blue shirt with white pants, beaded arm and ankle bracelets. Designed by Philip S. Heath. Signed with artist initials "PSH." Limited to one year's production. Doll was also available in a 20" limited edition of 25 in porcelain. The issue price in 1992 of the porcelain doll was $1,850.00. Collection of Beverly Dooms. $500.00.

Plate 1554: Reproduction dolls from molds sculpted by artist Maggie Head (Kane). All porcelain with painted eyes. 11½". Collection of Emma Ransom Hayward. $200.00 each.

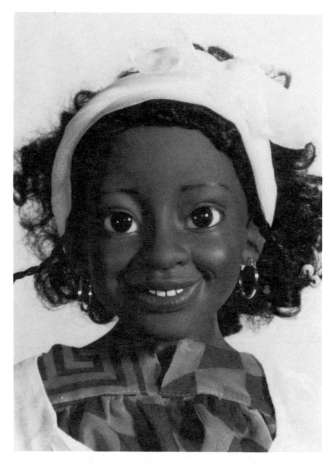

Plate 1555: Phillip Heath. "Jenné" for Gotz from "A World of Children" collection. 24" tall. Vinyl head and limbs, cloth body, crystal eyes, kanekalon wig. Jenné represents a 13 year old African girl and was made in a limited edition of 1000 dolls. Courtesy of Dolls of Color, Inc. $600.00.

Plate 1556: Heath. "Lema." 25" tall. Vinyl and cloth, dark brown wig, stationary brown eyes. Doll designed by artist Philip S. Heath and marketed by Gotz. Courtesy of Linda Boulware of Dolls of Color, Inc. $545.00.

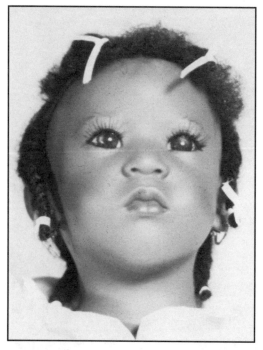

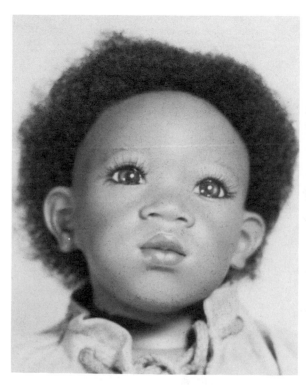

Plate 1557: Himstedt. "Sanga" from Tennessee from the "Summer Dreams" collection, #2295, 1992. 21". Hard vinyl head, upper body, lower arms and legs, brown velvet cloth lower body and upper limbs, stationary dark brown eyes, black hand knotted wig of human hair and mohair, closed mouth, pierced ears. All original in pink gingham dress and white undies. Himstedt signature is engraved on every limb. Doll was distributed by Timeless Creations, the Collectible Specialty Division of Mattel, Inc. Marks: (in cursive)/I ANNETTE HIMSTEDT©(in cursive), on head; I ANNETTE HIMSTEDT©, at waist in back. Won *Dolls* magazine 1992 Dolls Award for Excellence. $600.00.

Plate 1558: Himstedt. "Pemba" from Alabama from the "Summer Dreams" collection. 21" tall, 1992–93. Doll is of the same construction as Sanga. $600.00.

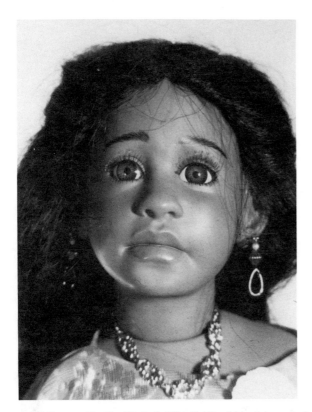

Plate 1559: Renate Hockh. "Naila." 27" tall. Vinyl head, breast plate, arms, and legs, cloth body, stationary brown eyes, lashes, closed mouth, black wig, pierced ears. Edition of 1000. Concept, design, and production by artist Renate Hockh. This doll is #70. Marks: NAILA/ RENATE HOCKH/1992, incised on head; 70/1000, handwritten on head. Collection of Beverly Dooms. $300.00.

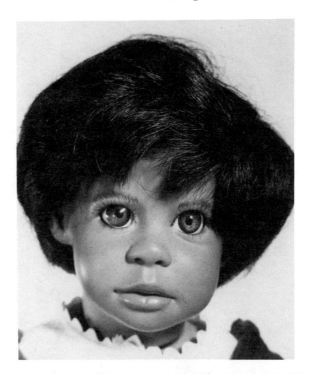

Plate 1560: Hockh. "Ari." 16". Limited edition "Balinese" child. Edition of 1000. This is doll #190. Vinyl head, arms, and legs, cloth body, black wig, stationary brown eyes. All original in purple corduroy romper with white shirt. Marks: ARI/RENATE HOCKH/1993, incised; 190, handwritten, on head. Collection of Beverly Dooms. $200.00.

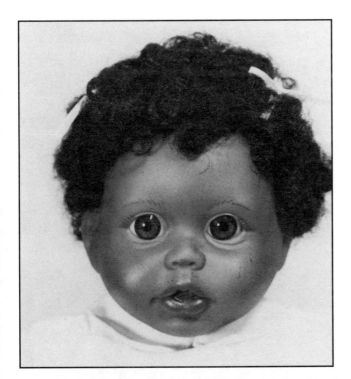

Plate 1561: Kathy Hippensteel. "Wheatsie." 15½" tall. Vinyl head, open-closed mouth, stationary brown eyes, black curly wig, vinyl arms and legs, brown cloth body stuffed with pelts. All original in yellow long sleeved romper with white eyelet trimmed bodice. Marks: ALL ORIGINAL/KATHY HIPPENSTEEL/©1989, incised on head. Each doll is hand signed and this one is numbered 152 by the artist. Limited edition of 2000 pieces. Courtesy of Xzena Moore of the Cubbyhole. $150.00.

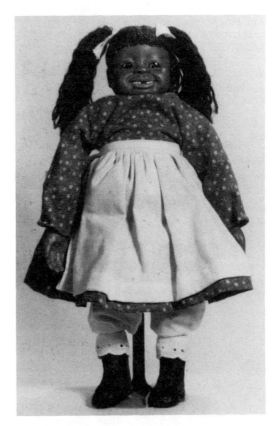

Plate 1562: Martha Holcombe. "Blossom," 11½", from "All God's Children" by Miss Martha's Originals. Wood resin head, hands, feet, and body, cloth upper arms and legs, painted eyes, molded hair with attached black yarn hair. All original in blue cotton print dress, white apron, and pantaloons. Represents a 6 year old child. Marks: G1987/HOLCOMBE/ (last line is unclear), on head. Collection of Joan Banks. $200.00.

Plate 1563: Jackson. "Union Sergeant" of Civil War Era. 19" tall. Original soft sculpture by doll artist Dianna Jackson. Head is made of stockinette fabric, painted eyes, attached ears, sculptured nose, attached hair and beard. Hang tag: DIANNA J'S COLLECTION/ UNION SERGEANT/CIVIL WAR ERA/ NOV. 1991/#3. Courtesy of Dianna Jackson. $100.00.

Plate 1564: Jackson. "Gardening Rosie." 16". Soft sculpture by artist Dianna Jackson. Painted eyes, applied nose and mouth, black yarn hair, cloth body. Dressed in overalls of floral print, mauve blouse and hair bows, holding a pot of flowers. Courtesy of Dianna Jackson. $65.00.

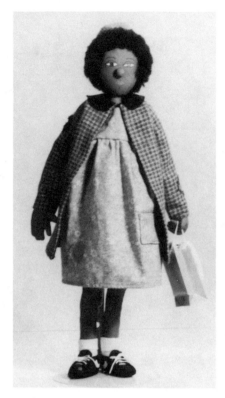

Plate 1565: Jackson. "Bag Lady." 15½". Cloth doll by artist Diana Jackson. Painted eyes and mouth, applied nose, attached black hair. All original in blue cotton floral print dress, tweed coat, white socks, black shoes, and blue knit hat. Doll is carrying a shopping bag filled with goodies. Doll is from Dianna J's Collection. Limited edition of 100. Marks: DIANNA JACKSON/SEPT. 1991 ©/#7 (slash) 100. Courtesy Dianna Jackson. $65.00.

Left — Plate 1566: Jackson. "Rosie With Doll." 16". Limited edition cloth doll by Dianna Jackson. Painted eyes, applied nose and lips, black yarn hair. All original in blue print cotton dress under white eyelet pinafore, white eyelet bloomers, black lace-up high-top shoes. Doll is holding a 5" cloth doll in a pink print dress. Edition of 50 from Dianna J's Collection, ©April, 1991. Courtesy of Dianna Jackson. $65.00.

Right — Plate 1567: Jackson. "Monday Night Football" by doll artist Diana Jackson. One-of-a-kind sculptured cloth. $300.00.

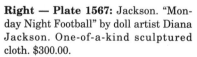

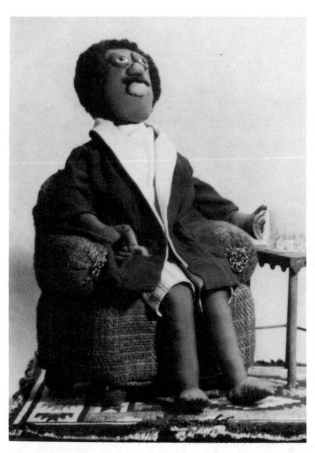

Plate 1568: Janada. "Jade." 10". Original artist doll by Janada Dolls. Resin and cloth baby girl. Collection of and photograph courtesy of Phyllis Schlatter. $50.00.

Plate 1569: January. 16". Handcarved wooden dolls made by West African artist Kor January. Dolls have glass eyes. $600.00 each.

Plate 1570: January. 16". Handcarved with glass eyes. 1993. Photograph by Kor January. $600.00 each.

Plate 1571: January. 16". Handcarved with painted eyes. 1993. Photograph by Kor January. $600.00.

Plate 1572: January. 16". Handcarved with painted eyes. 1993. Photograph by Kor January. $600.00.

Plate 1573: January. 16". Handcarved with painted eyes. 1993. Photograph by Kor January. $600.00 each.

Plate 1574: January. 16". Handcarved by Kor January. 1993. Doll has molded hair as well as attached hair. Photograph courtesy of Kor January. $600.00.

Plate 1575: January. 16". Handcarved with painted eyes. Doll has molded hair under attached wig. Photograph by Kor January. $600.00.

Plate 1576: Johnson. "Miss Baby Heirloom Dolls," 15", from "The Kinfolks" by artist Sue Johnson, ©1991. Set number one in an edition of 300. "Monroe" is the boy, "Odie" is the girl. Composition head, painted features. Girl has painted and applied hair, boy has painted hair. She is holding a cloth doll, he is holding a bag of sugar. Collection of Michael Wolk-Laniewski. $500.00.

Plate 1578: Johnston. "Jazz Player." 21" tall. One-of-a-kind made by doll artist Jack L. Johnston for the 1991 National Institute of American Doll Artists Convention in New Orleans, Louisiana. Doll is sculpted of Cernit over wire armature and sculpted cloth body. Marks: TJ 91, on back of the neck. Courtesy of Jack L. Johnston. Photograph by W. Donald Smith. $2,900.00.

Plate 1577: Johnston. "Santa." 21". Original artist doll by Jack L. Johnston. One-of-a-kind sculpted of Cernit over a wire armature cloth body. Photograph courtesy of Jack L. Johnston. $900.00.

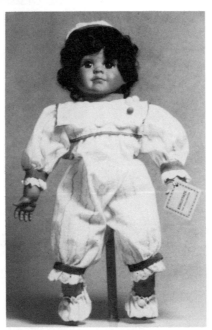

Plate 1579: Kingstate. "Yvonne." Porcelain head, stationary brown eyes, dark brown curly wig, closed mouth, porcelain arms and legs, white cloth body. 15½" tall. All original in white satiny dress with mauve accessories, white lace tights, and white slippers. Marks: BL NO 6, on head. $75.00.

Plate 1580: Kingstate. "Steve," #2236. Porcelain head, stationary brown eyes with real eyelashes, closed mouth, black synthetic wig, dimpled chin, porcelain arms and legs, white cloth body. 14" tall. All original in white striped romper with matching booties. Unmarked. Doll was purchased from QVC, item #C9614, 1992. Also available was a girl from the same mold named Stella. $65.00.

Plate 1581: Kingstate. "Stella," #2237. 14" tall. Porcelain head, hands, and feet, brown stationary eyes with real lashes, dimpled chin, closed mouth, white cloth body, black wig. All original in pastel striped dress with pink pantaloons. Unmarked. $65.00.

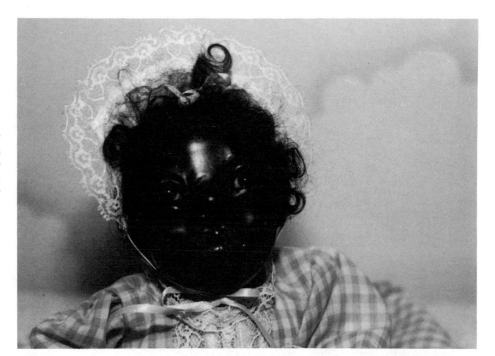

Plate 1582: Pat Kolesar. "Sparkle." One-of-a-kind prototype. 15" tall. Fimo head, weighted cloth body. Seymour Mann is reproducing the doll in porcelain. Courtesy of Pat Kolesar of Kolesar Kreations. $500.00.

Plate 1583: Kolesar. "Proud Lucy" by doll artist Pat Kolesar. 18". 1989. Artist proof from the "Ugly But Snuggly" limited edition. All original in blue print dress. Collection of Michael Wolk-Laniewski. Edition was limited to 1000. $400.00.

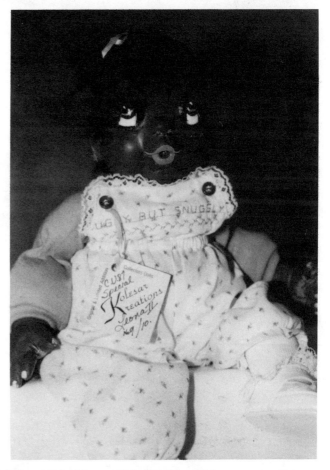

Plate 1584: Kolesar. "Ugly but Snuggly" by artist Pat Kolesar. 18" tall. Vinyl head, hands, and feet, cloth body filled with plastic pellets, painted features. Tag reads "C.U. 87 Kolesar Kreation Leona II No. 9 of 10." Limited edition of 10. Doll is holding a balloon that reads "It's a Girl." Collection of and photo courtesy of Etta Houston. $300.00.

Plate 1585: Kruse. "Lea," "Malou," "Trixie," "Ricardo," and "Wilma," left to right. 1993. 10" tall. Photograph courtesy of Kathe Kruse Puppen GmbH. $260.00 each.

Plate 1586: Kruse. "Badebaby India." 1993. 13" tall. Photograph courtesy of Kathe Kruse Puppen GmbH. $500.00.

Plate 1587: Kruse. "Ethel," 13", on the right, 1993. Photograph courtesy of Kathe Kruse Puppen GmbH. $500.00.

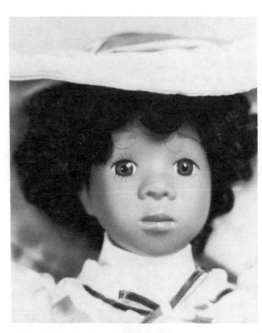

Plate 1588: Liberty Bell Christmas Inc. "Janet." 16" tall. Porcelain head, arms, and legs, white cloth body, black wig, stationary brown eyes, closed mouth. All original in lavender sateen dress trimmed with lace, white sateen pantaloons. Unmarked. Box marked: MADE IN TAIWAN FOR/LIBERTY BELL CHRIST-MAS INC./CENTRAL ISLIP, N.Y. 11722. $20.00.

Plate 1589: Wendy Lawton. "Little Sarita — Carnival Brazil," 1992 from the "Cherished Customs" collection. 14" tall. Doll #140 from a limited edition of 750. Porcelain head, stationary brown eyes, pierced ears with hoop earrings, black curly wig, jointed porcelain body. All original in a costume made of tissue lame in green, blue, pink, purple, and copper. Headpiece is quilted from matching fabric. Marks: LAWTONS/©1992, on head. $425.00.

Plate 1590: Wendy Lawton. "Wee Bit O' Bliss" from the "Wee Bits" collection. Limited to 250 dolls. ©1989. Porcelain doll, dark brown eyes, black lambskin wig. 12" tall. Photo courtesy of the Lawton Doll Company. Issue price $295.00.

Plate 1591: Wendy Lawton. "Topsy" from *Uncle Tom's Cabin* 1988. Issued approximately $350.00. Sold along with white doll "Little Eva," 12" tall. All porcelain. Photo courtesy of the Lawton Doll Company. Limited edition of 250 dolls.

Left — Plate 1592: Long. "Julianna," creole naughty lady by art doll sculptor Marlene Sagar Long. 17" tall. Limited edition of 100. All porcelain with five joints, inset eyes. ©1989. Photograph courtesy of Marlene Sagar Long of Violet Vision. $550.00.

Right — Plate 1593: Long. "Janie and Jamie." 24". Mulatto twins by doll artist Marlene Long. Edition of 25. Porcelain and cloth with inset eyes. ©1987. Photograph courtesy of Marlene Sagar Long of Violet Vision. $455.00 each.

Left — Plate 1594: Long. "Ooma," Danakil woman. 17". Edition of 100 by Marlene Sagar. Ooma is holding a Danakil baby, 5", limited edition of 100 boys and 100 girls. Woman is all porcelain with five joints, inset eyes. Baby is all porcelain with four joints, painted eyes. ©1989. Woman was issued at $513.50, baby at $162. Photograph courtesy of Marlene Sagar Long of Violet Vision. $675.00 set.

Right — Plate 1595: Long. "Aberrah," Danakil man. 18". Limited edition of 100 by Marlene Long. All porcelain, six joints, inset eyes. ©1990. Photograph courtesy of Marlene Sagar Long of Violet Vision. $513.00.

Left — Plate 1596: Long. "Kemo." Danakil child. Limited edition porcelain doll by art doll sculptor Marlene Sagar Long. Photograph courtesy of Marlene Sagar Long of Violet Vision. $385.00.

Right — Plate 1597: Long. "Josephine Baker" by doll artist Marlene Sagar Long. 16½" tall. All porcelain with five joints, inset eyes. Doll was part of a set that included a Josephine Baker doll, a pet animal, and a complete wardrobe of clothing. Limited edition of 20 sets were made. Photograph courtesy of Marlene Sagar Long of Violet Vision. $2,500.00.

Plate 1599: Luth. "Chamarra." 21" tall. Limited edition by Marika Luth for the House of Windsor. Porcelain head, arms, and legs, white cloth body, stationary brown eyes, black wig, closed mouth, pierced ears with goldtone stud earrings. All original in African inspired dress, matching hat, beads on neck and on left wrist, aqua string sandals. Edition of 5000, excluding prototypes and samples. This is doll #466. Nominee for 1992 Dolls Award of Excellence. Marks: MARIKA, incised on head; ARTIST EDITION/BY MARIKA/ 466 OF 5000, stamped on head (except for 466 which is handwritten) $150.00.

Plate 1598: Lyles. "Santa Claus" by doll artist Carrie L. Lyles. 1991. 20" tall. Santa's outfit is trimmed in real mink fur. $150.00.

Plate 1600: Reproduction. "Zobe" from original mold by Frances Lynne. Marks: ZOBE/BY FRANCES LYNNE/©1990/REPRODUCTION, on head. 22" tall. Doll was made by Clara Clark. Courtesy of Clara Clark. $195.00.

Plate 1601: Marian Yu Designs. "Oprah and Gerald." Porcelain shoulder head, porcelain arms and legs, stationary brown glass eyes, black curly wigs, smiling mouths with painted teeth, cloth bodies. Numbered limited edition dolls. These are #2537 of 3500 sets. 16" tall. Oprah is all original in red print cotton blouse and brown print cotton skirt, white pantaloons. Gerald is all original in brown velvet pants and hat with brown gingham shirt. Marks: 2537/3500 (written by hand)/MARIAN YU/MYD INC./MARIAN YU DESIGNS (stamped on). $150.00 set.

Plate 1602: Madison. 15". Cloth dolls by doll artist Dale Madison. Dolls are dressed in African fabric with beads and earrings. Removable clothing. Dolls come in colorful pouches made of African fabric. Marks: ©93/DGM, on feet. $45.00 each.

Plate 1603: Madison. 24". Cloth doll by Dale Madison. Black synthetic curly hair, face in profile, attached earring, African type beads, two piece outfit in African fabric. Marks: DGM, on front of left foot. 1993. Back of feet are personally autographed to author. $125.00.

Plate 1605: Maphis. "Keera." 26" tall. Artist edition of 25 by Jackie Maphis. Porcelain flange neck, head, arms, and legs. Marks: KEERA/BY/JACKIE MAPHIS/©/1992, etched in back of head. Hand signed in gold ink "Jackie Maphis" with thumb print. Photograph courtesy of Jackie Maphis. $700.00.

Plate 1604: Jackie Maphis. "Clemmy." 26". Doll artist edition of 50 dolls from Jackie Maphis' first limited edition porcelain series, the "Sunday School Kids." Clemmy is the first doll in the series and is based on a little girl from Jackie's multi-racial neighborhood. Markings on back of shoulder-plate: ©1992/CLEMMEY/BY/JACKIE MAPHIS; hand signed in gold ink and numbered "Jackie Maphis." Photograph courtesy of Jackie Maphis. $800.00.

Plate 1606: Maphis. "Saffron." 28" tall. Limited edition of 400 by artist Jackie Maphis. Porcelain head and limbs, cloth body, dark brown wig. Her dress is a black and white mock pinafore style with yellow piping with a matching hat. Photograph courtesy of Jackie Maphis. $800.00.

Plate 1607: Mann. "Oprah," ©1991. Porcelain head, chest plate, arms, legs; stationary brown glass eyes, open mouth, white cloth body, black wig. All original in white and pink dotted dress and long pants. Production limited to 2500 dolls. Marks: THE CONNOISSEUR/DOLL COLLECTION/SEYMOUR/MANN/SEYMOUR MANN/MCMXCI, on head. 13" tall. $95.00.

Plate 1608: Mann. "Amber" from the "Moments in Time" collection designed for the Seymour Mann signature series by American doll artist Michele Severino. 12" tall. Porcelain head, black curly wig, stationary side glancing brown eyes, open-closed mouth with two upper painted teeth, dimples in both cheeks, porcelain arms and legs, white cloth body. All original in white baby dress trimmed with white lace, matching pantaloons, and slipper shoes. Marks: ©SEYMOUR MANN INC. 1992, stamped on head; MICHELLE SEVERINO/MANN 1991, incised on head; 252(slash) 5000, hand written on head. This is doll #252 out of edition of 5000. Dress is tagged. $100.00.

Left — Plate 1609: Mann. "Fleurette." 16" tall. Porcelain head, arms, and legs, short black curly wig, stationary brown eyes with real eyelashes, open mouth, white cloth body. All original in African-like print dress and matching gelee with white sandals, beads, and earrings. Marks: THE CONNOISSEUR/ DOLL COLLECTION/SEYMOUR/MANN, on head. Edition is limited to 7500 dolls. $85.00.

Right — Plate 1610: Mann. "Almira." 17" tall. Porcelain collectible doll. Porcelain head, arms, and legs, white cloth body, black wig in long curls, stationary brown eyes with real upper eyelashes, pierced nostrils, closed mouth. All original in blue dress with lots of lace trim. Numbered limited edition of 1500 dolls. This is #1162. Marks: CONNOISSEUR DOLL/COLLECTIONS/SEYMOUR/MANN/ SEYMOUR MANN INC. 1990, stamped on back of head; 1162 (slash) 1500, written by hand on back of head. Made in Taiwan. $90.00.

Plate 1611: Mann. "Creole." 19" tall. Porcelain head, arms, and legs, long black curly wig with bangs, stationary brown eyes with real lashes, closed mouth, pierced ears with goldtone hoop earrings, white cloth body. All original in long pink gown trimmed with baby blue lace, matching hat and parasol. Numbered edition limited to 7500 dolls. This doll #16. Marks: 15 (slash) 7500, written by hand; THE CONNOISSEUR/DOLL COLLECTION/SEYMOUR/MANN/SEYMOUR MANN, INC./ MCMCII, stamped on head. Made in China. $160.00.

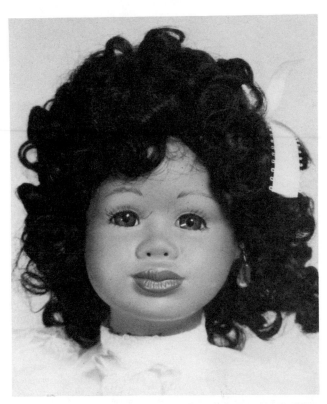

Plate 1612: Mann. "Bernetta," #EP-40V/C-11096. 17"tall. Porcelain head, arms, and legs, white cloth body, stationary brown eyes with lashes, pierced nostrils, closed mouth, pierced ears with pearl drop earrings. All original in white fancy dress with lace. Numbered limited edition of 2500. Marks: 170 (slash) 2500/ CONNOISSEUR DOLL/COLLECTION/SEYMOUR/MANN/ ©SEYMOUR MANN INC. 1992, on head. $90.00.

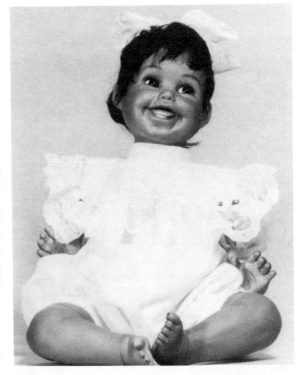

Plate 1613: Reproduction. "Tippy," 19" tall. Mold by doll artist Cindy Marschner. Porcelain head, brown stationary glass eyes with real upper lashes, black wig, open-closed mouth with four teeth, porcelain arms and legs, cloth weighted body. Marks: TIPPY/A CINDY MARSCHNER/ PRODUCTION/©1991, on head. Doll made by Clara Clark. $200.00.

Plate 1614: Linda Mason. "Rachel Williams" by artist Linda Mason for the Georgetown Collection from its "American Diary Collection." Rachel depicts a girl from Chicago in 1893. An 18 page booklet about her life comes with the doll. Porcelain head, arms, and legs, brown cloth body, black curly wig, stationary brown eyes, closed mouth. All original in peach dress with matching hat and parasol. 16" tall. Marks: LINDA MASON/©1992, on head. Doll was made in Taiwan. Rachel was painted by hand and is limited to 100 firing days. Collection of Beverly Dooms. $130.00.

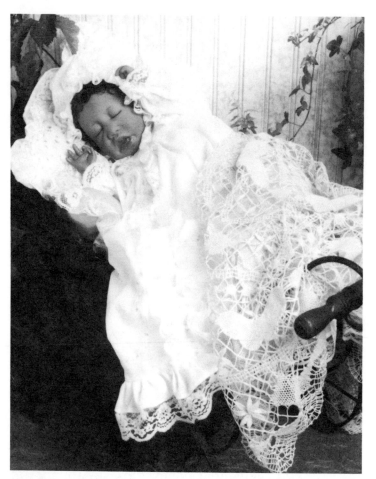

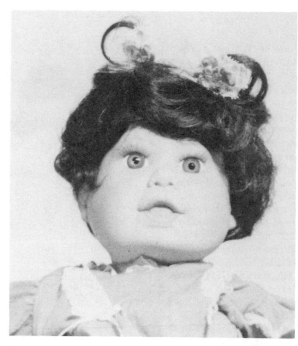

Plate 1616: Lee Middleton. "My Lee." Vinyl head, lower arms and hands, lower legs, and feet; brown stationary eyes with real upper lashes, painted lower lashes; open-closed mouth; glued on black wig; white cloth body and upper limbs. 22" long. All original in red footed sleeper in cotton knit. Marks: 092287/©LEE MIDDLETON 1987/USA/LEE MIDDLETON 3,456 (hand written). Doll comes with miniature bible. $190.00.

Plate 1615: Middleton, Lee. "Dear One/Sunday Best." 18". 1992. Vinyl limited edition of 5,000 by doll artist Lee Middleton. Rooted dark brown hair, real lashes, dressed in batiste white day gown with embroidered flowers and vines, matching bonnet. Courtesy of Lee Middleton. Doll was available in 1986 with porcelain head, hands, and feet, cloth body. 18". Limited edition in porcelain was 750. $140.00.

Plate 1617: Middleton, Lee. "Amanda Springtime." 21" tall. 1993. Original vinyl doll by Lee Middleton. Dark brown eyes, real lashes, jointed arms and legs, curly brown wig. Limited edition of 2,000. Courtesy of Lee Middleton. $175.00.

Plate 1618: Milano. "Tissy." Shoulder head, arms, and legs for a reproduction china head doll. Kit was purchased in the mid 1970's from a doll supply catalog. Head is unmarked but directions for completing and dressing the doll are written by Geri Milano and are copyright 1974. Completed doll would be approximately 12" tall. $30.00.

Plate 1619: Geri Milano. Kit to make a china head "Harriet Tubman" doll. Included are a china shoulder head with molded, painted hair, painted eyes, closed mouth, two sew holes in the front of the shoulder-plate and two holes in the back; china legs with molded, painted black boots; china arms; pattern for a cloth body and clothing. Completed doll would be 12" to 14" tall. Marks: GM 84, on back of shoulder head. $20.00.

Plate 1620: Moments Treasured. "Jumoke." Porcelain doll in authentic African clothing with fruit basket on top of her head. #1703 in a limited edition of 2000 dolls. 19" tall. $120.00.

Plate 1621: Moments Treasured. "Brittany," ©1991, from the "Moments Treasured" collection. A numbered, limited edition doll, this is number 1301 of 1500. Porcelain head, arms, and legs with white cloth baby body, black curly wig, stationary black eyes with real lashes, open-closed mouth with molded tongue. Doll came with a small all cloth doll with black button eyes, glued on black wig and embroidered mouth. Both dolls are all original in white baby gown trimmed with lace and ribbon. Brittany is 20" long, small doll is 5½" and is unmarked. Marks on Brittany: 1301 (slash) 1500/MOMENTS/ TREASURED, on head. Made in Taiwan. $120.00.

Plate 1622: Moments Treasured. All cloth baby doll that came with previous doll "Brittany." 5½" tall. $15.00.

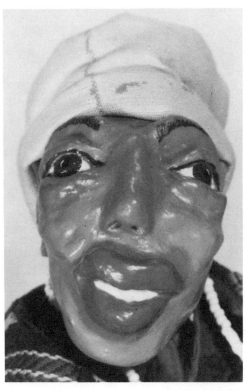

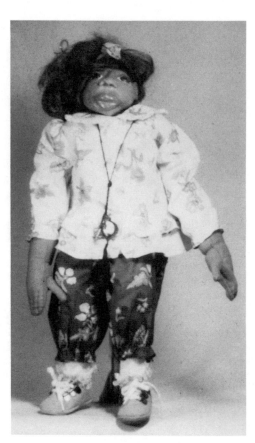

Plate 1623: Hannah T.W. Mumin. "Abu Salat El Nasir." 22" tall. One-of-a-kind. Fima and clay head, painted features, cloth body jointed by strings and buttons. All original with ecru kufi hat, tapestry pants and vest, cotton print shirt, print underpants, prayer beads around neck. Marks: H. UMIN, on head. Doll won two awards at the 1992 Michigan Doll Maker's Guild Competition: First Place and Best of Division Rosette. Courtesy of Hannah T.W. Mumin. $2,000.00.

History of Brother Nasir by Hannah Mumin: Brother Nasir represents an important part in the foundation of a Muslim brother's life — THE JAMAT! During which, he leaves his home to study, pray, do charitable work as well as fast. He may stay close to home or travel throughout his country or go anywhere in the world. Jamat can be a devotion of three days or a whole year of study and travel — reliant totally on God for worldly needs. This is an extremely significant period in a man's life. Not only does he benefit from his prayers and awakening knowledge, but his family and those who have the privilege to worship and study with him, feed, or house him during Jamat are similarly blessed.

Plate 1624: Mumin. "Bajainah." 25" tall. One-of-a-kind dol by doll artist Hannah Mumin. 1992. Clay head, reddish-brown synthetic wig, painted eyes, closed mouth, brown gabardine body and limbs. All original in floral print blouse and pants, white socks, pink shoes. Collection of Mr. and Mrs. Russell Thompson. $450.00.

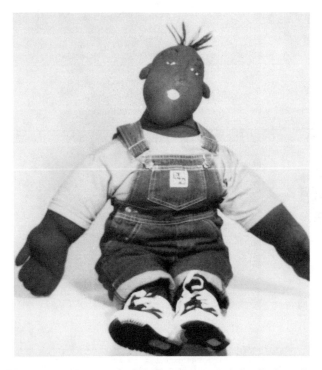

Plate 1625: Mumin. "Jami," (The Gatherer). 28" tall. One-of-a-kind by doll artist Hannah Mumin. Brown cotton flannel head, body, and limbs, painted eyes, sculptured eyebrows embroidered eyebrows, sculptured nose, applied ears, painted mouth, tuft of black yarn hair. All original in overalls, red shirt, white athletic shoes. Anatomically correct. Collection of Harry Mumin. $600.00.

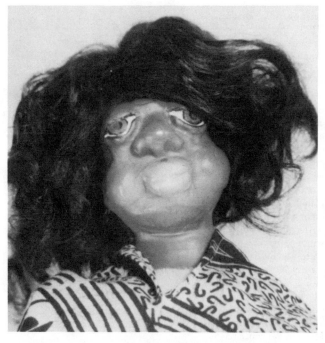

Plate 1626: Mumin. "Zena's Buelah." 22" tall. 1992. Clay head, mixed black and brown human hair with a few strands of gray, painted features, tan cotton body and limbs. All original in two piece outfit made of fabric from Senegal. Marks: HANNAH MUMIN/1992, handwritten on the back. Courtesy of Hannah Mumin. $500.00.

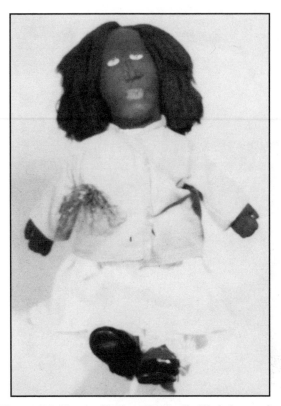

Plate 1627: Mumin. "Hakim." 20" tall. One-of-a-kind by doll artist Hannah Mumin. Sculptured features, painted eyes, rooted brown yarn hair. All original in red and purple two piece outfit, purple hat, white lace-up shoes, neck beads. Courtesy of Hannah Mumin. $200.00.

Plate 1628: Mumin. "Rasheen." 22" tall. All cloth one-of-a-kind by doll artist Hannah Mumin. 1992. Soft sculptured face, painted eyes, rooted black yarn hair. All original in pink corduroy jacket, pink print dress, white cotton pantaloons, black shoes. Courtesy of Hannah Mumin. $250.00.

Plate 1629: Mumin. "Nina." 3½". One-of-a-kind by artist Hannah Mumin. Clay head, painted features, black macramé cord hair, clay body, cloth arms and legs. Dressed in yellow hand crocheted dress. Marks: H M, on back. Courtesy of Hannah Mumin. $75.00.

Plate 1630: Mumin. "Sister." 5". One-of-a-kind soft sculptured doll by artist Hannah Mumin. Cloth sculptured face, painted features, black yarn hair, cloth body. Dressed in two piece hand crocheted dress. Courtesy of Hannah Mumin. $50.00.

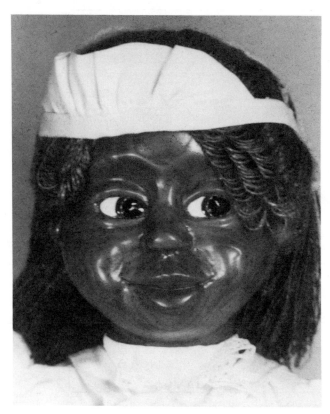

Plate 1631: Naber. "Maxine," #807. 1987. 18" tall. The material used to make the head, arms, legs, and torso consists of a secret blend of woodchips, pigments, and high density urethane that expands during the curing process, creating pressure as much as two tons. The molded wood parts are cleaned and stained and a coat of polyurethane clear satin finish is applied to seal the surface. The initial carving was sculpted by Harold Paul Naber from yellow cedar. All dolls are completely hand crafted in the U.S. Painted eyes, brown yarn hair. All original in white romper with aqua overskirt and bibbed apron, matching booties. Marks: MAXINE BY H.P. NABER/NABER GESTALT CORP., carved on head. Each character is only made for 1001 days after the original carving is completed. Doll was issued June 8, 1987, and retired March 4, 1990. Collection of Dr. Ingrid Dooms-Cook. $450.00.

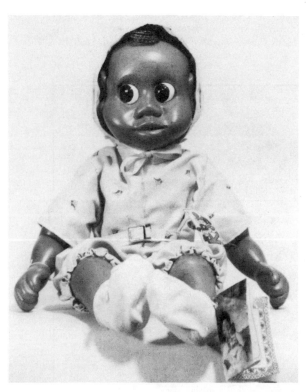

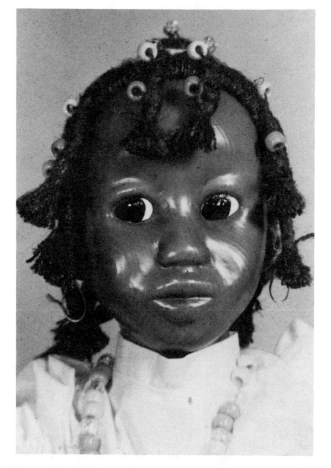

Plate 1632: Naber. "Sami," #874. 17". 1989. Baby doll, made of urethane from mold of original carving yellow cedar by Harold Paul Naber. Bald head except for tuft of brown yarn hair on top of head, painted dark green side-glancing eyes, closed-mouth. All original in blue print tagged romper, matching bonnet, white booties. Marks: SAMI ©1989 H.P. NABER, on head. Issued 7/18/89; retired 4/13/92. Collection of Dr. Ingrid Dooms-Cook. $350.00.

Plate 1633: Naber. "Josi," #378, 1993. 19" tall. Doll is made of "molded wood," brown yarn hair, painted eyes, closed mouth. All original in white blouse and burgundy dotted skirt with mauve ruffle and waistband, pearl and silver cord earrings. Marks: 387 JOSI ©1992 H.P. NABER, on head. Courtesy of Xzena Moore of the Cubbyhole. $300.00.

Plate 1635: Maryse Nicole. "Letisha." 16" tall. 1990. Number 21 from a limited edition of 500 dolls. Porcelain swivel head, dark brown wig, stationary brown eyes, with upper lashes, open mouth with two upper teeth, porcelain body. All original in pink cotton dress with pink striped pinafore, white lace stockings, pink buckle shoes. Marks: MARYSE/ NICOLE/1990, on head. Courtesy of Clara Phillips Hill. $300.00.

Plate 1634: Napier. "Sojourner Truth." 14" tall. Original artist doll, sculpted and made by Sharon Napier for the U.F.D.C. Region 12 Conference, sponsored by the Battle Creek Area Doll Club, held October 26–28, 1989. Title of the conference was "Sojourn to Battle Creek." Doll has a porcelain head, shoulder-plate, arms, and boots, cloth body, black persian lamb's wig, set in brown plastic eyes. Limited to an edition of 500. Doll is marked on the back of the head and on the cloth body with her name, the artist, the date, and the conference. $250.00.

Plate 1636: Reproduction. "Tala" and "Muhammed" from a mold made by artist John Nissen. 26" tall. Porcelain head, arms, and legs, cloth body. Dolls were made from the mold and dressed by Clara Clark. $300.00.

Plate 1637: Marie Osmond. "Cindy," from the "Children of the World" collection. Porcelain head and shoulder-plate, stationary brown eyes with real upper lashes, closed mouth, black human hair wig, porcelain arms and legs, white cloth body. 18" tall. Cindy's face was sculptured by Karen Blandford, an Australian sculptor. This doll is #1397 of a limited edition of 2500 dolls. A gold Marie Osmond doll bracelet with the initial "M" came with the doll. Marks on doll conflict with the name doll was marketed under. Marks: ORIGINAL WITH THE NAME DOLL/"BLOS-SOM"/REPRODUCTION, incised on head; MARIE OSMOND/ ©1991/1397/2500, handwritten and stamped on head. All original in one piece flowered old-fashioned styled jumpsuit. $175.00.

Left — Plate 1638:
Reproduction. "Lucinda" from Lucinda mold set by Mary Van Osdell. Marks: LUCINDA/BY/MARY VAN OSDELL/©1992, on head. 26" tall. Made by Clara Clark. $225.00.

Right — Plate 1639:
Osdell. "Elmo," 2993. 23½". Original artist doll by Mary Van Osdell. Porcelain head, arms, and legs, cloth body. Molds were sold to make reproduction. Photograph courtesy of Mary Van Osdell. No price available.

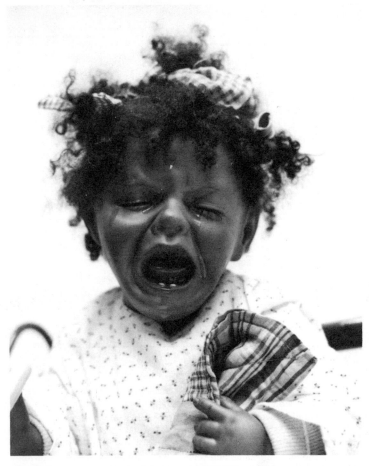

Plate 1640: Osdell. "Sweetpea." 1993. 18" tall. Another original porcelain artist doll by Mary Van Osdell. Head molds were sold for reproduction Sweetpea dolls. Photograph courtesy of Mary Van Osdell. No price available.

Plate 1641: Heidi Ott. "Saddie." 12". Jointed vinyl doll with handpainted brown eyes, human hair wig. All original in pink dress under blue pinafore. Issued 1993, Collection of Patricia B. Whittler-Martin. $100.00.

Plate 1642: Heidi Ott. "Tom." 12". Jointed vinyl doll with handpainted eyes, human hair wig. All original in brown corduroy jacket, print shirt, and brown pants. Issued in 1993. Collection of Patricia B. Whittler-Martin. $100.00.

Plate 1643: Ott. "Baby Harry." 9". Jointed vinyl doll, brown painted eyes, molded hair. All original in red knit shirt, navy and white striped overalls, and matching cap. Collection of Patricia B. Whittler-Martin. $100.00.

Plate 1644: Ott. "Baby Ruby." 9". Jointed vinyl baby girl with painted brown eyes, molded hair. All original in peach print dress, peach underclothes. Issued in 1993. Collection of Patricia M. Whittler-Martin. $100.00.

Plate 1645: Ott. Boy by artist Heidi Ott. All original. Numbers on neck: 90-88-205. Handwritten on head: Heidi Ott. Collection of and photograph courtesy of Shirley Jackson. $1,000.00.

Plate 1646: Ott. Girl by Heidi Ott. All original. Number of head: 93-89-45. Collection of and photograph courtesy of Shirley Jackson. $1,000.00.

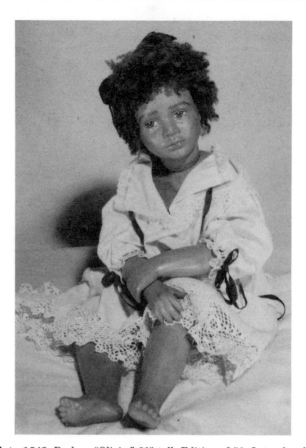

Plate 1647: Parker. "Madelyn." 28" tall. Edition of 50. Latex head, limbs, and full breast/chest, pellet-filled jointed cloth body, painted brown intaglio eyes, Border Leiciester sheepskin wig. Gown is constructed of vintage fabric, lace, and trim. Doll designed and handmade by artists Jim & Sue Parker of Parker People Dolls. Photograph courtesy of Jim & Sue Parker of Parker People Dolls. $900.00.

Plate 1648: Parker. "Olivia." 20" tall. Edition of 50. Latex head, limbs, and full chest, pellet-filled jointed cloth body, painted brown intaglio eyes, Border Leicester sheepskin wig. Gown is constructed of vintage fabric, lace, and trim. Designed and handmade by artists Jim & Sue Parker for Parker People Dolls. Photograph courtesy of Jim and Sue Parker of Parker People Dolls. $700.00.

Left — Plate 1649: Parker. "K-Lynn." 23" tall. Edition of 23 dolls. Constructed of latex with a faux antique wood finish, jointed body with a swivel waist, glass paperweight brown eyes, Icelandic sheepskin wig. Dressed in vintage fabrics, ribbons, and Irish-crochet lace, hand dyed leather shoes. Teddy Bear courtesy of Jenny Murphy. Dolls designed and handmade by artists Jim & Sue Parker of Parker People Dolls. Photograph courtesy of Jim & Sue Parker of Parker People Dolls. $700.00.

Right — Plate 1650: Parker. "Genie." 19½" tall. One-of-a-kind by artists Jim & Sue Parker for their daughter, Kristen. Latex with faux antique wood finish, painted brown intaglio eyes, sheepskin wig. Dressed in vintage fabrics, trim, and gemstones. Photograph courtesy of Jim & Sue Parker of Parker People Dolls. No price available.

Plate 1651: Parkins. "Rachel" from the "Tiny Treasures" series. 10" tall. All porcelain. Limited edition of 1000 by doll artist Phyllis Parkins. Photograph courtesy of Phyllis Parkins. $180.00.

Plate 1652: Parkins. "Marty & Matia," limited edition of 500 by doll artist Phyllis Parkins. Porcelain and cloth. Photograph courtesy of The Collectibles by Phyllis Parkins. $200.00 each.

Plate 1653: Pabst May. "Aurora" by doll artist Cheryl Pabst May. 24". Limited edition of 100. Porcelain head, shoulder head, arms, and legs, cloth torso, glass paperweight eyes, dark brown mohair wig. Dressed in blue and white cotton dress with white pinafore. Doll is holding a reproduction black Kestner, "Sweet Pea," which is sold separately. Photograph courtesy of Cheryl Pabst May. $900.00.

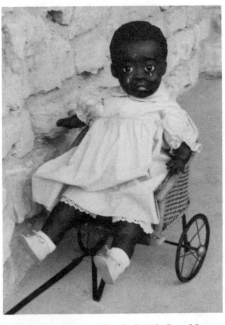

Plate 1654: Quintano. "Cicely." 23". Leo Moss type doll made by Rubin Quintano, an artist from Mexico, in the 1980's. Doll was purchased at the UFDC convention in Indianapolis, in 1992. Following is a description, given to the owner, of how the doll was made: "This man takes old compos and strips the painted off of them and repaints them. Then makes a new body for them and then he puts papier-maché on the head and molds it the way he wants it for the doll to look like the Leo Moss dolls. He sets glass eyes in and they're really very nice." It is also reported that he makes smiling Moss-like dolls. Collection Phyllis Schlatter. Information and photograph also reported that he makes smiling Moss-like dolls. Collection Phyllis Schlatter. Information and photograph also courtesy of Phyllis Schlatter. Doll was made by Rubin Quintano. $800.00.

Plate 1655: Rose. "Nicole" by artist Patricia Rose for Paradise Galleries. 14". Numbered edition from the "Treasury Collection," limited to 100 firing days. Porcelain head, arms, and legs, white cloth body, black curly wig, stationary brown eyes, closed mouth. All original in yellow cotton dress with white pinafore, white shoes and socks. This is doll #708G. Marks: TC 1992/PATRICIA ROSE/708G, on head. $50.00.

Plate 1656: Patricia Rose. "Amber." 7½" in seated position. Porcelain head, arms, and legs, brown acrylic eyes, cloth body. Signed limited edition of 100 dolls. Photograph courtesy of Patricia Rose Studios. $400.00.

Left — Plate 1657: Patricia Rose. "Pam." 14" tall. All porcelain, acrylic wig and eyes. Limited edition of 50 dolls. All original dressed as a flower girl in long white gown trimmed with pink ribbon with pink floral headpiece of dried roses. Made in 1991. Photograph courtesy of Patricia Rose Studios. $500.00.

Right — Plate 1658: Patricia Rose. "Brazilian Festival Dancer." 18" tall. All porcelain, one-of-a-kind, acrylic wig and eyes. Made in 1992. Photograph courtesy of Patricia Rose Studios. $800.00.

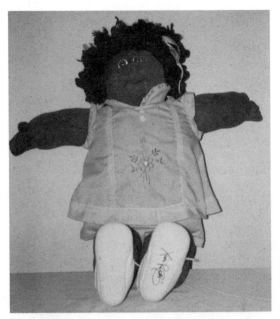

Plate 1659: Xavier Roberts. "Little People," Cabbage Patch Kids. All cloth soft sculpture. 23" tall. Painted brown eyes, black yarn hair, dimple in right cheek. All original in orange two piece outfit, white socks and white shoes. Marked Xavier Roberts on the bottom of the left shoe. Marks: XAVIER ROBERTS (brown signature) 85, on back. $250.00.

Plate 1660: Xavier Roberts. "The Little People," Cabbage Patch Kids Collection. Soft sculptured head, painted eyes, black cut loop yarn hair, cloth sculptured body. All original in blue and white baseball outfit with matching shoes lace-up attached, red baseball cap. 22". 1985. Marks: XAVIER ROBERTS '85, written on lower back. Tag sewn to body: XAVIER ROBERTS/THE LITTLE PEOPLE AND/CABBAGE PATCH KIDS ARE/TRADEMARKS OF ORIGINAL/ APPALACHIAN ARTWORKS/INC./CLEVELAND, GA 30528./©1978, 1980, 1981, 1983/ALL RIGHTS RESERVED. Reverse side of tag has bathing instructions. Bottom of left shoe is also marked. $225.00.

Plate 1661: Sarah's Attic. "Sassafras" from the "Sunday Best" series. 12". Wood resin head, arms, and legs, cloth body, painted features, molded hair with molded in ribbons. Courtesy of Xzena Moore of the Cubbyhole. $175.00.

Plate 1662: Sarah's Attic. "Hickory" from the "Sunday Best series. 12". Wood resin head, arms, and legs, cloth body, painted features, molded hair. Courtesy of Xzena Moore of the Cubbyhole. $175.00.

Plate 1663: Sarah's Attic. "Peace on Earth" Santa. 24". Limited edition of 200. 1992. Resin head, arms, and legs, brown cloth body, painted features, molded hair, full beard and mustache. All original in brown herringbone coat with fur-like trim and lining, matching hat, brown checked pants, molded on brown boots. Marks: SARAH'S ATTIC/#20 (slash) 200/ LIMITED EDITION/USA. Doll is from the "Spirit of Christmas" collection and is holding a "Peace on Earth" wreath made of wood resin. Collection of Joan Banks. $425.00.

Plate 1664: Sarah's Attic. "Emma." 10". Wood resin head, arms and legs, brown cloth body, molded on pink shoes, white socks, molded black hair, painted eyes, open-closed mouth. All original in off-white dress with tiny mauve print, checked headband and waist sash. Marks: EMMA/SA©1991, on back of shoulder head. White cloth heart sewn to lower back: SARAH'S ATTIC/#75 (slash) 500/LIMITED EDITION/USA. Collection of Joan Banks. $175.00.

Plate 1665: Sarah's Attic. "Edie." 12½". Limited edition of 500. Wood resin head, lower arms, and legs, brown cloth body, molded on straw hat, painted eyes, painted smiling mouth with two upper teeth, molded pink shoes, and white socks. All original in mauve gingham dress, white print apron, and matching underpants. Marks: EDIE, on head. Tag sewn to back on body: SARAH'S/ ATTIC/#63 (slash)/ 500/LIMITED EDITION/USA. Collection of Joan Banks. $175.00.

Plate 1666: Sarah's Attic. "Edie" and "Emma" in other all original outfits. Photograph courtesy of Sarah's Attic, Inc. $175.00.

Plate 1667: Sarah's Attic. Left to right: "Wooster," #3602, 14½" tall; "Whoopie," #3597, 21" tall; "Harpster," #3591, 22½" tall; "Banjo the dog," #3622, 9½" tall; Banjo's dog bowl, #3732. Dolls are retired. Photograph courtesy of Sarah's Attic, Inc. Price guide values: $160.00, $200.00, $250.00, $100.00 and $10.00, respectively.

Plate 1668: Sarah's Attic. "Enos" and "Adora," angels from "Granny's Favorites" collection. Limited edition of 500 each. Dolls are #79 and #76 respectively. 14" tall. All cloth, hand painted faces, black yarn hair, attached framed brown cloth wings. Collection of Joan Banks. $100.00 each.

Plate 1669: Sarah's Attic. "Muffin and Puffin." 19". Cloth limited editions of 500 each from "Tattered and Torn" collection. Painted faces, black yarn hair. Boy has red gingham shirt, striped pants. Girl has red gingham dress under striped dress which is over striped trousers. Puffin is doll #65 and Muffin is #64. Dolls were retired December 31, 1991. Puffin's hat is missing in the photograph. Collection of Jan Banks. $100.00 each.

Right Above — Plate 1670: Sarah's Attic. Quilting Lady Dolls. Left to right: "Granny," #3576, 20"; "Millie," #3586, 19" tall; "Lilla," #3581, 18" tall. Mystery Limited date. Photograph courtesy of Sarah's Attic. $437.00.

Plate 1671: Reproduction. "Bye-lo Baby." 15" tall. Porcelain head and hands, painted eyes and hair, white cloth body. Unmarked. Collection of the Museum of African American History (Detroit). $50.00.

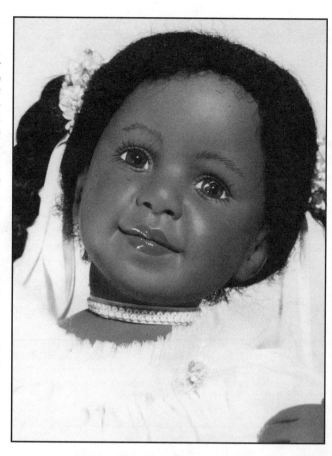

Left — Plate 1672: Schrott. "Ricardo." 27" tall. Designed by artist Rotraut Schrott for The Great American Doll Company (GADCO). Vinyl socket head, stationary brown eyes with upper and lower lashes, brown wig in soft curls, vinyl upper body, lower arms, and legs, remainder of body is brown cloth. Marks: RICARDO/AN ORIGINAL/ROTRAUT SCHROTT/ DESIGN/THE GREAT AMERI-CAN/DOLL COMPANY ©1990/ ANAHEIM CALIFORNIA 92806, on back. Limbs are also marked. Doll is available in porcelain. Vinyl edition limited to two years production, porcelain edition limited to 2500. Collection of Dr. Ingrid Dooms-Cook. $300.00.

Right — Plate 1673: Schrott. "Jasmine." 28". Designed by Rotraut Schrott for GADCO.Vinyl and cloth, stationary eyes. All original in white ballet outfit. Doll was limited to two years production. Collection of Beverly Dooms. $600.00.

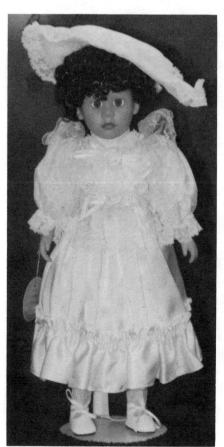

Left — Plate 1674: Show Stoppers. "Tamara." 18" tall. Porcelain head, arms, and legs, cloth body. Original in apricot dress and pantaloons, loose tights, shoes. Photograph courtesy of Faith Wyse. $60.00.

Right — Plate 1675: Smelser. "Renee." 28" tall. Original doll by doll artist Sharon Smelser. Limited edition of 50. Porcelain head on a jointed hard body. Copyright 1990. Courtesy of Sharon Smelser. $1,200.00.

Plate 1677: Shumaker. "Teaka." 23" tall. 1992. Limited edition of 750 by doll artist Gail J. Shumaker. Courtesy of Gail J. Shumaker Originals. $300.00.

Plate 1676: Shumaker. "Cotton." 24" tall. 1990. Porcelain limited edition of 50 by Gail J. Shumaker. Courtesy of Gail J. Shumaker Originals. $500.00.

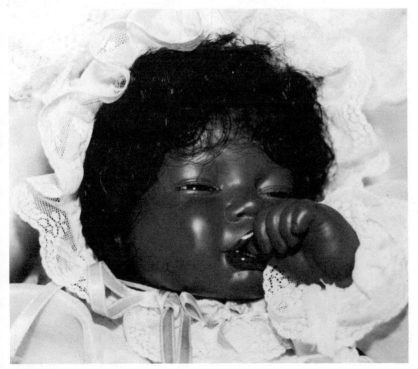

Plate 1678: Shumaker. "Patra." 23" tall. 1990. Porcelain one-of-a-kind by artist Gail J. Shumaker. Included are cradle, pillow, quilt, and handmade christening outfit. Courtesy of Gail J. Shumaker. $1,000.00.

Plate 1679: Shumaker. "Latisha." 1991. Limited edition of 27 by Gail J. Shumaker. Courtesy of Gail J. Shumaker Originals. $600.00.

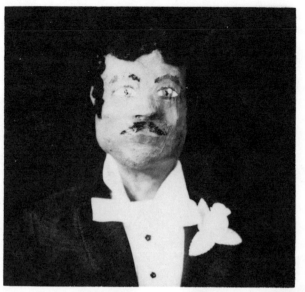

Plate 1681: Smith. "Groom." 27". One-of-a-kind papier-maché by artist Frances L. Smith. Doll is based on dollmaker's husband on their wedding day. Painted features, yarn hair. Doll is dressed in a tuxedo made of man's suiting. Created in 1992. Photograph courtesy of Frances L. Smith, FLS Designs. $750.00.

Plate 1680: Smith. "Bride." 24". One-of-a-kind by artist Frances L. Smith. This papier-maché doll was inspired by the artist's wedding photos. The papier-maché arms and legs are attached with doll joints, hair is curly dark brown wig, facial features are hand painted with acrylic paints. Elaborate bridal outfit includes gown, headpiece, stockings, pantaloons, petticoat, and shoes that coordinate with her dress. Created in 1992. Photograph courtesy of Frances L. Smith, FLS Designs. $750.00.

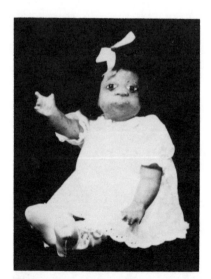

Plate 1682: Smith. "Baby Glenda." 18". One-of-a-kind papier-maché doll by Frances Smith. This doll was inspired by a photograph of the dollmaker's mother as an infant. The body is painted with acrylic paints. The arms and legs are movable, stationary acrylic eyes, black wig. Doll is dressed in white eyelet dress, white shoes and socks. Photograph courtesy of Frances L. Smith, FLS Designs. $300.00.

Plate 1683: Smith. "Heart and Soul Children." 27". Cloth dolls from the "Folk Art by Frances" line by Frances L. Smith. Cloth dolls have felt faces and hair made of dried flowers. Photograph courtesy of Frances L. Smith. $100.00 each.

Plate 1684: Smith. "Miss Veatrice." 24". One-of-a-kind papier-maché doll by Frances L. Smith. Miss Veatrice won the theme award in Wilberforce, Ohio, at the Holiday Festival of Black Dolls in 1992. The theme was "Dolls: The Fabric of Life Cultural... Traditional." The doll is a portrait doll of the artist's paternal grandmother at age 19. She wears a natural color straw hat adorned with flowers. Her dress is bright blue with a white lace collar. Created in 1992. Photograph courtesy of Frances L. Smith, FLS Designs. $2,000.00.

Plate 1685: Snow. "Sammy Davis, Jr." 24" tall by artist Diane Snow, 1978. Porcelain head, hands, and boots, cloth body. Yellow bellbottom pantsuit, jewelry, and pinkie ring. Marked on neck and bottom of right boot: ORIGINAL/DIANE SNOW 1978. Doll is probably one of a kind. From collection of and photo courtesy of Etta Houston. $700.00.

Plate 1686: Snow. "Redd Foxx" by artist Diane Snow. 18" tall. Porcelain head and hands, cloth body. All original. Unmarked and probably one of a kind. From the collection of and photo courtesy of Etta Houston. $700.00.

Plate 1687: Snow. Early "Mammy" doll by artist Diane Snow. 18" tall. Porcelain head, composition hands, cloth body. All original in long blue dress. Probably one of a kind. Unmarked. From collection of and photo courtesy of Etta Houston. $600.00.

Plate 1688: "Bud and Sarah." 14" boy and girl. 1985-87. Composition arms and legs, cloth bodies, painted side glancing eyes. Boy's hair is painted black. Girl's hair is black yarn and comes out in three holes in her head. Boy is marked BUD 33W on head. Girl is marked SARAH 33W on head. Marker unknown. Photography courtesy of Maureen Braeden. $175.00.

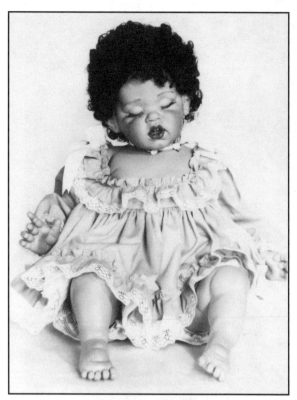

Plate 1689: Spanos. "Carmel Cream." 26". Vinyl head, breast-shoulder-plate, arms, and legs, brown cloth body. Jointed at arms with cloth, curly brown wig, molded eyes in sleep position with lashes, open mouth with two upper teeth. FAYZAH SPANOS/DESIGN G 1991/110 (slash) 2500. This is doll #110 out of an edition of 2500. Courtesy of Cultural Accents (Detroit). $280.00.

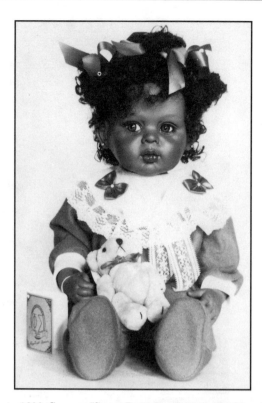

Plate 1690: Spanos. "Sugar Dumpling." 21½". Vinyl head, lower arms, body, and legs, cloth upper arms, lips slightly parted, stationary brown glass eyes with upper and lower lashes, dark brown hair, pierced ears with goldtone stud earrings. Doll comes with a 4½" jointed beige teddy bear with glassine eyes. Marks: FAYZAH SPANOS/1993/742 (slash) 100. This is doll #742 out of an edition of 1000. Courtesy of Cultural Accents (Detroit). $230.00.

Plate 1691: Sutton. "Elizabeth." ©1989. 21" tall. Sculpted from the likeness of a close family friend of the artist, Linda Lee Sutton. Dolls shown are #'s 64 and 65 in an artist studio edition of 100. Porcelain head, shoulder-plate, arms, legs, brown paperweight eyes, applied upper eyelashes. Marks: LINDA/LEE/SUTTON/ORIGINAL©1989/"ELIZABETH." Photograph courtesy of Linda Lee Sutton. $600.00.

Plate 1692: Sutton. "The Twins, Exie & Ernie" by artist Linda Lee Sutton. 17" tall. All porcelain, paperweight eyes, black afro wigs. Limited edition of 40 designed and made by the artist. Marks: LINDA/LEE/SUTTON ORIGINAL©1989/"THE TWINS." Photograph courtesy of Linda Lee Sutton. $1,000.00.

Left — Plate 1693: Sutton. "Cotton Candy Angel." Porcelain doll designed by artist Linda Lee Sutton. Paperweight eyes, black wig, pink iridescent dress with flower petal wings. Limited to 40 in the 3rd variation. Marks: LINDA/ LEE/SUTTON ORIGINAL/©1989. Photograph courtesy of Linda Lee Sutton. $475.00.

Right — Plate 1694: Pat Thompson. "Chantrell." 27" tall. Edition of 12 by doll artist Pat Thompson. Available in 1989. Photograph courtesy of Pat Thompson of Vlasta Dolls. $2,400.00.

Plate 1695: Pat Thompson. "Hattie." 23" tall. Artist doll available in 1989 in a limited edition of 1000. Hand painted cultured glass head and limbs, cloth body with wire armature, painted eyes, mohair wig. All original in peach outfit. Collection of and photograph courtesy of Phyllis Schlatter. $500.00.

Plate 1696: Pat Thompson. "Chardonnay." 25" tall. One-of-a-kind. Photograph courtesy of Pat Thompson of Vlasta Dolls. $5,000.00.

Plate 1697: Pat Thompson. "Livonia." Courtesy of Pat Thompson of Vlasta Dolls. $1,400.00.

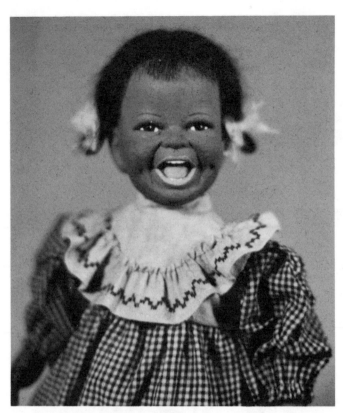

Left — Plate 1698: Thompson, Carla. "Liberty Jane — Sunday Best." 12" tall. Soft sculpture second edition of "Liberty" by NIADA (National Institute of American Doll Artists) member Carla Thompson. Edition of 75. The first edition was nominated for *Dolls* magazine's Award of Excellence in Cloth: All Prices category, 1992. It has an edition of 50. Photograph courtesy of Carla Thompson. $500.00.

Right — Plate 1699: Thompson. "Callie." 10". Original cloth soft sculptured doll by artist Carla Thompson. Edition of 100. Callie is the little sister of Liberty Jane. Photograph courtesy of Carla Thompson. $500.00.

Plate 1700: Thompson, Carla. "Tahira." 17" tall. Limited edition of 50 by artist Carla Thompson. Soft sculpture. Photograph courtesy of Carla Thompson. $700.00.

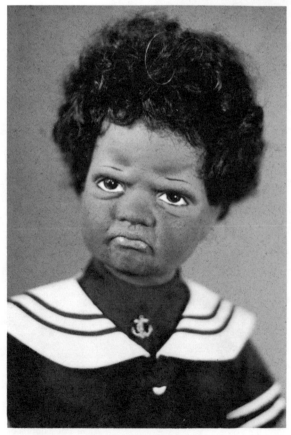

Plate 1701: Thompson, Carla. "Cyrus." 24" tall. Soft sculpture by artist Carla Thompson. Limited edition of 5. Photograph courtesy of Carla Thompson. No price available.

Plate 1702: Thompson, Carla. "Daddy's Home," mother and baby. Soft sculpture by Carla Thompson. This set won a DOTY in 1991 for cloth artist doll of the year. Photograph courtesy of Carla Thompson. $1,000.00.

Plate 1703: Treasures in Lace. "My Nanny." 1993. 16½" tall. Porcelain shoulder head, arms, and legs with molded on high-heeled red shoes, white cloth body, stationary brown eyes with upper lashes, closed mouth, black wig. All original in red print with white ruffled bottom. Unmarked. Collection of Patricia Hall. $30.00.

Plate 1704: Treasures in Lace. Collectible doll, 16" tall. Doll did not have a name, box only read "Treasures in Lace." Porcelain head, arms, and legs, stationary brown eyes, black wig, closed mouth, white cloth body. Doll is all original in calico print dress trimmed in lace. Doll is unmarked. $25.00.

Plate 1705: Treasures in Lace. "Pert N Pretty." 16" tall. Porcelain head, hands, and legs, brown curly wig, stationary brown eyes with lashes, closed mouth, white cloth body. All original in brown corduroy dress with cotton ecru trim. Marks: 1303, under the wig. Head is identical to that on "Cora" by Tussini except that Cora has painted eyelashes. $50.00.

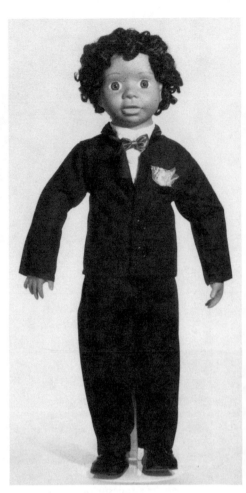

Left — Plate 1706: Tung. "Anita," designed by William Tung from the "Wedding Day" series. Porcelain head, arms, and legs, stationary brown eyes, black wig, closed mouth, white gown. Purchased from Home Shopping Club. 20" tall. Marks: W TUNG 1992©, incised on head; 84 (slash)200/W TUNG/1992©, stamped on head. This doll #84 out of an edition of 2000. $185.00.

Right — Plate 1707: William Tung. "Jeremy," mold #91206. Porcelain head, arms, and legs, cloth body. Bridegroom doll. All original in black suit. This is doll 793 out of 1500 dolls. Purchased from HSC in 1992. $185.00.

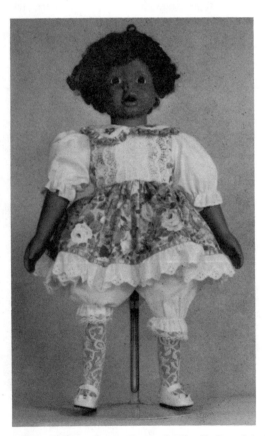

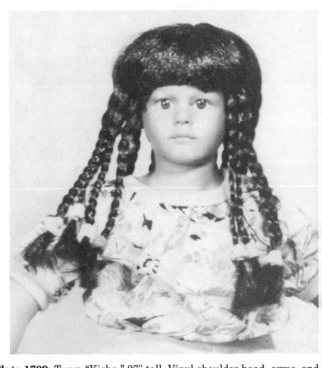

Plate 1708: William Tung. "Prissy." 20" tall. Porcelain head, arms, and legs, cloth body, open-closed mouth, black short curly wig, brown stationary eyes, pierced ears. Dressed in dress with white bodice and printed skirt, pantaloons. and lace stocking. Limited edition of 1500 dolls. Offered in 1992 on TV Home Shopping Club. $125.00.

Plate 1709: Tung. "Kisha." 27" tall. Vinyl shoulder head, arms, and legs, cloth body, rooted black hair, brown stationary eyes with real upper lashes, closed mouth, pierced ears with goldtone drop earring. All original in print top and green knee length pants, wearing goldtone coin bracelet, barefoot. Designed by William Tung in limited edition of 1000. This is doll #993. Marks: WILLIAM TUNG COLLECTION, on shoulder-plate back. Available in 1993. $230.00.

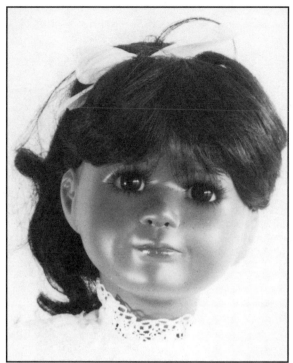

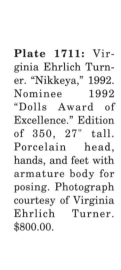

Plate 1711: Virginia Ehrlich Turner. "Nikkeya," 1992. Nominee 1992 "Dolls Award of Excellence." Edition of 350, 27" tall. Porcelain head, hands, and feet with armature body for posing. Photograph courtesy of Virginia Ehrlich Turner. $800.00.

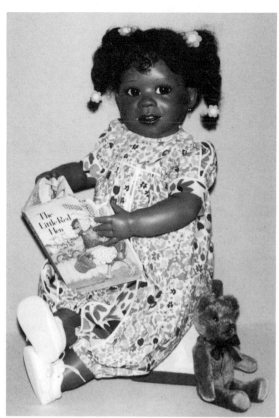

Plate 1710: Turner. "Cymbra." Original doll by doll artist Virginia Turner. Limited edition. Porcelain head, arms, and legs, wire armature cloth body, stationary brown eyes with upper and lower lashes, closed mouth, pierced nostrils, dark brown wig. All original in white dress trimmed with lace. Marks: NO. 69 (slash) 75/VIRGINIA EHRLICH TURNER/9-11-90, handwritten on head; ©VE TURNER 1990, incised on head. Collection of Xzena Moore of the Cubbyhole. $800.00.

Plate 1712: Virginia Ehrlich Turner. "Terrance," 1992. Porcelain head, hands, and feet, cloth body with wire armature for posing. 25" tall. Edition of 350. Photograph courtesy of Virginia Ehrlich Turner. $750.00.

Plate 1713: Turner. "Whitney," sculpted by Virginia Ehrlich Turner for the "Hamilton Collection." 18". Porcelain head, arms, and legs, white cloth body, black wig, stationary brown eyes with upper and lower lashes, pierced nostrils, open-closed mouth with two upper teeth, pierced ears with "gem" stone stud earrings. All original in blue print dress with white underskirt and matching blue print pantaloons. Marks: VIRGINIA 1991/EHRLICH TURNER, incised on head; WHITNEY/NO. 3125A/©VE TURNER 1992 ALL RIGHTS RESERVED, stamped on head except for the No. 3125A which is handwritten. $100.00.

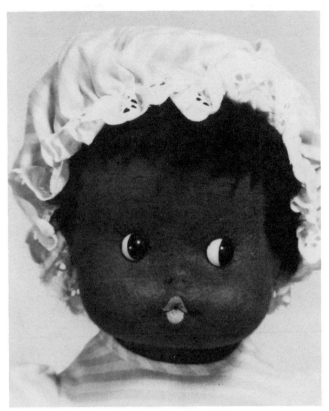

Plate 1714: Mary Vazquez. 22" tall. Baby doll with movable maskface felt head, black plastic googlie eyes, painted mouth, black wig that feels somewhat like mohair, stuffed felt body. All original in pink and white striped romper with matching cap, white knit booties. Doll wears a goldtone bracelet with charm imprinted: MARY/VAZQUEZ. 1980's. Courtesy of Xzena Moore of the Cubbyhole. $200.00.

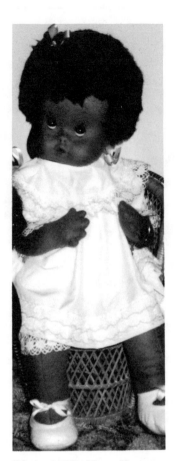

Plate 1715: Mary Vazquez (Vaz), Spain. 22" tall. Hard felt swivel head, closed mouth, glued on glass eyes, synthetic hair, soft felt body. All original in white dress with gold bracelet with heart, white shoes. Photograph courtesy of Phyllis Schlatter. $200.00.

Plate 1716: Wang's International. "Just for Keeps." 16" doll. Dressing doll made for doll collectors and sold at craft shops. Head, arms, and legs are made of hard vinyl that closely resembles porcelain, glued on black synthetic wig, stationary brown glassine eyes, closed mouth, white cloth body. Doll was sold dressed only in white lace tights with white buckle slipper shoes. Marks: NY — OH15014/OHIO — OH15014/MASS. — MA-T-835/PENNS — 2236/MADE IN CHINA/PRINTED IN HONG KONG/WANG'S INTERNATIONAL, INC./MEMPHIS, TENNESSEE. Reverse side: ...KEEP OUT OF THE/REACH OF CHILDREN,/©WANG'S INT. 1991. $15.00.

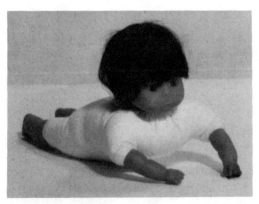

Plate 1717: Wang's International. "Just for Keeps," 10" crawling baby doll. Hard plastic head, arms and legs look like porcelain, cloth body, black synthetic glued on wig, stationary brown glassine eyes, closed mouth. Doll is marked the same as the previous "Just for Keeps" doll and came undressed. $15.00.

Left — Plate 1718: Tussini. "Cora." 16" tall. Porcelain head, arms, and legs, white cloth body, black curly wig, stationary brown eyes, dimpled cheeks, closed mouth. All original in red print dress under white lace trimmed overskirt. Head mold is identical to that used for "Pert N Pretty" by Treasures in Lace. Marks, if any, are covered by glued on wig. $40.00.

Right — Plate 1719: Welch. Cloth doll by artist Marcella Welch. Approximately 16" tall. Collection of Zenobia Holiday. $200.00.

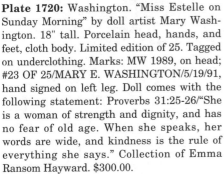

Plate 1720: Washington. "Miss Estelle on Sunday Morning" by doll artist Mary Washington. 18" tall. Porcelain head, hands, and feet, cloth body. Limited edition of 25. Tagged on underclothing. Marks: MW 1989, on head; #23 OF 25/MARY E. WASHINGTON/5/19/91, hand signed on left leg. Doll comes with the following statement: Proverbs 31:25-26/"She is a woman of strength and dignity, and has no fear of old age. When she speaks, her words are wide, and kindness is the rule of everything she says." Collection of Emma Ransom Hayward. $300.00.

Plate 1721: Wick. "Baby Plays Baseball." 14" tall. Original design by doll artist Faith Wick. 1977. Doll represents a baseball player. Porcelain shoulder head and hands, fingers on right hand are curled as if holding a baseball bat. Black wig, stationary brown glass eyes, closed mouth, brown cloth body, legs, and arms. Original shirt and socks. Pants, cap, and glove are missing. Marks: F-101-24/USA 1977/FWF (last "F" is written backwards)/WICKET DOLLS/PRODUCED/BY DOLL-LAW, on back of shoulder-plate. $250.00.

Plate 1722: Wimbleton. "Katrina," #A-017. 16". Porcelain head, hands, and feet, brown stationary eyes, black synthetic wig, closed mouth, dimpled cheeks, white cloth body. Face is hand painted, costume is hand sewn. All original stockings and shoes. Unmarked. Metal hang tag: THE WIMBLETON COLLECTION/BY LEXINGTON HALL LTD./HAND PAINTED, HAND SEWN/PORCELAIN COLLECTOR DOLLS. Reverse side: KATRINA #A-017. $85.00.

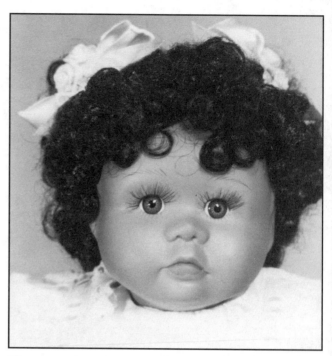

Plate 1723: World Gallery. "Tyrone Berry" from the "Family Tree" series of portrait dolls. Tyrone is the son of TV Home Shopping Club host Tina Berry. Doll was designed by Vincent J. De Filippo, a sculptor who worked at the Ideal Toy Company for 27 years and designed "Rub-A-Dub Dolly" and the Dorothy Hamill doll. Numbered limited edition of 2500 pieces. This doll #485. Porcelain head, shoulder-plate, arms, and legs, black curly wig, stationary brown eyes with real lashes, closed smiling mouth, white cloth body. All original in navy blue sailor outfit styled after one worn by Tyrone Berry. 18" tall. Doll came with a toy sailboat. Marks: VINCENT J. DE FILIPPO/TYRONE/©1991, incised on head: VINCENT J. DE FILIPPO/©1992/2500, stamped on head; #485, handwritten on head. $145.00.

Plate 1724: World Gallery. "Destina" from the "Tiny Treasures Collection," designed by Holly Hunt. 14" tall. Doll number 73 from a limited edition of 2500. Porcelain head, arms, and legs, stationary brown eyes with lashes, black curly wig, closed mouth, white romper with eyelet trim and tiny touches of peach ribbon. Marks: 73/2500, handwritten on head. $120.00.

Plate 1725: World Gallery. "June" from "The Little Jewel Collection." 10 tall. Edition of 2500 by artist Holly Hunt. Porcelain head and jointed body, black wig, stationary brown eyes, closed mouth. Marks: HOLLY HUNT/1992, incised on head; 1341/2500, handwritten on head; CAL-HASCO INC/CALIFORNIA; Holly Hunt, stamped on head. Collection of Valerie Burbank-Pugh. $65.00.

Plate 1726: Yvonne Heather. "Deborah Elaine," a hand numbered annual edition porcelain doll designed exclusively for Service Merchandise. 1989. Porcelain head, arms, and legs, long black wig, stationary brown eyes, closed mouth, white cloth body. 16" tall. All original in mauve print cotton dress with white cotton pinafore trimmed in lace. Marks: YVONNE/HEATHER/3245, on head. Doll came carrying a white cloth doll, 4½" tall. $125.00.

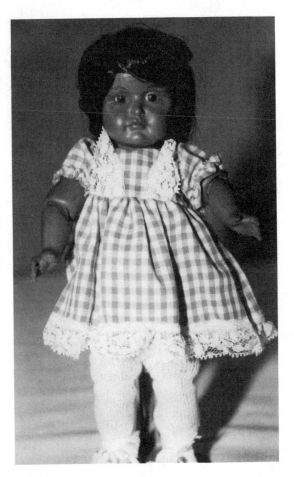

Plate 1727: Reproduction "Pouty." 9½" tall. All porcelain, glued on wig. All original in red check dress. Marks: K * R 114, on neck. From collection of and photo courtesy of Etta Houston. $160.00.

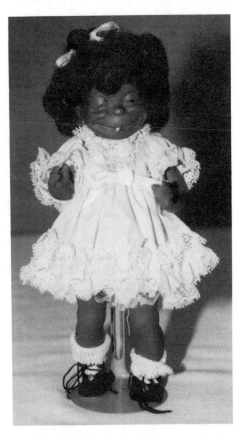

Plate 1728: Reproduction of Gene Carr Kid "Blink," wigged and dressed as a girl. All porcelain. 10½" tall. Unmarked. Collection of and photo courtesy of Etta Houston. $135.00.

Plate 1729: Reproduction "Kewpie" doll. 10½" tall. Porcelain head, molded painted hair, stationary brown eyes, porcelain jointed body. Reproduced by Clara Clark from an unmarked mold. All original. Courtesy of Clara Clark. $75.00.

Plate 1730: "Lily," on left and "Ruby" on right. One-of-a-kind hand painted cloth dolls by artist Robert Zacher. Photograph courtesy of Robert Zacher. $185.00 each.

Plate 1731: Zook. "Chloe." 22". Limited to 1000 dolls. Vinyl head, arms, and legs, cloth body, stationary brown eyes, closed mouth, black wig done in many braids with bangs. All original in lavender print jumper with white shirt, lavender shoes, white socks. Photograph by Rich Hines Photography. $178.00.

Plate 1732: Johannes Zook Originals. "Tonya." 22" tall. Limited to 1989. Vinyl head, arms, and legs, stationary brown eyes with lashes, black wig, closed mouth, white cloth body. All original in pink dress, white shoes, and socks. Marks: PAT SECRIST/©1988, on head. Photograph by Rich Hines Photography. $200.00.

Plate 1733: Johannes Zook Originals. "Shalequa." 22" tall. Limited to 1000 dolls. All vinyl. Photograph by Rich Hines Photography. $162.00.

Plate 1734: Johannes Zook Originals. "Whitney." 20" tall. Whitney was produced in 1990 and was limited to 1000 dolls. Issue price was $160.00. Vinyl head, arms, and legs, cloth body. Photograph by Rich Hines Photography. $160.00.

Plate 1735: Porcelain doll from the "Collectible Porcelain Dolls" collection distributed by J.C. Penney Company. Lot #5577. 16" tall. Porcelain head, arms, and legs, white cloth body, black curly wig, stationary brown eyes, closed mouth. All original in red and white gingham dress with matching pantaloons and red straw hat. Made in Taiwan. Unmarked. 1992. $20.00.

Plate 1736: "African Initiation Doll." 15½" tall. Bead doll made by the tribeswoman of the Nbedele tribe of South Africa. Doll is given to a girl after the initiation ceremony which celebrates her reaching teenage years. It means she is now old enough to be a mother. It is also wished that she should marry a man as handsome as the doll. The glass beaded apron symbolizes the marriage and the blanket is for warmth in the future. Purchased new in 1993. $100.00.

Plate 1737: Black Mammy, maker unknown. 15" tall. Porcelain head, arms, and legs, cloth body, painted features. All original in print long dress with matching headscarf, orange apron, painted on black boots. Unmarked. 1980's. From collection of and photo courtesy of Maureen Braeden. $125.00.

Plate 1738: "Willie's Wedding." Both dolls are 14" tall. Porcelain heads, arms, and legs, stuffed cloth torsos, painted eyes, closed mouths, black hair. Willie has on a brown, green, and lime plaid jacket, white shirt, black tie, beige pants, brown belt, and black painted shoes. Bride is dressed in white satin and lace bridal dress with painted black shoes. Dolls were made in Colorado Springs, Colorado. Collection of and Photograph courtesy of Mary June Hill. $125.00 set.

INDEX

14R......................................181
A&H Doll Co. 142
A.J. Moon............................279
ABC Triplets........................316
Abe.....................................376
Aberrah................................402
Abraham..................................8
Absolutely Abigale 164
Abu Salat El Nasir.................410
Abyssinian Baby 14
Ace Novelty Co. 106
Aces....................................142
Acme Toy Co. 121
Adama.................................353
Addy...................................295
Adora...................................421
Africa..........................140, 180
African Contempo 332
African Girl and Baby..............22
African Initiation Doll 437
Agent Telepathy 279
Aggie and Argus Whipple..........101
Aimee..................................189
Alabama Baby.........................12
Alexander Doll Co. ...11, 23, 52, 118,
                     121, 143–147
Allesandra 390
Almira 406
Alona....................................19
Alton...................................355
Amanda — Springtime 408
Amanda Jane.................147, 148
Amandla................................277
Amber..........................148, 406
Amelia..................................164
Amer. Stuffed Novelty Co. 110
America's Kids...............299, 300
American Doll Co. 108
American Trading Inc. 148
Ami.....................................391
Amosandra 134
Amy....................................230
Anabas.................................148
Angel Doll.............................178
Angelique...................305, 314
Anguish, Vickie......................352
Anisha and Forest....................354
Anita...................................430
Anna....................................147
Anne Shirley.........................122
Annie At Play.........................382
Anthony................................346
Archees................................353
Ari......................................393
Armand Marsielle 14, 40

Army Barbie............................257
Army Ken 257
Arnold Print Works..................51
Arrow Hawk............................280
Art Novelty Co. 112
Asha.....................246, 252, 258
Ashley..................................305
Ashton Drake Galleries 362
Atlanta.................................162
Atlanta Novelty......................186
Attic Babies...........................101
Audrey.................................381
Aunt Cloe..............................66
Aunt Dinah............................108
Aunt Jemima.............8, 48, 49, 50,
                     51, 110,128
Aunt Peachy 67
Aunt Sally..............................44
Aurora.................................417
Austin, Virginia......................116
Authentic Models 137
Averill Manufacturing Co. 15, 107,
                          116
Avon 95, 98, 148–149, 353
BBI Toys..............................149
Babe Bouchard.......................374
Baby....................................284
Baby All Gone 218
Baby, Baby.............................207
Baby Be Good.........................300
Baby Beans............................264
Baby Betty.............................128
Baby Check-Up........................221
Baby Coon.........................34–35
Baby Cries For You 233
Baby Crissy...........................288
Baby Cuddle Soft.....................334
Baby Doll.................294, 297, 298
Baby Dreams..........................206
Baby Elisa.............................309
Baby Face....................167, 184
Baby Feels So Real 325
Baby Floyd..............................33
Baby Gift Set.........................336
Baby Giggles 'n Go...................327
Baby Glenda..........................424
Baby Go Bye-Bye.....................232
Baby Grows Up.......................233
Baby Grumpy.................107–8, 123
Baby Grumpykins....................108
Baby Harry............................415
Baby Huggins.........................122
Baby Jesse.............................373
Baby John..............................347
Baby Laugh and Cry.................205

Baby Loves to Talk...................321
Baby Makeda 296
Baby Needs Me 221
Baby Oh-No!...........................189
Baby Peek-a-Boo......................188
Baby Pele...............................344
Baby Plays Baseball 433
Baby Rollerblade......................240
Baby Ruby.............................415
Baby Say 'N See.......................231
Baby Sez So............................263
Baby Shivers...........................324
Baby Sofskin 204
Baby Sofskin Tears 201
Baby Talk..............................183
Baby This 'n That......................301
Baby Tummy Talks....................329
Baby Two Year Old....................161
Baby Walk 'n Roll.....................241
Baby Wanna Walk....................189
Baby Winkie...........................167
Baby Won't Let Go 217
Babyland 9, 12, 76
Babysitter.............................344
Babysitter's Club......................299
Badebaby India.......................400
Bag Lady 394
Bahai....................................69
Bahamas...............................312
Bailey, Elinor Peace 100
Bajainah...............................410
Baker, Josephine..............45, 403
Balica Dolls...........................337
Ball, Bette.....................388, 389
Ballerina..............................146
Banneker, Benjamin 356
Barbie.......................242–261
Barbie Color Change.................261
Barbie Fashion Brights 251
Barbie For President..................249
Barona P.S.B. Enemy.................280
Barray........................354–355
Barval.................................149
Baseball Kids 343
Bashful Baby Abby 184
Basile...................................337
Bath Blast Barbie.....................257
Bath Magic Barbie...................248
Bathtub Baby Face 184
Baton Twirling Skipper 257
Bayou Jack............................220
Be My Baby 148
Beach Blast Steven...................242
Beach Dazzle Asha...................246
Beach Dazzle Nichelle 246

Beach Dazzle Shani 246
Beach Streak Asha.....................252
Beach Streak Nichelle 252
Beach Streak Shani 252
Beecher.......................................47
Beehler Arts Ltd. 149
Belcam Inc..................................150
Bell Doll....................................142
Bell Mfg. Co. 111
Bell, Floyd 17, 356–359
Bell, I. Roberta 18, 360–361
Bello, Yolanda...........................362
Beloved Belindy..2, 12, 13, 46, 47, 98
Benamy......................................150
Benetton Christie......................249
Benjie 16, 23, 317
Benny...216
Berea College Student Ind 52
Beri Ann....................................218
Berjusa 149, 150, 151
Berkeley Design 151
Bermuda Sailor 11, 87
Bernetta.....................................407
Berry & Ross Mfg. Co. Inc...110, 111
Berry, Tina.................................380
Berry, Tyrone.............................434
Bessie...376
Bethel Mfg. Co. 111
Bethune, Mary McLeod 357, 358, 361
Betsy..155
Betsy Wetsy 211, 212, 288
Betty Jane Carter Dolls..............388
Betty's Gift Set 336
Biarritz..53
Bibber, Grace...............................45
Bilan of Burkina Faso.................20
Billye..374
Birthday Party Barbie................255
Birthday Surprise Barbie ...248, 261
Bitter Sweet...............................174
Black Angel Doll 178
Black Baby..................................20
Black Flat Heel Doll 178
Black Sambo...............................57
Black/White Klown 213
Blackeyed Susan 105
Blake, Sandra M.........................362
Blanca..143
Bless You Baby Tenderlove........232
Blink 435
Blossom......................................393
Blue Box 151
Blue Challenger 262
Bo Jangles 19
Bonecas.......................................61
Bones..118
Bonnie Bride..............................217

Bonnie Lou 16
Bottle Doll 347
Bottle Time Baby 234
Bouncin' Babies.........................183
Bradley Dolls.............................151
Brandi..216
Brandon 149
Brazil...138
Brazilian Festival Dancer 418
Brenda..181
Brewington, Beatrice W.............363
Bridal Party Renee 215
Bride 142, 307, 424
Brinn...363
Brittany 329, 409
Bro, Lois 363
Bronze Bombers 267, 279–280
Brooke..304
Brother.......................................292
Brown-Eye Baby Whistle............302
Brown-Eye Baby Laugh-a-Lot....302
Brown-Eye Jumpsy.....................302
Brown-Eye Polly Puff.................302
Brown-Eye Tina 302
Brown-Eye Tiny Tumbles 302
Bruns, Nancy..............................364
Bubble Bath Bottle Doll 150
Bubble Gum 212
Bubbles 16, 95, 108
Bud..425
Bullet Proof 195
Bunch, Dr. Ralph........................356
Bundle of Joy.............................160
Burger King Corporation...........152
Busy Dressy Bessy......................98
Buttercup...................................168
Butterball 167
Butterick....................................101
Buysse, Barbara.........................365
Buzzy 33
Bye-Lo Baby 421
Byerly, Mary 18
CPK 10th Anniversary 194
CPK All Stars 154
CPK Heart to Heart Baby 193
CPK Kissin' Kids........................191
CPK Little Lullabye 191
CPK My First Cabbage Patch 192
CPK My Own Baby 192
CPK Newborn/Magical Monit 192
CPK Peek 'n Play 193
CPK Pretty Crimp 'n Curl 192
CPK Splash 'n Tan Kids 193
CPK Teeny Tiny Preemies..........193
CST 155
Cabaret Dancer 356
Cabbage Patch Kids..........153, 154, 191–194

Cabbage Patch type 317
Calico Critters............................102
California Roller Baby 327
Callie..................................32, 428
Calumet Baking Co....................115
Calypso Jill................................158
Camelot 366–367
Cameo Doll Products 152
Cammi Goes to College..............154
Can't Break 'Em 132
Canada.......................................158
Candy...264
Candy Girls Spring Fashons 188
Candy Kid...................................16
Captain Planet/Planeteers 318
Care For Me Baby 285
Carmel Cream 426
Carmen 379
Carnival Brazil............................401
Carol Anne Dolls........................388
Carolyn 164
Carribean Islands 72
Carver, Dr. George Washington...18, 359, 360
Cassandra...................................389
Cassini, Oleg 314
Cavel-Greant, Deborah..............365
Cavester.....................................293
Celebration Sandi 319
Chad Valley Chiltern 56
Chad Valley Co. Ltd...11, 56, 87, 152
Chamarra 403
Champ..315
Chantrell 427
Chardonnay................................427
Charlene 143
Charles Chilly Pop Battle...........280
Charleston..................................162
Charlie Ragg................................92
Charlotte Russe..........................284
Chase, Martha.......................12, 44
Cheer Girl..................................346
Cheerleader 145
Chelsea 21
Cherise.......................................314
Cherry.......................................140
Cherry Merry Muffin 235
Chicago Mail Order Co. 107
Children for Children 180
Chiltern.....................................152
Chipper 168–169
Chloe..436
Chocolate Delight......................199
Choo-Choo 375
Christie...............245–247, 249, 255
Christine 319, 335
Christopher 335
Chubby 265

Chubby Tub-a-Tot 328
Cicciobello...........................307
Cicely 417
Cindy 413
Cititoy 153
Clark, Clara........367, 383, 384, 404,
                            407, 413, 435
Classic...............................181
Clemmy................................405
Cleo..................................384
Cleodine..............................306
Clippo Puppets 116
Clothes Brush Doll....................138
Clown.............................212, 297
Club Kids..............................96
Cobabe, Laura.........................367
Coca-Cola.............................149
Coca-Cola Santa.......................306
Cocheco Manufacturing Co.....17, 45
Coconut Doll..........................139
Coconut Kids 157
Coleco............................153, 154
College Bound Dolls...................154
Collette Toy and Novelty 154
Color My Dress Pretty 177
Combat Man............................340
Combex 135
Comfy Karen 346
Commander Clash.......................318
Commando Ops, Chief 322
Commonwealth Toy & Novelty.....93
Communion 305
Compos, Ray..........................354
Consuela 379
Coochy Coodles........................228
Cool Breeze P.S.B. Enemy 279
Cool 'n Sassy Barbie 251
Cora 433
Corolle...............................155
Cory 381
Cosmopolitan..........................156
Cotton 423
Cotton Candy Angel....................427
Country Chums.........................101
Cowboy Curtis.........................230
Cream of Wheat 89
Creata 156
Creative Story Puppets................384
Creche..........................26, 27, 132
Creole.............................6, 407
Crete Mills...........................59
Crimp 'n Go Imani 275
Crumpet...............................217
Crunkleton, Marge.............368–369
Crying Baby...........................181
Cuddle Kidztm 151
Cunningham, Cynethea.............369
Cunningham, Randall 106

Cupcakes 216, 218
Curious Baby Cara....................184
Currier & Ives 165
Cute Looks...........................159
Cutie Cammie 190
Cutie Club Kids......................183
Cutoy Coop Assoc.....................188
Cymbra 431
Cynthia 143
Cyrus 18, 428
DKP 158
DVP 157
Daddy's Home 429
Daddy's Long Legs 370–378
Daisy 332
Dakin, Inc. 332
Dale 140
Dallas 163
Dan Doll.............................157
Danakil 402, 403
Dance Club Devon.....................243
Dance Magic Barbie 243
Danielle 362
Darice 157
Darkey Doll 17, 45
Darling Dena 190
David 362
Davis Milling Co. 2, 8, 49, 50, 51
Davis, Jr., Sammy 425
Dawn 216
Deana 388
Dean's Childsplay Toys, Ltd. 54
Dear One/Sunday Best 408
Debbie 140, 330
Debbie Dear.........................190
Deborah Elaine 434
Dee & Cee 158
De Filippo, Vincent 434
Definitely Dinosaurs................293
Della 100
Delton Product Corp.................97
Denamur, E. 41
Dengel, Diane.......................378
Denise 337, 389
Denney, Elsie.......................158
Deserie 380
Design Debut........................379
Designer Row Dolls..................380
Desk Set............................268
Destina 434
Determined Products...........96, 103
Diana 2, 8, 48, 51
Dill, A.G. 25
Dilsie 8
Dinah 8, 44
Dinner Bell Doll...................136
Dionne Quint.......................127
Disneyworld 340

Dixie...........................44, 140
Dixieland Minstrels...........118–119
Doc Moses..........................373
Doll Collectors....................380
Doll Parts 157
Dollhouse Dolls...............136, 292
Dollhouse Family..................292
Dolls by Christina.................97
Dolls by Pauline 105, 283
Dolls for the Dressmaker...........155
Dolly Dingle..................107, 124
Dolly Mine 103
Dolly Shopper......................164
Double Dutch 384
Douglass, Frederick 357
Dr. Denton 202
Drayton, Grace......23, 107, 124, 130
Dream Babies.......................216
Dream Dollhouse Family...........179
Dream Dolls 380
Dubois, W.E.B. 25
Duck House 380
Dune Buggy Baby 301
Dusty 21
Dy Dee Baby....................169, 170
Dynasty Doll..................381–382
E.M.S. Novelty Co. 36
Earring Magic Barbie 252
Eason, Yla 267
Easter Sunday......................147
Eavenson, K. 365
Ebony 143
Ebony and Ivory 320
Eclair 284
Edgar 387
Edie 420
Edward Mobley Company 264
Eegee 105, 158–161
Effanbee.........15, 16, 108, 116, 122–
                        123, 132, 162–173
Effner, Dianna.....................383
Egyptian 121
Elizabeth 74, 179, 426
Ellisse Gift Set 273
Elmo................2, 22, 414
Embry, Jacqueline..................383
Emily 283
Emma 420
Emotions...........................17
Emson 174
Enesco.............................296
Enos 421
Entertainer, The...................363
Ernest Enterprises.................383
Ernie 426
Especially Yours 203
Esteban, Jennifer..................384
Esther 377

Estrella 124
Ethel 400
Etsie 100
Eubank, E'dee 384
Eugene Doll Co..................174–177
Ewing, Patrick 106
Excited Baby Becca 184
Exie 426
Ezra 373
Faith 378
Falcon 264
Family Circle................................99
Fashion Play Barbie, 1990 244
Fashion Play Barbie, 1991 247
Father-To-Be 215
Federica 385
Felicia 382
Felisha 96
Fern 355
Fibre Craft..................................178
Fiesta International............319, 320
Filipino 30
Fishburne, Sandra 230
Fisher Price 179
Flagg..................................135, 180
Flapper 213
Flashfire 228
Fleetwood Toys 180
Fletcher's Castoria.................16, 46
Fleurette 406
Flip 'n Fancy......................290–291
Flip 'n Fancy Twins.....................291
Flip 'n Fancy Fun Friends 291
Flip 'n Fancy Honeymoon 291
Flora 33
Flory, Anita 385
Flower Festival Sandi.................320
Flower Girl 145
Formaz, Betty.....................386, 387
Formaz, Tony...............................387
Fortune Toys......................149, 180
Fountain Mermaid Barbie..........257
Foxx, Redd 425
Francoise 165
Frierson, Annie Davis.................361
Fun-to-Dress Barbie 256
Fung Seng 181
Furga 181, 182
G.W. Bridge 321
G.I. Joe..............................194–198
G.I. Joe Alpine............................196
G.I. Joe Bullet-Proof 195
G.I. Joe Colonel Courage 197
G.I. Joe Hardball........................197
G.I. Joe Heavy Duty....................195
G.I. Joe Roadblock 196
G.I. Joe Stalker 195, 197
Gabriel Industries......................182

Gadsden Doll Co. 36, 37, 38
Gallagher, Donna 100
Galoob 183–185
Galperin, Jan 387
Gama 186
Gambina 186
Gardening Rosie 394
Gaultier, F. 40
Gay Nineties Picnic.....................361
Gem Doll Corp. 108
Gemette 160
General Hawk 148
Generations 18
Genie 416
Gentle Dreams 311
Georgene Novelties 2, 13, 46
Gerald 404
Gerber Baby 130, 186
Germany, Karen 370
Giggles 209
Gigo Toy 336
Gimbel Bros. 9
Ginger 156, 187
Ginnette.......................................333
Ginny 140, 332–333
Gladiator Gemini 262
Gladys 140
Glamour Girl 322
Glitter Beach Christie 255
Glitter Beach Steven...................255
Global Enterprises 92
Gloria 388
Gobo, South African Boy.........14, 58
Goebel Inc.........................388–389
Golberger 158–161
Gold Dust Twins............................44
Golberger 123
Goldberger Doll Mfg. Co. 175
Golden Ribbon Playthings..........187
Golliwog (Golliwogg)........23, 44, 54,
                                            55–57
Goodfellow Doll 128
Good Housekeeping 63
Goss, Dee 389
Gotz.......................................140, 187, 390
Gowron the Klingon....................287
Grace..387
Grace Drayton.......23, 107, 124, 130
Grandmother and Child 17
Granny 421
Griffey, Ken Jr. 106
Griffith, J. Art Co. 37
Groom 424
Grow Time 188
Gruelle, Johnny............................47
Grumpy...107
Guinan 286
Gunzel, Hildegard.......................143

Gutsell, Ida A. 45
Gwendolyn...................................105
HCN Enterprises, Inc. 188
Haas, Ella....................................390
Hair Doodler Cinnamon..............211
Haiti......................................130, 312, 362
Hakim 411
Hallmark..98
Hamilton Toys 188
Hammer, M.C. 260
Hammertime 260
Handy, W.C. 360
Happy Birthday Hannah.............184
Happy Birthday 145
Happy Birthday Barbie 243, 261
Happy Birthday Billy..................145
Happy Holidays Barbie.......244, 251
Happy Returns 207
Harmonica Joe 109
Harpster 421
Hasbro 140, 188–200, 267
Hassan 125
Hattie 427
Hazelle 117
Heart Family Kiss & Cuddle......262
Heart Family New Arrival 262
Heart and Soul Children 424
Heath, Philip S.............18, 390–392
Heavy Duty 195
Heinrich Handwerch.....................41
Hendren...............................107, 124
Henson, Matthew..............357, 361
Here Comes Niya 188
Heubach Koppelsdorf..12, 14, 34–35
Hi Babies 296
Hi Heidi 301
Hi Tech..280
Hickory 419
Hilary...383
Himstedt, Annette 392
Hippensteel, Kathy 393
Hitt, Oscar.....................................35
Hockey Players............................389
Hockh, Renate 393
Holcombe, Martha.......................393
Honey Child.................................108
Honey Combs 282
Honey Suckle................................53
Hopes, Nancy 108
Horsman.....................76, 200–205
Hug 'n Love Baby........................176
Hug-N-Talk...................................233
Hugga Buds 151
Hugga Bunch................................95
Huggy Bean Kulture Kids 187
Huggy Stylette 187
Hunt, Holly...................................380
Hush Little Baby.........................318

Hyacinthia 200
I Say Da Da 330
I Say Ma Ma 331
I'm Amanda 102
Ice Capades Barbie 242
Ida Bean 295
Ideal 15, 16, 17, 124,
206–212, 288, 325
Imagination Factory 96
Imani 268, 271–275
Imani African Fantasy................272
Imani Goes Shopping..................274
Imani Holiday Fun......................272
Imani Kente Fun.........................273
Imani Loves to Swim 272
Imani Prom Time 271
Imani Royal Princess 268
Imani Wedding Magic 271
Imani and Menelik Wedding 272
Import Billing............................212
In Time Products........................212
Irwin 318
Irwin Toy Limited 213
Issac, The Love Boat 263
It's a Small World........241, 242, 340
Izahia 368
Jaci 343
Jackson, Dianna.........................394
Jackson, Michael................226–227
Jacqueline.................................165
Jade..395
Jamaica 90, 278
Jamaican Barbie 247
Jamal 248, 253, 276, 258
Jambo the Jiver...........................116
James 376
James River Corporation............265
Jami 410
Jana 219
Janada 395
Janet 400
Janie and Jamie 402
January, Kor................19, 395–397
Jasmine 21, 300, 370, 368, 422
Jaws 152
Jazz Player 398
Jazzabelle 97
Jean Gift Set 277
Jed Gibson 230
Jelly Belly................................212
Jelly Jeans................................328
Jem and the Holograms...............189
Jenne 392
Jennifer 277
Jennifer Lauren 194
Jeremiah 370
Jeremy 430
Jesco.................................213–214

Jessi & Becca............................299
Jessica 381
Jiggly Jigglies............................301
Jill 285
Johanna Art Dolls......................365
John Henry 358
Johnny Cool..............................313
Johnny West Adventure 230
Johnson, Magic..........................106
Johnson, Sue 397
Johnston, Jack L. 19, 398
Jolie..362
Jones, Joyce Stokes.....................97
Jonina 337
Joplin, Scott..............................358
Joseph 20
Josi 412
Josie 375
Joy 390
Joyce Marie 95
Joyner, Florence Griffith 225–226
Judge 374
Judith Corporation 215, 264
Julianna....................................402
Julie 363, 380
Jumeau 6, 35
Jumoke 409
Jumpsy 302
June 434
Junel Novelty Company 79
Junior 372
Junk Yard Dog...........................225
Just Born 161
Just Born Baby 175
Just for Baby Set........................292
Just for Keeps 432
Justin Products 215
K*R 35, 42, 43, 435
K-Lynn.....................................416
KVK, Inc. 370–378
Kamiko 385
Kane, Maggie Head.....................391
Kanika 22
Kareema 278
Karen 297
Karen & Her Magic Carriage 210
Karoler (Kewpie)................213, 214
Karsuji 216
Kate Smith's Mammy Doll..........115
Kathe Kruse Puppen 400
Katie 223
Katrina 433
Katy 375
Keats, Ezra Jack 96
Keera 405
Kemba and Bintu.......................390
Kennedy, Karen.........................389
Kenner 95, 216–221

Kenya......................................326
Kesia.......................................381
Kewpie 152, 213, 214, 340, 435
Kewpie Flower Girl....................214
Kewpie Sleeper..........................152
Kid Kore 222–223
Kid Sister..................................294
Kid's Goods 224
Kidco 224
Kim 308
Kimmie 298
King of Cartoons 230
King, Dr. Martin L. 268
King, Frank 110
Kinstate 398
Kinky 107
Kirschner, David 158
Kisha 430
Kiss Me Baby 175
Kito 385
Knickerbocker 95
Koko B. Ware............................198
Kolesar, Pat 399
Konigseer Puppen 224
Kotton Kandy Kid 310
Kow Toy's 224
Krissie 189
Kuddlee Kids.............................316
Kumbah 18
Kwame.....................................318
L.J.N. 225–227
L.L. Fresh 275
LA Blading Club 222
LIN Toys, Inc............................228
La Baby 149
Ladies Boudoir Doll 281
Lady Ascot 166
Lady Luminous 314
Laiko 228
Lamin 18
Lanard Toys..............................228
Lando Calrissian 221
Lange, Ted 263
Lara 297
Lark 318
Larry, Sandra Fishburn..............112
Larvelle Jones 220
Latisha.....................................423
Laurie 103
Lawton Doll Company 19, 401
Leeana 156
Lema 392
Lenci 45, 76, 87
Leo 32
Leroy on a Carousel Horse 359
Les Creations Gama 186
Leslie 23, 144
Lester......................................160

Letisha...413
Li'l Dee Dee Diapers 229
Li'l Just Born...............................176
Li'l Miss Magic Jewels................235
Li'l Miss Singing Mermaid 236
Liberty Bell Christmas Inc.........400
Liberty Jane-Sunday Best...........428
Liddle Kiddles 231
Lieutenant Worf..........................287
Life Size Walking Pretty.............158
Lights & Lace Barbie..................244
Lilla...421
Lillian..32
Lily..435
Linda...276
Lindsey, Drucilla.........................257
Lip Gloss Secret Beauties..........199
Lipstick Secret Beauties.............199
Lionel..369
Lisa...318
Lisbet..100
Lissi Dolls and Toys 228
Littauer & Bauer 9
Little Baby Water Babies 285
Little Black Sambo 108
Little Brown Koko..........91, 92, 110
Little Chief of Kango.....................20
Little Lou.....................................113
Little Love 283
Little Lovums...............................170
Little Luv.....................................170
Little Miss Dolly Surprise 289
Little Oopsie Daisy 323
Little People 419
Little Sarita.................................401
Little Treasure 328
Little Wishes Baby......................240
Little Wishes Wet 'n Cry.............240
Littlest Angel 332
Lively Sofskin.............................204
Livonia..427
Liza...283
Liza Lee 116
Lo-Lo...276
Lois...278
Lois Locket 231
Lolly Surprise.............................289
London Toy & Model Museum......87
Long Legs Entertainer................234
Long, Marlene Sagar 402–403
Lonnie...140
Look Around Velvet.....................211
Lorrie...................................174, 177
Lotta..140
Lovable Babies 239–240
Love Boat, The 263
Love 'n Touch Real Sister 233
Lovee..229

Lovely Baby.................................224
Lt. Cmdr. Geordi La Forge 286
Lt. Geordi La Forge 286
Lucille...187
Lucinda.................................22, 414
Lucky the Gambler 377
Lulu Belle 113
Lusciously Lilac 198
Luth...403
Luv-a-Bubble Tenderlove............233
Luvy...369
Lyles, Carrie 403
Lynne, Frances 404
M.C. Cool 275
M.C. Hammer 260
M.N. Thomas 317
Maddie 355
Madelyn.......................................416
Madison, Dale 404
Magic Bottle Baby......................325
Magic Nursery....................236–238
Magic Talker................................331
Magical Mermaid, The.................156
Mahji...362
Major Gil Jones 140
Make Me Pretty Barbie 261
Makin' Music Birthday
    Celebration 223
Malou...400
Mamie..182
Mammy.................44, 53, 100, 142,
                              266, 334, 425
Mammy Castoria 16, 46
Mammy Chloe 44
Mammy and Friends....................100
Mandy..63
Mandy Lou 140
Mann, Seymour...................406–407
Maphis, Jackie 19, 405
Mapman Jackson 279
Marama................................15, 124
Marc Kaboom Walters 280
Marcellino...................................229
Mardi Gras King 131
Maria...319
Marian Yu Designs 404
Marie-Luic 229
Marine Corps Barbie 249
Marine Corps Ken.......................249
Marionette 116–121
Mark International.......................230
Marschino, Marty.........................101
Marschner, Cindy........................407
Marty...417
Marvel...321
Marx...230
Mason, Linda...............................407
Matchbox 230

Matia...417
Mattel, Inc. 17, 140, 231–262
Maurice Andre Dubos 364
Maxine...363
May, Cheryl Pabst.......................417
Mazie, American 296
McCalls Pattern Company 52, 90,
                            99, 100, 101
McDonald's Happy Meal.....194, 261
McLeod, Barry.............................354
Mego 263–264
Melanie..329
Melody..................................352, 366
Menelik..272
Menelik Kente Fun 273
Meritus..264
Mermaids.....................................265
Merry Mint Violet 241
Merrythought Limited...........44, 56
Micah...375
Middleton, Lee 408
Middleton, Pauline........................20
Miguel...320
Mike...355
Milano, Geri 409
Millie...421
Minene...150
Minifon..229
Mini Thirstee Baby.....................201
Minstrial Man 118
Miranda...90
Miss Baby Heirloom Dolls 397
Miss Dinah....................................44
Miss Estelle................................433
Miss Hattie..................................372
Miss India....................................166
Miss Veatrice.......................19, 424
Mobile..163
Modern Bride 265, 382
Mollye..125
Moments Treasured 409
Mommy's Little Girl.....................224
Mommy's Having a Baby 327
Mommy-To-Be 215, 264
Monet...300
Monica...389
Moon, Warren..............................106
Moonlight Magic Barbie 259
Morocco.......................................241
Moss, Leo.........................32–33, 417
Mouseketeer 203
Movin' Groovin' Crissy................211
Moza..103
Mr. 'E' Wrestler 315
Mr. Baseball 315
Mr. Basketball.............................315
Mr. Football.................................315
Mr. T...303

Mr. Track & Field......................315
Muffin.....................................421
Muhammed..............................413
Multi Toys................................265
Mumin, Hannah.................410–411
Music Box Doll..........................178
Musical Movements....................104
My Big Sister.....................222, 223
My Bottle Baby.........................210
My Buddy.................................294
My Bundle Baby.........................238
My Crawling Baby......................323
My Fair Baby............................170
My First Baby...........................276
My First Barbie...242, 243, 245, 256
My First Cabbage Patch.............192
My First Ken.....................247, 256
My Gal.....................................200
My Lee.....................................408
My Little Mahji.........................362
My Little Sweeheart..................146
My Love...................................310
My Nanny.................................429
My Old Kentucky Home...............75
My Own Baby.............................192
My Pretty Mermaids..................289
My Slumber Party......................215
Myla..386
N.V. Sales Company..................115
Naber Gestalt Corp...................412
Nafti.......................................313
Naila.......................................393
Nancy Ann Storybook..........15, 266
Naomi......................................367
Naomi Fashions................269–271
Naomi Hair Dryer......................269
Napier, Sharon.........................413
Nassau....................84, 86, 312
National Company.....................113
National Negro Doll Co........35, 36
Natural Doll Co. Inc..................265
Ndeko/Zaire...............................19
Negro Dude...............................138
Nera.......................................151
Nesting Mummies......................137
Nesting Dolls............................137
Nesting Santas.........................137
Nettie.....................................371
New Orleans.......................70, 94
Newborn Baby Alive..................219
Newborn Baby Doll....................174
Newborn Baby Shivers..............324
Newborn Baby Tenderlove.........232
Newborn Thumbelina.................206
Nicole, Maryse.........................413
Nichelle.................246, 252, 258
Nigeria..................15, 242, 267
Nikkeya...................................431

Nina.......................................411
Nissen, John............................413
Niya.......................................188
Noelle.....................................389
Noma Toy Co............................108
Nun..107
Nurse.....................................296
Nurse Garnet...........................374
Nut Head Doll...........................139
O-K Colored Doll Company........111
Odelia.....................................186
Odessa....................................105
Odette.....................................366
Old Friends Collection...............363
Olivia...................163, 377, 416
Olmec Toys, Inc.................267–280
Oma Green...............................372
One & Only, The.......................334
Onyx.......................................185
Ooma......................................402
Oprah................................404, 406
Opt 4 Kids...............................103
Orange Blossom.................218, 322
Orchid.....................................158
Osdell, Mary Van.............2, 22, 414
Osmond, Marie.........................413
Ott, Heidi.................22, 414–415
P.S.M.I...................................281
PM Sales, Inc...........................281
Paint 'n Dazzle Barbie...............259
Pam................21, 149, 180, 418
Panosh Place............................282
Paradise Galleries.....................418
Paramount Pictures...................282
Parker People Dolls...................416
Parkins, Phyllis..................21, 417
Parks, Rosa.............................353
Parsley Bunch............................17
Party 'n Play Stacie...................256
Pat...140
Patches and Petunia.....................7
Patra......................................423
Patricia...................................335
Patsy Joan...............................108
Patsy................108, 127, 132
Patsy, Jr...........................15, 123
Patsyette..........................15, 123
Patsykins................................123
Patti Cake...............................159
Patti Jo....................................23
Patti Playful............................207
Patty Play Pal..........................209
Paulette..................................379
Payton, Walter.........................281
Peace on Earth.........................420
Peaches & Cream......................162
Pearl..32
Peck, Myra Linn..........................65

Pedigree.................55, 140, 283
Peek-A-Boo Baby......................183
Peggy.................................32, 151
Pelham....................................118
Pemba.....................................392
Peppers, Billie..........................363
Perfume Secret Beauties...........198
Pert 'N Pretty...........................429
Pet Pals Skipper.......................245
Pete.......................................204
Peter..96
Phoebe....................................377
Phoenix...................................284
Phyllis Fairchild.........................96
Piccaninny Dolls..................98, 108
Pillow Doll...............................178
Pittman, Jane...........................358
Planet of the Apes....................263
Plastic Molded Arts...................281
Plated Moulds..........................284
Play Vogue Ind. Co. Ltd............284
Play-Doh Hairdo Dolly...............218
Playgroup................................285
Playmates.........................285–287
Playskool...............98, 289–294
Playtime..................................288
Pleasant Company....................295
Pocahontas..............................167
Police Officer Barbie.................259
Polly.................................339, 364
Poly.......................................151
Poppy.....................................382
Porgy.....................................151
Posable CPK............................191
Positive Image Enterprise.........296
Postcard..........................87, 312
Posy Pixie...............................140
Potty Time Drink &
    Wet Quints.........................324
Powell, General Colin.........212, 353
Praise Unlimited Inc.................296
Precious Moments.....................296
Pretty Bonnet Beans.................234
Pretty Crimp 'n Curl.................192
Pretty Cut & Grow....................182
Pretty & Me.............................321
Pretty in Pearls Sandi...............320
Pretty in Purple.......................251
Princess Krystal.......................293
Pringle, Helen............................96
Prissy...................32, 147, 430
Proud Couple............................384
Proud Lucy...............................399
Puffalump Kids.........................179
Puffin.....................................421
Pullan.....................................339
Pun'kin...................................171
Pupee Nobel............................107

Purple Blossom 199
Pussy Cat.................................144
Quaker Oats Co.............................8
Quilted Northern Doll................265
Quilting Ladies 421
Quintano, Rubin........................417
Quints 324
Quints Cousins.........................324
R. Girls 297
Rachel 110, 417
Rachel Williams 407
Radiant in Red Barbie 250
Raffoler 297
Raggedy Ann & Andy 13, 365
Rainbow Classics 94, 102, 297
Ramp Walker.............................136
Rapid Deployment Force 212
Rappin' Rockin' Christie............245
Rasheen 411
Rastus.....................................8, 89
Razzle Dazzle Dolly 161
Rebecca 379
Reed, Butch 185
Regal 298
Reliable Toy Co. Ltd...................298
Remco 299–302
Renee 215, 422
Rev. Crow and Mrs. Crow 139
Rev. Johnson.............................372
Rhea 228
Ricardo...............................400, 422
Richmond.................................163
Rippy, Rodney Allen...................386
Roberta Doll Co. 9, 303
Roberts, Xavier.........................419
Robin's Pals 95
Rock & Roll Soul Imani 275
Rockabye Lullabye.....................347
Roddy.......................................303
Rojus 303
Rolle, Esther.............................92
Rollerblade Christie...................247
Rolly Twiddle............................231
Romantic Bride Barbie 256
Rope Doll 139
Rosa 368
Rose................................33, 366
Rose Bud..................................144
Rose, Patricia 21, 418
Rosedust 200
Rosemary...........................108, 140
Rosey Renee 290
Rosie Hip 213
Rosie With Doll 394
Ross, Diana..................17, 206, 263
Royal House of Dolls, Inc....304–305
Ruby 435
Ruby Red 199

Rufus.......................................107
Rumbero and Rumbera.........11, 121
Rushton 306
Russ Berri & Co. 104
Russian Gift ITC.......................137
Ruth 371
SFBJ 41, 42
Saalfield Publishing............7, 8, 45
Saddie 414
Saffron 405
Sally Secrets 241
Saloon Girl, The 385
Sam 166
Sambo.........................90, 117, 118
Sami 412
Sandi Comb 'N Color..................319
Sandy.................................105, 277
Sanga 392
Santa Claus................306, 370, 376,
                          398, 403, 420
Santone Mfg. Sales Co. 113
Sanyko 104
Sara..172
Sarah 425
Sarah Midgley Budgerree............62
Sarah's Attic....................419–421
Saralee Negro Doll............208–209
Saratoga 166
Sarg, Tony 118
Sassafras 419
Satin 'n Lace......................174, 222
Saturday Night Football............394
Saucy Walker 140
Sauerkraut Bunch 337
Saved by the Bell 318
Sawdust Doll 64
Schildkrot Puppen 133, 306
Schoenhut.........................12, 138
School Fun Barbie......................250
School Teacher, The 363
Schrott, Rotraut 20, 21, 422
Schuetzmeister and Quendt........42
Scorpion 228
Sea Island Sugar 14, 58
Sebino 307, 347
Secret Hearts Barbie 252
Sgt. Apone 220
Shaka Johnson 280
Shalequa 436
Shana 189, 388
Shani..........246, 252, 253–254, 258
Shani Fashions................253–254
Shannon...................................381
Sharing 307
Sharley "Tom Boy".....................369
Sharmell 320
Sharon 367
She-Ra 234

Sheena 389
Sherbet 176
Shillman 307
Shindana 150, 308–309
Shining Star 323
Shirley Temple 15, 124
Shontay...................................228
Show Stoppers..........................422
Shumaker, Gail J. 22, 423
Simba Dolls 310
Simmons, Ron 185
Simon & Halbig........13, 35, 43
Simplicity 98, 99, 101, 260
Sindy.......................................283
Singing Sam 63
Sipes, Jean 93
Sis 124
Sissy.......................................166
Sister................................292, 411
Sister Mary Kathleen 373
Skaters....................................165
Skatie......................................153
Skipper 245, 257, 354
Skippy......................................108
Skye 217
Sleep Over Dolly 217
Sleepy 204
Sleepy Susie 190
Slick 225
Small World..............................149
Smelser, Sharon 21
Smile Internatinal Inc. 310
Smith, Francis L. 19, 424
Smith, Louis S..........................309
Snap 'n Play Barbie 248
Snooky 110
Snow White 16, 124
Snow, Diane.............................425
Snowball..................................107
Snowflake..................................35
Snuggles..................................210
Sofie 371
Soft P.J. Sparkles 234
Soft-Luv Ltd. 311
Soft-n-Wet................................332
Softhearted Friends 93
Softina 161
Soul 140
Soul Train Asha 258
Soul Train Jamal.......................258
Soul Train Nichelle 258
Soul Train Shani 258
Southern Gentleman 358
Souvenir type 127, 130, 312,
                            313, 351
Spanos, Fayzah 426
Sparkle 399
Sparkle Eyes Barbie 248

Spatz 311
Special Expressions Barbie 245, 251, 255
Special Ops 322
Spool Cotton Co. 63
Spring Parade Barbie 245
Spring Song 198
Squeak Babies 188
Stacie 256
Stacy Two Wheeler 216
Stalker 195, 197
Starla 190
Starlight Girls 189
Starlight Splendor Barbie 244
Star Trek 286–287
Starry Stephanie 290
Steiner, Hermann 125
Stella 398
Stereopticon photo 39
Steve 398
Steven 242, 246, 255
Storm 321
Strawberry Shine 200
Stuart Co. 53
Style Me Pretty 239
Sugar Dumpling 426
Summer Dream 224
Summit Barbie 244
Sun Rubber Co. 134, 135
Sun Sensation Christie 246
Sun Sensation Steven 246
Sun-Dee 134
Sunbabe 264
Sunday Babies 277
Sunday Best 166, 353, 408, 419
Sunlight Soap 34
Super Doll Corp. 311
Super Style Huggy 187
Sure Fire 279
Susan 341
Sutton, Linda Lee 426–427
Suzanne 165
Suzette 15, 122
Suzie Sunshine 172–173
Sweet Kandi 161
Sweet Lavender 250
Sweet Little Miss 278
Sweet Scents 322
Sweet Susan Layette 153
Sweetheart Sadie 290
Sweetie Pie 172
Sweetie Pops 289
Sweetpea 414
Swingy 232
Syndee's Crafts 311
Synia 313
TCA Toy Corp. of America 314
TPI Distributing 315

TV Stars Fashion Collection.......263
Tahira 428
Tak-Uki 83
Takara 314
Tala 413
Talen-Toy 116
Talking Baby Alive 218
Talking Rag Doll 102
Tamara 422
Tamika 367
Tanline Products, Inc. 317
Tanteen 22
Tanya 388
Tanzania 103
Tap Dance Twins 359
Tap Dancer 117
Tara 316
Tea Pot Tots 213
Teaka 423
Teen Talk Barbie 250
Teensie Sofskin 201
Teeny Tiny Premies 193
Tell Me Tots 190
Teri Saturday/Sunday 368
Terrance 431
Terri Lee 16, 23, 317
Terry 345
Thirstee Walker 200
Thirsty Quints 324
Thomas, Marilyn 112
Thompson, Carla 18, 428–429
Thompson, Pat 427
Thumbelina 206, 210
Tiger Toys 318
Tim 364
Timothy 378
Tina 103, 334, 380
Tina Fashion 346
Tiny Powder Puff 330
Tiny Tears 288
Tippy 407
Tippy Tumbles 207
Tissy 409
Tobacco Leaf Doll 139
Tobias 371
Tod-L-Tyke 134–135
Tom 415
Tom Stone 194
Tonka Corp. 318, 332
Tonya 219, 436
Topsy 8, 44, 45, 51, 108, 117, 266
Topsy-Turvy ..7, 9, 29, 34, 44, 76–81, 126, 138, 350, 401
Topsy and Eva 78, 79
Totally Hair Barbie 235
Totally Hair Christie 247
Tots, T.J. 96
Totsy 140, 319–320

Touch 'n Talk 330
Toy Biz 321
Toy Headquarters 322
Toy Island 322
Toy Works, The 46
Toy-O-Rama 323
Toys 'N Things 322
TreBelle 323
Treasures in Lace 429
Trendy Wendy 290
Trica's Fashion Ensemble 153
Trion Toy Co. 125
Trixie 400
Troys Toys 95
Truth, Sojourner 359, 413
Tubman, Harriet ...97, 357, 360, 409
Tummy Talks 329
Tung, William 430
Turkish Boy 83
Turner, Virginia Ehrlich 431
Tussini 433
Tutanahamen 15
Tweaker 95
Twinkie 173
Twinkle 173
Twinkling Thumbelina 323
Twins 213, 336, 426
Twistee 319
Two Hearts Collection................228
Ty & Pup 369
Tyco 323–327
Tyrone 434
U-Shab-Ti 15, 116
Unica 125
UNICEF Kids 103
Ugly But Snuggly 399
Uhura 282, 383
Uncle Mose 48, 50
Uncle Tom 117
Uneeda 140, 328–331
Union Sergeant 394
Unis France 41, 42
Valerie 231
Vanessa 224
Vazquez, Mary 432
Vesa 32
Victor Flour 59
Victoria Ashlea Originals 389
Victoria Doll Co. 113
Vintage Bride 304
Violet Bouquet 199
Virga Play-mates 149
Virgin Islands 17, 60, 65, 127
Virginia 186
Vogue Dolls 140, 332–333
Volland 12, 47
Voodoo 94
WPA 108

Wade 8, 48, 51
Wake Up Sleepy Head 301
Walkin' Baby & Her Walker 183
Walking Annette 158
Walking Mammy.........................108
Wang's International 432
Washington, Booker T...............356
Washington, Harold 361
Washington, Mary......................433
Wayne Golden Alexander 279
Wear-A-Doll..............................148
Wedding Bells...........................265
Wee Bit O' Bliss........................401
Wee Li'l Miss Bedtime 236
Wee Li'l Miss Makeup........235, 236
Weigand, Hugo 126
Welch, Marcella.........................433
Welcome Home..........................146
Welcome Home Chubby 317
Wellings, Norah........11, 82–88, 126
Wendy Walkalong 285
West Indies Girl 82
Western Stampin' Barbie...........259
Western Sugar Refinery 14, 58
Wheatsie...................................393

Whispering Wishes 185
Whispy Walker 328, 331
Whistling Rastus........................107
Whistling Rufus 107
Whitney 431, 437
Whoopie 421
Wick, Faith 433
Wilco 334
Williams, Billy Dee 221
Williams, Dr. Daniel Hale 360
Willie...............................387, 437
Willie Talk 205
Willie Tyler's Lester 160
Willie's Wedding.......................437
Wilma......................................400
Wilson Walkie...........................136
Wimbleton 433
Winston Zeddmore 220
Winterbride 304
Wis-Ton Mfg. Co. 334
Women's World...........48, 49, 50, 57
Woodford, Ann...........................92
Wooster 421
World Championship
    Wrestling..............................185

World Doll.................................334
World Gallery 434
Wrestling Superstars 225
Wright, Beatrice........................335
YDC 105, 336
Yah Sah....................................44
Yankuba....................................18
Yo' Aunt Cloe 66
Yolanda....................................364
Yoromong..................................391
Young & Lovely 307
Your Dream Bride 175
Yvonne 398
Yvonne Heather..........................434
Zacher, Robert 435
Zambardon Corp. 334
Zaninni & Zambelli....................336
Zapf...337
Zeb 8
Zena's Buelah 410
Zobe...404
Zoletta.......................................32
Zook, Johannes.............22, 436–437
Zuri 150

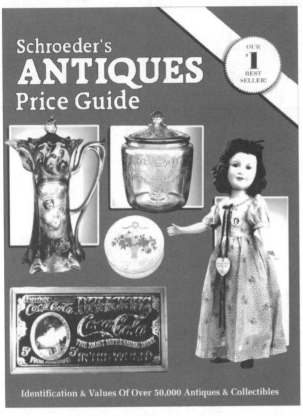